MY LIFE AND WORK

HOFRATH PROFESSOR DOCTOR ADOLF LORENZ

My Life and Work
THE SEARCH FOR A MISSING GLOVE

By

Dr. Adolf Lorenz
Hofrath and Professor of Orthopædic
Surgery, University of Vienna

CHARLES SCRIBNER'S SONS · NEW YORK
CHARLES SCRIBNER'S SONS · LTD · LONDON
MCMXXXVI

This book is dedicated to my wife

EMMA

*who has been my faithful assistant
for over half a century*

FOREWORD

A foreword is the writer's opportunity to excuse himself to the reader. Of that opportunity I shall not avail myself. If I have failed in my endeavor to interest the reader, I feel that I am to be pitied rather than excused. But I am presumptuous enough to nourish the conviction that my book will appeal to old and young people, to physician and layman, because it is a simple and human story of ups and downs. Among the many super-sophisticated volumes of present-day literature, a human book may not be amiss.

I think that every man beyond eighty feels the urge to tell people something of his life. Yielding to that urge, I wrote the book without the slightest idea that it would ever be baptized with printer's ink. I shelved it in the hope that my grandchildren would sometime find it and perhaps read it.

When I celebrated my eighty-first birthday in New York, about half a dozen sturdy young knights of the "Order of the Pad and Pencil," as the late Harry Acton called them, came to congratulate me and to remind me of my old age. They asked me whether I had written the story of my life. "Certainly I have, but who cares?" The next day came the avalanche—now I could choose a publisher.

I feel that I must thank Scribners for their efforts to bring forth what I have written in an agreeable form. I trust that the content of this book will be worthy of its frame. Should any of my readers find in it the hundredth part of the pleasure which I felt as its writer, the purpose of the book will be fulfilled. Further, I wish to offer my thanks to my secretary, Lilli Hartung Rohlin, for her great care and assistance in preparing the manuscript.

ADOLF LORENZ

NEW YORK,
March 1, 1936

CONTENTS

		PAGE
FOREWORD		vii
I.	A BOY IN SILESIA	1
II.	THE MISSING GLOVE	15
III.	THE CHOIR-SINGER	32
IV.	OUT IN THE WORLD	42
V.	A STUDENT OF MEDICINE	54
VI.	JUDGING MY TEACHERS	68
VII.	CALAMITY CREATES A "DRY" SURGEON	76
VIII.	BUILDING THE "FATHER-HOUSE"	86
IX.	DEVELOPING BLOODLESS OPERATIONS	95
X.	ROYAL RECOGNITION	109
XI.	I RIDE MY HOBBIES	118
XII.	IMPORTED BY AMERICA	130
XIII.	A HARD-WORKED TOURIST	148
XIV.	IN THE BANKERS' CLUTCHES	163
XV.	QUEENS AS MOTHERS	176
XVI.	SOUTHLAND JOURNEY	190
XVII.	HAZARDS OF THE THEATRE	208

PAGE

XVIII. Lorenz Hall or Bust! 217

XIX. An Arabian Nights Fantasy 231

XX. The Conflagration 248

XXI. Life in the Ashes 265

XXII. Reconquering America 280

XXIII. Dimples and Indemnity Suits 302

XXIV. Abdication 311

XXV. What Hope for the Crippled? 322

XXVI. Your Own Missing Glove 337

XXVII. I Attend My Funeral 347

Index 355

ILLUSTRATIONS

Hofrath Professor Doctor Adolf Lorenz   *Frontispiece*

FACING PAGE

St. Paul's Benedictine Monastery in Carinthia   38

The Famous "Uncle Gregor"   38

During Choir-Boy Days   39

As a Medical Student   39

The Young Doctor Adolf Lorenz   72

My Adviser, Professor Eduard Albert   73

Professor Billroth, Famous Viennese Surgeon   73

Congenital Club-Feet   100

Professor Adolf Lorenz in 1902   101

Operation before a Great Audience, Chicago   142

Professor Adolf Lorenz Operating on a Spanish Artist Who Had Painted a Picture for Him   143

Lorenz Hall and the Lion Staircase   226

One of the Terraces at Lorenz Hall   227

Examination in Consultation Room at Board of Health, New York, 1921   288

Professor Adolf Lorenz Distributing Bacon to Starving Children   289

Professor Adolf Lorenz and Harry Acton   344

Professor Adolf Lorenz with His Son   344

Professor and Mrs. Adolf Lorenz   345

xi

MY LIFE AND WORK

I

A BOY IN SILESIA

IN the little country town of Weidenau in Silesia (then Austria), a boy was born on April 21, 1854, to humble parents. He was given the name Adolf. His mother was very proud of her first-born, especially because he was a boy. She was the daughter of Silesian peasants of the type who live in little towns and on Sundays go to church in high silken hats and long black frock-coats, white gloves in hand; while any week-day finds them, according to the season, plodding behind the plough or measuring their fields with equal steps and at every second step throwing a handful of seed on the brown earth, like automatons. There used to be a saying: "When the citizen is not at home, the peasant is on his acres."

The young mother was the eldest of the three daughters of old Mr. Ehrlich. He had also had two sons who left home as boys and who did not come home for so long that they became legendary in the family as well as in the little town. But they were not legendary to the new mother. At least not the younger of the two brothers, who was named Johann, and with whom she kept up a good friendship, especially while he was a student. Many a *gulden* which she had saved went to the ever-needy brother Johann, whom his father, old Mr. Ehrlich, as well as his mother, used to call an indolent and lazy fellow, not able to earn his bread as a student. Nobody knew how the unheard-of thing came about that two boys of rather poor Mr. Ehrlich should leave the town to study in Troppau, the capital

1

of the province of Silesia. And yet, after the boys had finished the Gymnasium, they continued their studies in Graz, the capital of Styria. Eduard, the older brother, became a physician. Johann, the younger, had begun to study law, but it did not please him to earn his bread giving lessons, and so he threw himself on the bosom of the church. As this narrative will show, he fell softly, and made a very easy and comfortable career. Under the name of Father Gregor he became a capitular of the Benedictine Monastery of St. Paul, in Carinthia, where the monks directed the first four classes of the Gymnasium, called the *"Untergymnasium,"* and were obliged to provide the four classes of the *"Obergymnasium"* in Klagenfurt, the capital of the province of Carinthia, with teachers from the monastery.

It is necessary to describe in brief the career of Father Gregor, because on it hinged the fate of the newborn baby boy.

In St. Paul, as in all big Austrian monasteries, church music was a matter of great importance. Choir-singers were much sought for. Father Gregor had given his sister, as an inexpensive wedding-present, the promise that he would try to install her first-born boy as a choir-singer in St. Paul, provided he had a good voice and could play the violin. Besides singing in the choir, he could study the first four classes of the Gymnasium in St. Paul. Therefore the proud mother already saw her tiny baby a student of Latin and Greek and probably also a learned Benedictine monk, a vision which was less unlikely than it may seem at first sight. Thus the newborn boy was apparently destined to become either a musician or a clergyman. His mother did not doubt for a moment that her Adolf in the course of time would become *"ein grosser Herr"*—a great gentleman. As the boy grew up, it was preached at him that he must become a grand gentleman. Then and later on, when he was asked jokingly, "Adolf, what are you going to be?" he would steadfastly answer, "A Grand Gentleman."

Adolf's father was a harness-maker, and also kept a little inn where the coachmen could refresh themselves while they waited for their new or repaired harnesses. He not only made belts and leather trunks, but all kinds of upholstery for coaches and cabriolets. He varnished the wooden bodies and the wheels with a steady hand. He drew straight lines on the spokes, and while he let the wheel spin, he applied nicely curved lines on the felly. This handcraftsman was an artist. Surgeons and physicians, who usually are overproud of their dexterity, should watch craftsmen do their work and then become modest.

Adolf, then about four years old, was not yet in school when he had the first experience that was to stay in his memory forever. On a hot summer afternoon, a low-wheeled cart, drawn by four horses, rattled over the cobblestones of the big square in the center of the town. The vehicle was heavily loaded with big pieces of polished marble which glittered in the sunshine. The surface of one of them was covered with golden letters, engraved in the stone. All the urchins of the town followed the slowly progressing team, which took the way toward the cemetery outside the town. It did not interest them that the biggest of these marble stones was to be the socket of the new marble cross in the center of the cemetery. Their interest was exclusively concentrated on the golden letters upon its side. The letters were illegible, but the figures aroused discussion, as the block stood upside down on the platform of the wagon. On this occasion a little, lean, flaxen-haired boy learned for the first time to know certain figures; but not one of the many boys tried to make out what the series of numerals "1859" meant, because time meant nothing to them, and war in Italy even less.

Although one recollection of Adolfla's earliest youth concerns a night-time experience—and a night of pitch blackness at that—the many decades that have passed since have not been able to dull its vividness.

The resort of Lindewiese was then already held in high regard, but enjoyed especial popularity among the youngsters of the little city of Weidenau. Unavoidably the intimacy of these many boys suffered almost daily grievous disturbances. Their differences were not always of such a nature that they had immediately to be decided by a fist-fight; the insulted one in certain cases was satisfied merely with injured, sulking retreat, but he was "mad"; then the cocky insulter would add mockery to injury and declaim:

"If you're mad, go to Lindewiese—
Then be glad, put an old hat on your beezer!"

Not very clever, but a piece of propaganda for Lindewiese.

One fine day little Adolfla was to learn that his father had a relative at Lindewiese, an old great-uncle whom he was planning to visit soon, taking with him his whole family.

The intended visit was made, but Adolfla later remembered neither the trip there nor the trip back, nor the house in the town, nor the old great-uncle—in short, nothing; but he did recall vividly enough a terrifying, night-time experience. The Lindewiese relatives were not prepared to have so many visitors stay the night with them. They were short of beds, and the guests consequently had to sleep on the floor in the large, first-floor parlor. This of course was the lot of Adolfla, who was put to bed on a straw sack in a corner of the room.

He spent a restless night, perhaps because of his unaccustomed position, since he was actually sleeping on the floor, which suggested a fear of mice; but perhaps it was because he had eaten too much crumb-cake.

In the middle of the night he awoke and, not quite conscious, raised himself upright from his couch. Then, on his back, which was left bare by the slit shirt, he felt a soft tickling, and at the same time an icy cold touch. He shuddered; the next instant the uncanny touch recurred, and now it seemed to him even colder. He shrank forward and screamed out loud in fright.

The other sleepers awoke; his mother cried: "What's the matter with you, Adolfla?" He did not answer but began to howl anew as if he were sticking on a spit. It was not the screaming of a naughty child but of one tortured by fear. The cold presence had crept from Adolfla's neck down across his back to his legs, and he grabbed for it, trying to ward it off with his hands.

Thereupon the cold snake wound itself about his fingers and slipped down his legs to his feet. He fought in desperation with the icy serpent, which drew itself ever tighter about his arms and hands; he kicked his feet and beat about with his arms, which resulted only in his presently feeling the cold embrace around his neck.

If the child had fallen in that nocturnal battle with

the snake, and if help had not been near at hand, he would have been choked. However, Adolfla did not fall, but leaned against the wall, wrestling with the monster.

The whole house had become aroused. People rushed about confusedly in the room looking for matches. When lights were lit, the mother found that Adolfla was resting worn out against the wall, with a long snake twined about his arms, legs, and neck. But the embrace was not the work of the snake, but of the struggling child.

And the explanation of the nocturnal adventure? When Adolfla stood up, his neck and back had come in contact with the long, cold, pliant brass chains which were pulled up by the clock-weights.

Grandmother said one day to her favorite grandson: "Adolfla, gray Mietze is sick. Couldn't you put her on her feet with some *Hasenbrot?*"

Adolfla found the old cat curled up in a corner of the stable. He picked up the furry gray ball; it felt stiff and cold. This cat could not be helped any more; she was dead.

But the young cat-doctor, having come too late, wanted at least to provide for his client's honorable burial. With his brother, he dug a shallow pit in the Kingdom of Earth beside the dung-heap. The cat, moreover, was not to be interred as a curled-up, furry ball, but was to be laid comfortably to rest with her body properly stretched out, then covered with earth.

The children played funeral; they lifted the newly turned earth between their hollowed hands and, rubbing their palms against each other, strewed it in a fine coating over the body of the dead cat. Gradually the contours of the cadaver disappeared under a thick shroud of the finest earth. In solemn mood the young grave-diggers looked at the brown, long-stretched hillock.

Suddenly to their amazement they thought they noticed a soft movement of the brown particles of earth against each other. Longer observation removed all doubt. The sifted veil of earth was rising and falling rhythmically, very gently, betraying along its sides cracks which alternately opened and closed.

There was no doubt the cat still lived and, with her breathing, was bursting the loose chains of her light grave-hillock.

In complete consternation the boys freed their old house-companion, whom they had thought dead, from the suffocating embrace of Mother Earth; they bedded her in soft hay and cared for her till her early and blessed demise.

The story became public and brought raillery upon the cat's doctor: "He'll be a swell doctor—who buries his patients alive!" Thus joked the malicious. And the old people said: "Well, yes—the doctor and the grave-digger, they always work hand in hand."

Adolfla was always uncombed and usually unwashed, but in spite of all that, a fine boy with a frank, fresh-colored face and beautiful, blue eyes. His rich yellow mane, which might have been white-yellow flax, suited his complexion. Of course this bright wealth was not cared for, for time was lacking, as well as the right comb to bring the tangled locks into order.

If his nose had been less broad, his chin somewhat broader, one might have considered the boy's features handsome. At any rate, the total impression was favorable and engaging.

The fact that his right ear stood out a little farther from his head than his left was covered up by the yellow mop and only came to light when the mane fell victim to the scissors. Then this little blemish often became the cause of battles with slandering comrades, who would insist on tracing the right ear's divergence to the frequent repetition of painful handling under punishment, thereby deeply wounding the conscious innocence of the derided one.

But that happened only in the summer; winter found his ears always abundantly covered by the yellow flax, a natural head-covering. Only after ten years was it desecrated by the first hat.

Adolfla was strikingly large for his age when he was perhaps five years old, but at the same time was tough and lean. Unfortunately he was a bit bowlegged, too slightly to have been caused by illness; it was a paternal inheritance which persisted in the family. But this flaw, despite its unimportance, had not been overlooked by Max, his malicious, impish cousin. Max was sufficiently mean to compose a mocking verse, which went:

"Adolf, funny Adolf,
Bowlegged Adolf!"

But Adolf wasn't slow. He responded:

"Max, stupid Max,
Walks like a Dachs!" *

For this he reaped blows, for Max was the stronger, actually destined to be a butcher.

* Dachshund.

The boy's winter and summer dress consisted of a shirt
and fustian breeches with an attached vest that buttoned
in back. The buttons of the vest fortunately were beyond
reach of his manipulation, otherwise they would have been
taken care of just as negligently as the buttons over that
more accessible part of the body which in the near future
was to press the school bench. It was quite unavoidable
that the shirt should hang out of the gaping slit, giving him usually a triangular little tail; that was characteristic of the type of the street urchin in general. The
oft-heard question: "Adolfla, what's the price of a quart
of white beer?" therefore made no impression on him. But
he was painfully aware of the disordered state of his toilet
when they said, "Adolfla, what's the price of a quart of
yellow beer?" When cherries and plums were in season
this jibe was usually justified.

From the middle of March till toward the end of November his feet wore only their own skin, and that was
firm leather. The stubble fields of autumn could not hurt
him, for the hurrying foot knew how to tread them flat;
the March snow indeed enjoyed some favor because of the
hot, prickly feeling of the skin it caused afterward. The
barefooted boy also was spared the care of his toenails.
The roughness of the miserable street pavement took care
of that, and indeed the whole nail often would remain
hanging in the cracks. This unpleasant experience was
so frequent that it created its own special terminology.
"Adolfla has knocked his toe off again," his grandmother
would say, and for this event she had small scraps of linen
handy, which she bound on the injured toe in the form of
a neat little cap.

Then, when the first frost of winter came—and in

Silesia that admits of no joking—the only pair of shoes that could be covered by the family budget had to be bought willy-nilly. Stockings were a luxury quite unknown; even thoroughly damp shoes were put on again and again over bare feet. The insufficient footwear was compensated for by a brightly colored woolen shawl for the neck and a pair of cloth mittens which hung from it on a strong cord. As a result, both were always lost at once, and usually very soon after the last Christ Child had brought them.

Winter was and still is a bad time for children of poverty. Adolfla has an unhappy recollection of it; he did not like it even later when its harshness could no longer affect him. Even in later years he would say: "In summer one lives, in winter one vegetates."

But summer's heat and winter's frost could not harm the boy's health. Not a single illness remains in his memory. Malnutrition and faulty care, however, seem to have caused, if only transitorily, a tendency to sickliness. It was at the time of brightest sunshine, when Adolfla, perhaps four years old, suffered for some time from a painful sensitivity to light, and had to grope in the dark with bandaged eyes. Still he could move about freely in his grandmother's back room, for he knew every nook and corner of the large parlor. As a consolation, his grandmother had bought him a small carved wooden cow which he pulled around after him on a string. The clatter and squeak of the little wheels of the toy became unforgettable music for the child. Just as unforgettable remained the bump on his head, when the unsympathetic cord wound itself about his feet and caused him a sudden fall. Loud screaming and lively protest against the continued bind-ing of his eyes gave evidence not so much of self-pity as of the firm will of the boy. What a joy for him when with blinking eyes he could see for a moment the roughly carved and brightly painted cow instead of having always to feel it with his fingers!

It can be considered a miracle that no further symptoms of scrofula or rickets came to light in the boy, for his diet consisted of little more than bad coffee and coarse rye bread. The fault was not his parents', but an unfortunate consequence of his grandmother's unreasonable love and of the child's own strange aversion to meat.

As often as Adolfla asked his mother before lunch (and he never omitted to do so): "Mother, what've we got today?" the stereotyped answer would be: "Well, what would we have? Smoked beef, sauerkraut and dumplings."

"Well then, I don't want it," came the answer just as regularly, and Adolfla was gone—to his grandmother in the back room. She always had a "little drop" of coffee standing on the stove to share with her pet. Luckily, though the coffee was bad, the milk was good, and rye bread with salt butter was also not to be sneered at. At any rate it tasted delicious and to the boy it was incomprehensible that there could be people who preferred fatty meat.

In general, then, the boy was badly cared for; no one troubled about his education. His freedom was all the more delightful; no one stopped him from pattering along the street at a run, spattering passers-by after a rain; he enjoyed wading in the thickest mud in the streets to practise the art of letting it rise between his toes in four spirals. His comrades did the same; this was an art that gave one prestige. The children were left to decide for themselves how to fill the long hours of the day.

In the fine season they stopped at home only as long as frugal meals necessitated, then they were out again in the fields or the street. Adolfla and his friends were gamins in the worst sense of the word. Even the severe winter did not make stay-at-homes of them. The boy, trained in freedom, developed so well physically in spite of his poor nourishment, that his mother was wont to exclaim: "I'd like to know what makes that boy grow so, he eats no meat!"

There were entertainments by rope-walkers on the great square, but there were also at times productions of plays in a closed hall, by a travelling troupe which had strayed into the quiet little city.

The youngsters naturally were less interested in such performances. To such a troupe, Adolfla is indebted for his first impression of the theatre, which was a great disappointment to him.

The title and content of the play that was performed have escaped his memory. But one scene remained ineffaceably in his recollection, perhaps because it agreed completely with reality as he himself had experienced it.

In a poor room stood a lean, pale, tall woman, bent over a washtub, from which she picked up white plates, dried them with a cloth, and stacked them. A man came in the door and reproached the woman in excited tones. She stopped her work and began to cry.

Such scenes, of course, were not alien to the reality of Adolfla's own home; but he had never stopped to think about them. Yet the theatre posed him the riddle: Why is the man so angry? The woman had not done anything to him! He had to get to the bottom of this question.

He pushed curiously along the wall of the little hall toward the front, as far as the low stage, in order to observe the woman, who had resumed her handling of the plates, from the closest point. Then all became clear to him. The woman was only pretending to wash and dry the plates.

"She hasn't got any water in the tub," he shouted loudly in his pride of discovery, and in the same instant felt his mouth covered not too gently by the rough hand of a neighbor.

"Will you be quiet, you little fool!" he was warned in a low voice. But Adolfla would not give up, and answered, likewise in an audible whisper: "If the plates aren't clean, the man will get even angrier at the woman."

"Adolfla, go home—you're still too stupid for the theatre," the neighbor replied, amused, and shoved the youngster behind him.

The boy remained unalterably convinced that the people in the theatre were merely being fooled by the actors; actually in this opinion he had hit the nail on the head.

At five the flaxen-haired boy went to school. It was the first time order had come into his life. Until now he had lived in boundless freedom, like the chickens in the street. He began also to learn to play the violin and to sing with his playmates. His mother told him why he had to learn the violin and to sing: he was to be a choir-singer and a student at eleven; he was never to forget that he must learn more and better than his playmates, of whom not one was destined to become a student and later a grand gentleman. To tell the truth, the boy did not heed these admonitions very much and was a rather bad and negligent scholar. On one occasion, however, he felt deeply ashamed of his behavior and resolved to do better in the future. It was the day when the school was visited by a school reviser (a sort of higher teacher), and a general examination was held. The quizzing by this new teacher interested the ordinarily lazy boy; he paid attention and answered questions which were met with silence by the rest of the class. The reviser could not fail to perceive that the lively boy had brains under his flaxen hair; he praised him and asked his name. "A very intelligent boy," the reviser said to the teacher. But the teacher was of a different opinion, and availed himself of the occasion to accuse the boy publicly of laziness, negligence, and a tendency to truancy; the boy was, he said, all the more to blame because he was talented. Never in his later life did Adolf feel so ashamed. His buoyancy turned into desperate dejection; he burst into tears, and felt himself already a better boy who would take to heart what the teacher had said of him. Hadn't he behaved shamefully—he, who was destined to become a student? At home he said nothing of his experience at school, but hid himself in a little garret which was used as a lumber-chamber, and meditated on his utter depravity. By chance he found there an old, dilapidated book which probably had once belonged to his uncles when they were students. It was a Latin vocabulary. This book impressed the boy more than any admonitions of his mother on the theme of becoming a grand gentleman. This, then, was Latin at last. He resolved at once to learn the vocables, at least one page every day, and to progress as far as he could until his study should begin in earnest.

II

THE MISSING GLOVE

As a schoolboy of about seven years of age, Adolfla used to watch his father while he mended harnesses, first boring holes through the hardened leather and then introducing the blunt needle threaded with the strong, waxed thread. When he drew the thread taut, it was dangerous to stand at his side because he would throw out his arms regardless of any curious bystander. Adolfla admired the skill and steadiness of his artisan father's hands. Sometimes the boy would carefully search through heaps of junk, crammed upon shelves in the workroom, in the hope of finding tools, playthings, and the like. Once he found a small, black, round ball, the surface of which looked corrugated, like a snakeskin. He tried to penetrate with a boring finger between the wrinkles of the questionable object, and to his amazement brought forth the body of one short, black serpent; he pried further and out came another serpent, then still another, until there were five of them emerging out of a black bag. It took the boy some time to realize that he had found a left-handed glove—probably a relic of a funeral of many years ago, for gloves, if worn at all, were used only on such occasions.

The boy stuck his left hand into the mouldy tubes and ran to his mother in the kitchen. "Look here, Mother, see what I have just found, a real glove!"—and he reached his hand up to her triumphantly, adding, "Am I not a real big gentleman now?" His mother looked thoughtfully at the boy, smiled, and at last said, "My dear Adolfla, if you want to be a big gentleman, you must have two gloves. Go find the other glove!"

This little incident remained in the memory of the grown-up man throughout his life. Decades elapsed before he thought, "Now you have found the other glove"— only to lose it again. Once he thought he had lost both of them, and almost gave up the search.

But a man who gives up hope, gives up himself. At last he found out that he had long been in possession of both gloves, though he thought he had lost them—but he still had them, because he had not only always enjoyed his own life, but had done something to help others also to enjoy their lives.

Life is nothing but a frantic search for the missing glove. Woe to him who thinks himself not concerned with the search for the other glove because he is convinced that he was born with a glove on each hand.

At that time, those tradespeople who occupied themselves with the preparation of church decorations were called "trimmers." Probably they have the same name today.

The more common name "gilder" fell far short of designating the arts of trimmer Bauch, who not only gilded frames and saints' figures and tabernacles, but also knew how to restore pictures and to repair church ornaments. He knew how to draw beautiful angels, how to make artificial flowers, and so on.

His wife was tall and thin. She and the small, spare

man with sparse reddish beard and thin hair, whose build belied his name,* made an unequal pair.

The trimmer's workshop, especially in severe winter, was Adolfla's paradise, not only because the walls of the low room were decorated with so many gaily shimmering saints, and because little angels' heads with gilded wings swayed from the ceiling, but also because of the comfortable warmth there—a warmth that derived partly from the past summer, when the windows had last stood open. In winter, the airing of the room would have been a hair-raising extravagance. And consequently there was always a great variety of odors in the workroom, odors of oil paint, of glue, alcohol, turpentine, and many other more animal scents. One lived in a visible cloud of smells, which, even in bright daylight, filled the room with a soft twilight. In the midst of this cloud stood the ruler of the tinselled kingdom, Herr Bauch.

When he turned and twisted a Resurrected Christ in one slender white hand and with the other applied the glittering gold-leaf to the points of the crown of thorns from the tip of a fine brush, little Adolfla would think that he could recognize the Lord Father out of his Bible in the mild and yet earnest face, and would look up at him with reverent awe.

Was it any wonder then that the observation of these holy things in the process of creation aroused in the boy thoughts of possessing such objects for himself and of grouping them on an altar?

He carpentered for himself a little chest and on it nailed upright a small board, which his father, by means of an old green carriage-lining, transformed into a beautifully

* *Bauch* means Belly.

folded canopy. The chest, upholstered with old linen, formed the altar-table. Flowers were made out of paper; little saints' pictures were not hard to procure; but the small candlesticks offered difficulties. They were finally made of molten window-lead poured into a clay form.

The only thing lacking was the most important—the tabernacle, which, according to the model in the church, had to have three revolving niches around a vertical axis. It was something not to be reproduced off-hand, and seemed to Adolfla a possession as unattainable as it was desirable.

Then by chance he found a small model tabernacle in the shop of his friend, Herr Bauch. It was so perfect in detail that Adolfla could not suppress his longing for it. If the sin had not been too great, he might have felt tempted to steal the object so passionately desired.

He had to content himself with loudly admiring the beauty of the tabernacle and playing with it before Herr Bauch's eyes as obviously as possible. Often the words were on the tip of his tongue: "Say, Herr Bauch, this tabernacle looks just as though it was made for my altar." But again and again he bit his tongue on the words. From day to day he waited for the delivering pronouncement of Herr Bauch: "Well then, take the tabernacle, if you have such good use for it." But these passionately longed-for words did not come; Herr Bauch either did not understand or did not want to understand the gentle hints. For all the world the little boy could not have forced himself to ask for the tabernacle. Whether this was because of pride or because it seemed to him too impudent is uncertain.

And yet Adolfla was to come into possession of the jewel,

not as a gift, but after a difficult achievement had won him the right to demand it for himself. The occasion of this achievement was a very sad one for Herr Bauch. After many years of marriage, something unexpected, something long despaired of, had become reality: the stork left a very, very small Bauch at the house. The child resembled none of the fat-cheeked little angels' heads with the gilded wings on their short necks as they hung down from the ceiling of the workshop. Instead it was a greenish-yellow little worm with hollow cheeks and an old man's face. Too weak even to scream, it went off in sleep to the angel's kingdom, when it was scarcely a few days old. The grief of the parents was great. A solemn funeral was to give it expression.

In whose head did the crazy idea of making the little Adolf the pall-bearer originate? Probably many friends of the family must share the guilt. Since dead maidens and youths according to local custom were carried to the grave by those of their own age, it was thought the child's funeral would earn especial consecration if the dead child were laid in the arms of a living one.

The boy, then eight years old at most, did not question the wisdom of his elders; perhaps he was flattered to play an important part on such a solemn occasion; besides, he felt himself honored by the obligatory *boutonnière* of rosemary, which was put into his buttonhole. He willingly received the little wooden box with its meager content upon his outstretched arms.

In the beginning, the burden seemed light enough. But let any one try carrying a load, even a small one, on both arms held out in front of him, and in a short time he too will find that the smallest weight becomes a hundredweight; the very weight of his arms soon exhausts him. The road from the house of mourning to the church, traversed with slow steps, became endless, and the little coffin pressed the arms of its bearer lower and lower; soon he felt as though they must break off. He envisioned the coffin falling to the ground any moment and breaking to splinters on the pavement.

Such a horrible thing must not happen! The pallbearer gritted his teeth, flexed his arms, and drew himself up. It would have been an undying disgrace to fail in such a great moment in his life. But he was near to tears.

But there came a thought to help him through the final and hardest bit of the way, a thought that made him capable of superhuman effort—he remembered the tabernacle. Then at last the coffin was lifted from his arms in the church; he breathed grateful relief. He was free of the burden and he had won the tabernacle. With the walk to the church, the test of strength was over.

A few days later, Adolfla again visited his patron and found him at his usual occupation. Without beating around the bush, he brought forth the tabernacle, which he had hidden like a secret possession behind all sorts of litter, and said with matter-of-fact certainty, "Say, Herr Bauch, I could use this tabernacle very well for my altar."

The bereaved man looked up from his work and answered distractedly, "Yes, of course, Adolfla: take two angels for it, too, if you want." And after a brooding pause, "I've lost my angel forever."

At a certain early period of life, all boys want to become one and the same thing, but place their goal rather low. Their ideal is inevitably embodied in the coachman, the street-car conductor, or the locomotive engineer. This does not denote lack of ambition so much as it expresses a restless love of motion, which these professions promise to satisfy.

For Adolfla, not all these professions came under consideration, since at that time there were no street-cars, and the railroad had not yet progressed as far as Weidenau; thus the conductor and the motorman were pinnacles of greatness still unknown to him. On the other hand, he had become all the more closely acquainted with the coachmen from intimate observation, but what he had seen did not make him at all enthusiastic about their trade.

He despised just as heartily the idea of becoming apprenticed to some craftsman. For even then the boy had a gleam of perception of the immense importance to him of the promise made to his mother by his legendary uncle, Father Gregor. He saw before him the hope of possibly travelling another road than that of the craftsman. He even found the courage to answer the teasing question, "Adolfla, what would you like to become?" with the boasting words: "I'd like to be a great gentleman."

He had not pursued a choice of profession more definitely than this, but a decision was suggested to him by a few significant events.

Adolfla may have been about six or seven years old, when a grave worry took possession of the family. His father suddenly took sick, and his condition, from all that Adolfla heard, was serious if not hopeless. Doctor Münch went diligently in and out of the house, and often looked in on the sick man twice a day, where the latter lay on his back in bed, half-conscious, with burning face and strangely restless hands that groped over the bed-covers. There was a siege of typhoid in the village; several cases had ended fatally. In the opinion of the physician, the father was very, very sick and the worst was to be feared. Adolfla understood and shared the concern of his mother. The nearing crisis might bring death.

The small boy tortured himself with wondering whether he could not help in some way so that the dreaded crisis, to which he heard so many references, might bring new life to the sick man. Then the young *hasenbrot* (hare's bread) occurred to him, that grass whose chestnut-brown blossoms are the special adornment of the blooming June meadows. Only yesterday he had tasted some on his grandfather's meadow that was ripe for mowing, and had found that the hares show good taste in particularly preferring it. A beautiful, large bouquet of *hasenbrot*, if one cooked it and gave his father the broth as medicine, perhaps might still help! Early in the morning the boy gathered as much of the grass as his hands could clutch and carried the colorful, living greeting of the blooming spring meadow into the dim sick-room where a man struggled with death.

But the patient had already won the victory. That same morning he had returned to consciousness and had looked about in wonder at the familiar surroundings that had been eclipsed for so long. When Adolfla stepped into the room with the large bouquet of dainty little brown flowers and strewed the whole load on his father's bed, so that it resembled a blooming carpet of meadow, bright pleasure lighted up the man's lean face. "That's for medicine," called out the boy, who was glowing with eagerness. To which his father replied: "If I have a doctor like Adolfla, I'll surely get well."

Word was spread among the children that there were to

be "vaccinations" the next day in the large room of the Poppe Inn. The smallest children, who were still carried in arms and had no conception of things, played the main part in this event, but the school-children, who had naturally long since forgotten their own vaccination, puzzled their heads quite needlessly about the manner and purpose of the operation, and outdid themselves in wild speculation.

In front of the place of vaccination, the convergence of many mothers with screaming children in their arms became the nucleus of a large crowd, which was swollen to alarming proportions by the schoolboys who stood everywhere in the way, gaping curiously.

The commotion, the crying of the children, the apparent excitement of the mothers, some of whom had first to be converted to the idea of vaccination, heated the imaginations of the boys to exaggerated fantasy. Alternately one or the other of the lads would push his way into the vestibule of the house, and when a mother and child went in or out, would cast an eager glance into the room full of people. Then he would run out into the street to the others and tell what horrible things he had seen. One lad had seen a large, white dish in which red blood was beaten into foam. Another had seen the same blood streaming out of the opened neck of a calf into the white bowl.

Adolfla, too, was one of the impudent door-gazers; what he saw made his blood run cold. At a table sat a young girl with flowing locks, dressed only in a white garment that left her arms bare to the shoulders. Before her stood a shallow, white dish in which coiled a knot of reddish snakes, whose bodies the girl was stirring with blood-stained hands. From a knowledge of anatomy gained at the butcher's, the boy recognized the reddish snakes as fresh intestines—of course they could only be human intestines. His observation was received outside with a pleasant shock.

If Adolfla, then or at any later time, had had to swear a solemn oath by all that was holy to him, that he had really seen this with his own eyes, he would have sworn it with full conviction. The positiveness of this impression, which all his life remained unweakened, illustrates graphically the value of the testimony of children before a judge.

In Adolfla's grandfather's house, the house door opened into a passage which joined the front and the rear. In one wall of the passage was a cellar entrance kept closed by a wooden door, painted white.

One day, when the grandmother came out of her back room and walked through this passage, her scream as she reached the cellar door called Adolfla to her side.

"These beggars keep getting more brazen," she cried. "The creature sneaks into the house, so that one might get one's death of fright—get out!"

The beggar, a wasted, pale, little woman, not young and not old, stood motionless with her back against the low cellar door. Her head had fallen forward; she held her hands folded before her, and seemed to shrink into herself and get smaller and smaller. She neither raised her head nor answered.

But this sudden fright could not suppress the kindness of the old grandmother for long. She turned without a word and went back into the room to cut a generous chunk off the loaf of black bread.

"Give the woman a bit of bread!" she commanded her grandson, who was following at her heels. Adolfla, not particularly pleased by the order, hesitantly approached the beggar woman who was leaning against the cellar door like a statue. Several times he raised the chunk of bread, inviting her to accept it. But the woman did not move.

Adolfla now came quite near and laid the gift on her crossed wrists. She let this happen without moving, without a sign of gratitude.

Just as the boy was about to withdraw shyly from the puzzling woman, something terrible happened. The dark, half-crouching figure, whose outlines stood out sharply against the white cellar door, seemed to sway backward a little, then all at once to disappear, like a ghostly apparition, into a pitch-black abyss. There was a dull rumbling, then absolute stillness.

The cellar door had suddenly opened through the pressure of the beggar-woman's body, and she had plunged backward down the steep steps into the darkness. Horrified, the boy fled back to his grandmother. The house was aroused and the victim was quickly lifted back to daylight from the black depths. The woman presented a fearful aspect. It was not that she was bleeding from any wound, or that other injuries were apparent. Far more terrible was the bloated face with staring eyes and bloody, red foam at the mouth, as well as the convulsive twitchings of arms and legs and the whole body. The unfortunate woman was taken out of the house to the community jail; there the physician diagnosed her case as epilepsy.

On the evening of this memorable day, the grandmother asked her grandson: "Well, Adolfla, do you still want to become a doctor?" And the boy, who was much shaken by the experience, answered in a small voice: "It wouldn't just have to be a doctor for falling sickness."

Boys who receive blows in battle with their fellows, whether in a just or an unjust cause, consider these not punishment but honorable wounds. On the other hand, the beatings which are administered by parents or educators, no matter how well deserved, live on in their injured spirits as a disgrace. The future should be allowed to instruct them that injustice has been suffered or that justice has been done. Therefore children should never be beaten.

Only twice in his life did Adolfla get a thorough spanking from his father, the first time with perfect justice, the second time with equally marked injustice. A child's happiness is just as variable and as easily disturbed as that of a grown-up, and its loss is felt just as keenly as in later life.

One afternoon, in the company of his playmates, Adolfla was devoting himself to the harmless pleasure of jumping down from the dizzy height of the haymow in the empty stable onto a heap of juicy beet leaves, which had been prepared as feed for the cows. He was enjoying immensely the crackling of the brittle stalks breaking under his weight and the crackling of the leaves when pressed together.

Suddenly Aunt Karline rushed into the stable and shrieked in horror as she became aware of the children's wild game: "You pests, I'll show you not to ruin my cow-feed like that!" And biff, biff, the blows rained down on those of the scattering boys who were in reach of her coarse, workworn hands. Adolfla was among those who came within range. Deeply offended, he sneaked out of the stable into the courtyard. In this mood, he saw his father approaching him with a black bottle in his hand. "Adolfla, run quickly to the store and get me some fresh turpentine!" And already Adolfla had the sticky, smelly bottle in his hand.

To fall like that from the heavens into dull reality was too much for the child's spirit, so lately intoxicated with happiness. The corners of the boy's mouth showed distinct signs of a pout; he felt his father's broad hand on his back, starting him with a forceful push in the proper direction. "Shut up and be quick."

Adolfla let himself be shoved forward under the force of this impulse. For a while, lazily putting one leg before the other, he slowly strolled along until the strength of the push he had received was used up; then he slowed down his movements to a lifeless creeping. As if from a great distance, he heard the threatening voice of his father: "You, Adolfla, I'll give you legs!"

The threat only resulted in Adolfla's slackening his pace still further. He was just on the point of turning around to see whether a safe distance intervened when he felt his ear grabbed by his father, who had hurried up very quietly. Adolfla received retribution which the avenger in his sudden anger probably meted out too abundantly. "Get on," he ordered, and the howling boy trotted on, but certainly not so fast as he easily might have, to the shop of the merchant Reischel. Herr Reischel must have suspected what had happened to Adolfla, and as a consolation gave him a little horn called St. John's bread. For this Adolfla has remained eternally thankful to him.

Besides these blows, richly deserved if perhaps too generously administered, Adolfla remembers with unmollified resentment an unjust punishment. One winter evening the boy was the unobserved witness of a conversation in the inn. The card-players had stopped for a short pause;

then one of them proposed a sort of test whose execution
seemed to turn the inn into a classroom, and the phlegmatic,
dull-witted townsmen into first-grade schoolboys; this
the boy could not fail to notice. "Who can spell out correctly 'Neapolitanischer Dudelsackpfeifer' without slipping up once?"

And now the old card-players began to mouth with
heavy tongues: "N, Ne, A, a, Nea-, p, o, po, Neapo—"
and within half a minute the smoky room seemed transformed into a stable in which sheep baa'ed, little goats
bleated, pigs grunted, and cows mooed, until the multi-
vocal concert ended in ringing laughter. With that the
purpose of the joker was accomplished. "Are we here to
say a litany or to play preference? Klempner, cut and
deal!" Adolfla crept out of the room, and did not close his
eyes that night until he could spell the long words without making a single mistake.

The next morning his father was not in his best mood;
the meeting had probably lasted too late into the night.
In spite of this, Adolfla ventured the bold statement that
it was no trick at all to spell the long words; one only had
to pay a little attention and not to think of the cards at
the same time. But with that he touched a sore spot, and
could only thank his speed that the blow his father aimed
at his head partially missed its mark.

"Haven't you got anything more sensible to do than
such nonsense?"

"None of you yesterday was able to accomplish this
nonsense," answered the disrespectful boy, and ducked out
of dangerous proximity.

On another occasion Adolfla unwittingly heaped heavy
guilt upon himself, guilt which was all the more oppressive

because he had to answer for it to his good grandmother. The old woman had acquired a goat that was the joy of Adolfla's existence. His greatest pleasure was to visit the goat's stall and watch with tireless interest how daintily and delicately the animal would pick up the single leaves in the fodder strewn before her, try them out, then scorn them or cause them quickly to disappear. And when the gourmet had oats set before her! Every single little kernel was a delight for her. And the crackling music of her restless jaws! When the little bowl had been cleaned up, the scattered kernels had their turn; none was so well hidden that the searching mouth of the animal could not find it. Adolfla had the impression that the goat was always hungry, and decided secretly to double her ration in order to prolong the appetizing spectacle of meal-time.

One day the question occurred to him: Can a goat ever have enough to eat? It suggested a test, for the oat-bin was full. Well, then a third portion—a fourth—the goat continued to eat with undiminished appetite—a fifth!

The boy began to be uneasy, for by now the belly of the goat seemed to him to be unnaturally swollen. He slipped out of the stable with the uncertain feeling that he had possibly caused great misfortune.

His conscience bothered him during that night. Next morning the dreaded misfortune developed. Aunt Karline appeared with the news that the goat was very sick; she was lying on her side with a badly swollen belly and was probably near her end.

The half-empty oat-bin, which the patient could not possibly have opened herself, Adolfla's frequent visits to the stable, his guilty behavior—all these made it easy to fix the blame. The grandmother was genuinely angry at

Adolfla; of course he did not have to fear a beating, but her laments about the goat hurt him much more. She finally worked herself up to say: "Oh, you horrid little beast, you!"

Sobbing, the evil-doer clutched her apron. "Grandmother, dear, stop being angry at me—I didn't do it on purpose. She liked it so much."

"Sensible people often don't know when they've got enough—how can you expect it of the poor animal," his grandmother answered, softening before the distress of her favorite. But the goat recovered, and even the irreconcilable Aunt Karline was won over.

One punishment suffered without guilt remains ineffaceable in the boy's memory.

One day Adolfla heard his father call, "Come quickly! Hurry over to the cigar-store and get a *Portorico!*"

"What? A Pór—por. . . ."

"A Portorico—a cigar—you dumbhead," replied his father. The boy looked at him without comprehending, thinking more of the word than of the object. In order to remember the foreign-sounding name, he hit upon the idea of pronouncing methodically one syllable of it with each running step. "Por-to-ri-co—Por-to-ri-co."

He had reached the middle of the city square when he encountered a complication. His friends, idling about, had noticed their comrade running purposefully and rhythmically, and had followed him. In order not to let himself be distracted, he now began calling out in a loud voice: "Por-to-ri-co." But soon the beginning and end of the uncanny word were no longer distinguishable; it became "To-ri-co-por, To-ri-co-por"—and by the time a breathless Adolfla turned the doorknob of the cigar store, there was only a wild dance of exotic syllables jumping about in his brain.

He had to return with his errand unaccomplished; on the way home he made vain attempts to bring the chaos of syllables into order. Hesitantly he entered the inn-room. "What took you so long?" his father demanded. "Give me the cigar."

In a small voice the boy answered, "I haven't got it— I lost the name on the way!"

"You stupid fool—the boy isn't good for anything at all," and a very rough punch in the ribs was the reward of Adolfla's pains.

III

THE CHOIR-SINGER

TIME went by. After letters had been exchanged between his mother and Father Gregor, it was decided that Adolf was to leave for St. Paul, in Carinthia. It would be a rather long and complicated trip, and the eleven-year-old boy, inexperienced and uneducated as he was, could not be sent so great a distance alone. It was arranged that the wife of Doctor Eduard Ehrlich, the older uncle, who practised in Trofaiach, Upper Styria, should pay a visit to her parents-in-law in Silesia, and on her journey homeward should take Adolf as far as Styria. For the occasion, the boy became at least half civilized: he was given a thorough haircut; for the first time in his life a regular felt hat, and stockings, until now entirely unknown to him. He had moreover a new suit of clothes— long breeches, and a long black coat. He looked more like a very young sexton than a student, but for a choir-singer the outward appearance of the boy was not inappropriate.

Leaving home was not so painful as Adolf had feared, because the excitement of travelling over and beyond the ridge of low mountains which encompassed his world, of seeing new things, especially the railroad with the locomotives of which he had heard so much, led him to forget all other considerations. The boy got the seat on the box at the side of the coachman. The latter was no less a personage than Mr. Kluss, a rich peasant of the neighborhood, and Adolf's godfather. He drove his own horses. It was a long distance, a day and a half's journey, to the nearest railroad station. On the way Mr. Kluss talked to Adolf about his brother who was a high official in the Ministry of Instruction in Vienna, but the boy paid little heed to what was said to him because his new boots were too tight and his stockings too thick and coarse. He had to strip off his boots to rest his feet, and thereafter travelled barefooted. At Troppau he took leave of Mr. Kluss and his horses.

The railway was a marvel to the boy; he was dumbfounded by what he heard and saw. The first stop was made in Vienna. The hustle and bustle, the hubbub and turmoil of the streets bewildered the young traveller, and made him think longingly of the quietness of his little town. He did not see anything of Vienna during his stay of one day, which he had to spend in a very modest hotel room because his aunt forbade his going out barefooted. To while away the time, he studied the many new things he found in the room, for instance, the gas-jet. Petrol lamps had been called new-fangled things at home, where the tallow candle reigned supreme and where his grandmother used to spin by a torch of pinewood; you do not need much light for spinning, where the sense of touch is everything. And then the white knob on the wall above the nightstand. "Ring Once for the Chambermaid; Twice for the Butler." Never having seen an electric button, the boy was fascinated; he could not resist pressing it. A loud ring, another pressure, another loud ring. The boy thought, this electric ring works excellently. After a while the door opened and in came a tall, rather forbidding-looking man. "What do you want, boy?" he asked. Very much frightened, the young summoner answered, "Oh, nothing." The butler: "But you rang two times." The boy: "I didn't ring." Then the liar was called a very juicy Viennese name, something like *"Lausbub,"* or lousy boy. This epithet impressed the boy deeply, and he swore to tell the truth, henceforth, always.

In Trofaiach, Upper Styria, Adolf spent two months in the house of his uncle, Doctor Eduard Ehrlich. He found there many cousins who seemingly spoke a language quite different from his own. Both parties had difficulty in understanding each other, and the uninvited foreigner very often was laughed at and ridiculed. The big mountains, the Reiting, Reichenstein, etc., oppressed the child, who came from a more or less flat country in which low hills were called high mountains. He felt himself unwelcome in the family, and friendless. Whenever he took part in a boyish trick planned by his cousins, he was always made the culprit in the end. He felt instinctively that Uncle Eduard was not his friend. The doctor made no secret of his opinion that the whole idea of sending his nephew to the Gymnasium was wrong. To study one must have some means, the boy was as poor as a church-mouse. Who would take care of him later on? The Gymnasium would be an affair of eight years, and then would come the University. Quite impossible to get over a high mountain without being equipped for the trip. He thought it much better to send the boy into trade. He had in view a dry-goods shop in Graz, the owner of which was personally known to him. Perhaps he was right; perhaps the career of the poor Silesian boy might have been smoother this way. But it seems remarkable that the boy, though intimidated by his uncle and by the whole family, showed a stubborn resistance to all these insinuations. The dream of his childhood, continually renewed by his mother's encouragement, was to study and to become a grand gentleman. After an outburst of tears, the desperate boy even made bold to say that he was grateful for the hospitality of Uncle Eduard, but that he would have to leave very soon for St. Paul, where he had got a free place and so for the next four years would cost nobody anything. Uncle Eduard was astounded at this insolence, but he did not interfere again, and on occasion even showed some liking for the stubborn boy.

At the end of September, Adolf left Trofaiach for St. Paul. Uncle Eduard seemed reconciled with the situation and was kind enough to drive his nephew in a little cabriolet to the nearest railway station, Bruck-on-the-Mur. The boy sat silent at his side, deeply absorbed in thoughts of the near future. Uncle Eduard must have felt it his duty to say some friendly words to the departing student, and must needs touch again on the question of who was to pay the expenses. He declared himself unable to do it because he had not less than twelve children; otherwise, by God, he would do it. He was good at heart, but twelve children are very apt to make a man hard toward others. Adolf was touched by this last kindness of his uncle, but swore to himself that he would rather starve than knock at his uncle's door.

This time Adolf travelled alone in a slow train. Of course, he had been told to change cars in Marburg and to get off at a station named Unterdrauburg, at the frontier of Carinthia; there somebody would be waiting to take him to St. Paul. When Adolf descended from the car, he saw pacing the platform a tall clergyman who was evidently a Benedictine monk, clad in a long black gown which was circled at the waist by a black belt. At the front and back the habit was covered by a sheet of black cloth reaching down to the hem of the habit, called a scapular because it bedecked the shoulders. This scapular was the most conspicuous feature of the costume; being outside the waist-belt, it floated in the slightest wind. The costume was completed by a black collar with a white rim. Hat and overcoat were of civilian fashion. No, this was not Father Gregor, whom the nephew knew by his pictures, but Father Odilo, a friend of Father Gregor's; the latter had not been able to come this afternoon.

As they drove along a noisy, rather large river, Father Odilo asked whether the boy from Silesia knew its name. The boy was silent, feeling the blood rush to his face. "Not much geography, what?" said Father Odilo. "Of course, coming from Silesia you didn't care much about Carinthia. This river is called the Drave." The boy thanked him and then was silent. After a while the boy said, "The Mur empties into the Drave and the Drave into the Danube near Belgrade." Father Odilo retorted, "Are you quite sure, boy?" Yes, the boy was sure. While Father Odilo, a Bavarian by birth, had never cared much about the geography of the Balkans, the old rector at the school at Weidenau had been a very good teacher and had told his boys lots of things about Belgrade, about Prince Eugenius the noble knight, and the Danube. The rector had even told the boys that Lincoln in America had been murdered, but had failed to tell the boys who Lincoln was.

In that moment, Adolf felt grateful to his old teacher.

After a two hours' drive, the carriage rounded a hill and of a sudden the boy saw the Monastery of St. Paul looming in the background. Looking at the large, squat buildings on top of a hill, Adolf felt disappointed. And indeed, no one approaching it from this side can get an idea of the beauty and grandeur of the mediæval monastery as it is revealed in the view from the south. By good fortune the original plan of the buildings, which are not much less than a thousand years old, has never been carried out, so that the southern wing was never built. The gap allows one a beautiful view of the cathedral with its two mighty towers, protected and encircled by the three other colossal wings, which form two right-angles. Two of these wings are linked together by a colossal tower which rises from the side of the hill and makes an imposing picture to the visitor who comes from the north side.

Adolf was installed at the college of the monastery. This was called "Convict"; the boys were termed "Convictists"—not convicts! There he felt immediately at home. About thirty of the students of the Gymnasium were Convictists, who lived in the monastery; the others were Externists. Father Gregor, who at that time was at Klagenfurt, came to St. Paul to present his nephew to the abbot, then Prelate Augustin. The abbot lived *"extra Claustrum"*—outside of that large part of the building which was exclusively reserved for the monks and closed to any visitors, especially to women. The abbot's abode was called the prelature. At the door stood the prelate's valet, who announced the visitors. The boy felt awed by the big corridors with walls adorned by great pictures representing former abbots, bishops, and saints. The prelate gave the shy boy a friendly welcome and allowed him to kiss his hand. Uncle Gregor had previously informed his nephew that on such occasions not the hand but the big light-green emerald on the prelate's finger-ring was to be kissed. Adolf knew at once that he would never forget that kiss upon the green stone.

Prelate Augustin, a very good-looking man, wore around his neck a thick gold chain from which there hung upon his breast a precious, diamond-set golden cross. The poor boy felt very much impressed by the rather severe splendor of the prelate's reception-room, as well as by the serene dignity of his person. The Prelate hoped, he said, that Adolf would be a diligent boy; as far as the singing was concerned, he felt sure that the alto voice of the boy, which he had already heard, was all right—*"ad majorem Dei gloriam"* he added, and let his young visitor leave a parting kiss upon the big green emerald. Uncle Gregor told his nephew that the insignia of the prelate's dignity were once worn by the Abbot Princes of St. Blasien in the Schwarzwald, from whence the monks had emigrated to St. Paul after the closing of St. Blasien by Emperor Joseph the Second.

After this audience, Adolf felt himself no longer a visitor but an ever so humble member of the big monastery. His pleasant alto voice, which rang under the vaults of the cathedral often louder than necessary, made him conspicuous among his colleagues, although he was only a student of the first class. Shortly after his arrival at St. Paul a regiment of Austrian soldiers marched through the little village, and the name of Custozza and Koenig Grätz became known to everybody.

Learning never gave him the slightest difficulty. When he was in the second class he earned his first money as a *correpetitor* (helper) of some students in the first class. He was beloved by all who knew him, but felt himself hated and persecuted by a young monk, a rough peasant

ST. PAUL'S BENEDICTINE MONASTERY IN CARINTHIA

THE FAMOUS "UNCLE GREGOR," ABBOT OF ST. PAUL'S

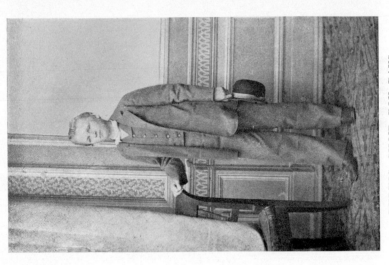

AS A MEDICAL STUDENT

DURING CHOIR—BOY DAYS

in spite of his clerical habit, who unfortunately was the prefect (overseer) of the Convictists. From what Adolf could gather from the sexton of the cathedral, Father Gregor and young Father Eberhardt were not great friends. It is hard to believe, but true, that Father Eberhardt persecuted the choir-singer on the ground that he had a "free" place in the Convict, even though as a compensation for food and instruction the boy paid with his voice in the choir. Nobody had found fault with Adolf as yet, and the boy knew very well that the prefect could not, of his own authority, carry out his threat to make Adolf take his meals not with his colleagues but with the farm-hands down in the big farmyard. Yet the threat terrified the boy, who resolved to be careful and on no account to give his persecutor any cause for complaint. Again the fact weighed upon his soul that he was so poor, and he felt it the task of his life to battle against this poverty. For his person he had money enough, since he earned money not only by his private lessons but also as ministrant at Mass. Father Richard, his professor of mathematics, was also the celebrating priest whom he served at Holy Mass. Unfortunately the elderly Father Richard was an early riser by habit, so his ministrant had to become an early riser by necessity. At six o'clock, winter and summer, the boy had to get up, with no time to wash his face or comb his luxurious yellow hair. He would say his *confitear* in an entirely unwashed condition—so to say, with ashes upon his head! When the priest at the beginning of Mass would pronounce, *"Introibo ad altare Dei,"* the ministrant would answer, *"Ad Deum qui laetificat juventutem meam"*—To God who makes my youth joyful—without thinking much that youth at six o'clock in the morning of a cold winter

day is happier in bed than kneeling upon the chilly marble
steps of an altar. For his daily services the ministrant
earned three *gulden* (florins) a month, which was then
about one dollar. The amount covered in addition to his
lesson fees the cost of neat clothing. The poorest of the
boys was always the best clad, because he took care of his
scanty wardrobe.

In the last year of Adolf's stay at St. Paul, rumors of
a battle at Sedan echoed faintly in the peaceful valley of
the river Lavant.

The four years of Untergymnasium in St. Paul were
the happiest of the boy's life. He loved all his teachers
and was loved by them. They were indeed excellent men,
all of them except the one who hated the boy with the free
place and was hated by him in turn. Adolf even got a
rough blow from the boorish priest because he had put on
his hat before leaving the room for a walk. All the boys
had put on their hats, but Father Eberhardt singled out
his darling and gave him a thrust on the head with his
iron-tipped cane; the hat flew to the ceiling and the iron
point of the cane scratched the boy's face. Adolf knew
that he would never forget his torturer's rudeness, for the
memories of youth are indelible.

Adolf was by this time a slender, tall boy of fifteen, with
yellow hair and blue eyes. He was two years older than
his colleagues of the same class, which gave him a certain
superiority. He made friends with the young novices;
there were always at least two of them in the house who
after having gone through the Obergymnasium had entered the monastery for a year of probation to see whether
or not they liked the monastic life. He tried on their habits
and felt very proud in the long black gown. Only four

more years of study and he should wear these clothes
rightly, he thought. And that thought would certainly
have come true if at that time the monastery had also had
the Obergymnasium which was established there some decades later. Then, of course, his way would have led from
the so-called "maturity examination" at the end of the
Eighth Class directly into the Novitiate. How different
and how much easier would have been his life under such
conditions! He had only to look at his Uncle Gregor, who
led a happy life as administrator of the large farm-lands
of the monastery.

IV

OUT IN THE WORLD

IT was with a feeling of sadness that Adolf—but now that he is sixteen years old and on the threshold of manhood, let me call him Lorz—left what for four years he had called home. From now on he was going to have to stand entirely upon his own feet; he was going to have to fend not only for his clothes, but for food and lodging as well. To continue his studies he went to Klagenfurt, where the St. Paul Monastery then maintained a small cloister inhabited by those Benedictine monks whom the monastery was required to send to Klagenfurt as teachers. To help the ex-choir-singer of St. Paul along, the prelate had given orders that the boy should receive a free lunch every day. That was certainly very kind of the abbot, but after some of these free lunches the boy very stupidly refused the gift. It disgusted him to have to worm his way through a crowd of beggars, men, and women, who thronged the kitchen door to get their free soup. "I am not a beggar yet," the boy said to himself, and was glad that he had saved some money in St. Paul. Living expenses were then very low in Klagenfurt; fifteen *gulden* a month would suffice to keep his head above water. With his letters of recommendation, it was not difficult for the ex-choir-singer to obtain private tutoring jobs which paid three dollars a month for one lesson-hour every day.

Lorz lived with some student friends in one room, and the old woman who let the room cooked for them. It was a

poor but a happy life, quite different from monastery life.
You were your own master, you could go where you
pleased, and you met people, although Klagenfurt was
then a very modest capital of Carinthia. And then you
saw what was quite new and rather exciting for a young
would-be monk; you saw nice girls. By good fortune on
his daily way to school Lorz met a young girl who went the
same way to her school. She was to be a teacher. It was
entirely natural that these daily encounters should lead
to occasional conversation, to appointments, friendship,
and to his first innocent love. This, his first meeting with
a nice girl, was enough to make the young man forget his
intention of becoming a Benedictine monk. He discarded
the thought entirely, laughed at his former predilection
for a long black habit and began to spend more money on
his wardrobe than on his food. With small outlay he
managed to become a provincial dandy, with frills on the
breast of his shirt and nice suits. As far as that was possible in Klagenfurt, he strove for sartorial perfection, all
for the sake of making a good impression in general and
especially on Josephine. It was a happy time. The young
dandy had never supposed it would be so easy to work his
way as a self-supporting young student. His studies concerned him little; once in a while he would spend a leisurely
hour on them, for things that others found difficult seemed
easy to him.

Quite a change came into Lorz's life when he was offered
the tutorship of a boy of bad reputation, the eldest son of
a very distinguished bourgeois family of the town. Former
tutors had failed to convince the boy that the Gymnasium
is a torture inescapable for all boys who want to achieve
anything in future life. Lorz knew the boy Hans to be as

nice and intelligent as his former tutor believed him to be
stubborn and obstinate. He thought, "Why not try where
others have failed?" And so he gave up his private lessons and went to live with Hans in the large house of his
parents. What seemed to be a good stroke of luck at the
moment turned out to be the worst luck Lorz had met with
in his young life. All was right in the beginning; Hans's
parents were lovely, especially his mother, a very beautiful
woman. She did her best to feed the new tutor all sorts of
delicacies to make him forget his troubles with Hans. But
to live with that boy and to work with him proved to be
martyrdom, for his tutor had to be not only his teacher,
but also his jailer. The boy thought and practised only
mischief, and was loath to learn anything; forcing him
only made him the more rebellious. Yet the tutor managed
to drag the boy through two classes.

Lorz began deeply to repent having given up his former
freedom and his work with willing, pleasant boys; the luxurious life at the rich house was no compensation. But
when he attempted to give notice to leave his position the
parents entreated him to stay because he alone had had
success with the boy. So he promised to stay. But there
came a morning in early winter when Hans was not to be
found in his bed, nor anywhere else in the house. He had
left during the night, not to kill himself as his mother
feared, but to go to the parents of his former tutor, with
whom he had once spent his vacation. But this was not
known at the time, and the parents were very much frightened. Now their tune changed; now it was the cruel
tutor's insistence that Hans should learn his lessons that
was the obvious and only cause of his flight; Lorz had
driven him to desperation; Hans simply could not stand

the torture any longer. It was self-evident that the torturer must leave the house at once and go where he liked.

The tutor-torturer assured Hans's father that he was
very sorry ever to have come into the house at all. As for
the "torturing," not he but the father himself was the
torturer, because he insisted that Hans should become a
Doctor of Laws. Hans would never be that if he could
help it, and therefore Hans had fled from his father. "If
I were in your place," said the tutor, "I should put Hans
into business and make a good stationer of him." This
remark was spiteful because Lorz knew that Hans's father
had been made a stationer by his own father because he
had absolutely refused to learn Greek and Latin. Like
father, like son.

But this easy revenge did not alter the fact that the ex-
tutor was thrown out on the street, this time without any
savings at all, because young *"homo stultus"* had spent
the little money he got beside board on finery, mostly ties
and nice boots. Hadn't he even had to buy pince-nez to
look stylish, although he felt blind looking through the
glasses? His present situation sobered him, however.
Scornfully he hurled the glasses upon the floor and
tramped upon them. He cut off the frills from the breast
of his shirts to make the washing less expensive and begged
shelter from one of his good friends. To pay for immediate needs he sold his summer suits for a tenth part of
what they had cost him, and felt himself to be in the
deepest hole of his life. The question of how to continue
his studies did not bother him; the only problem was how
to go on living.

News of the flight of Hans and of the downfall of his
tutor spread through the town like fire. The director of

the Gymnasium understood the situation of the dismissed
tutor, and said that the parents had behaved shamefully,
but could not help him because at this time of the year
there were no private lessons to be got. As chance would
have it, one of Lorz's friends remembered that a remote
aunt of his, living on her estate in southern Hungary beyond the city of Arad, wanted a home tutor for her son
Arthur, who was ready to begin his Gymnasium and could
not be sent to the city.

The dismissed tutor accepted in advance, hoping that
the post would still be free, and so it came to pass that a
newly appointed tutor changed Carinthia for Hungary.
He was loath to leave Klagenfurt where he had made many
friends as a member of the Society of Singers of Klagenfurt. He could no longer attend their singing-lessons and
concerts. It was a sad leave-taking. Many of his friends
thought he should have stayed; they felt he was in danger
of breaking off and giving up his studies. But that was
Lorz's least concern. He now had something to live on,
the rest did not trouble him. He would miss his teachers,
but he could study by himself and would come back to
take the final maturity examination with his colleagues.

The place where the mother of his future pupil Arthur
resided was a tiny village, or rather a cluster of mud-built
huts in which Roumanian peasants lived. There were no
chimneys; the smoke filtered out through the thatched
roofs. Beside the village, near the river Körös, lay a rather
badly kept park containing a low, squat, one-story building rather euphemistically called the *"castell"* (castle).
The valley was surrounded by Carpathian hills covered
with beech trees; the estate consisted chiefly of beech woods
and had only a small acreage. There was no railway to

transport the beeches, and so they were left to fall and rot on the spot where they had grown to mighty giants. Lady R, the owner of the estate, was very hard up, and everything was mortgaged to the limit; her chief problem was how to sell the estate to some advantage. The rare guests in the house were prospective buyers who usually withdrew after a short inspection of the decaying farmhouses.

The low squat house in the beautiful though neglected park was loneliness in essence. It happened very often that Lady R was suddenly called to Budapest to deal with threatening creditors, and then the tutor would be left alone in the house with the children—his pupil Arthur, a smaller boy who had not yet begun to study, and two little girls, Helen and Misa, of about five and six years, the most charming and lovely creatures imaginable. On many a winter evening the children would gather around the big fireplace and sing Carinthian songs which the tutor had taught them. These concerts were opened and closed with the motto of the Society of Singers of Klagenfurt: "What the dew is to the meadows, song is to the soul." It was engraved in the bark of the hazelwood baton with which the tutor beat the time. When Lady R was at home, these gatherings around the fireplace would begin with an English lesson, for Lady R was of English descent and spoke English fluently. But the lesson always wound up with the concert. Lady R was a very noble-looking and highly educated woman, who spoke Hungarian and Roumanian as fluently as English and German; she was the first competent teacher of manners the young tutor had ever had. She was bent on making a gentleman of the rude boy, who learned to thank her for criticisms.

There was never the slightest disagreement between Lady R and the tutor except on one occasion. While the Baroness was absent on one of her business trips, the tutor received an invitation to attend a ball to be held in a neighboring village and accepted it. He was hungry to see people; besides, there would probably be nice girls at the ball. He rode to it on an old mare; it took him more than an hour to get there because the road was slippery with ice, and his feet became very cold in the stirrups. It worried him that he had no gloves while the gentlemen at the ball had not only white gloves, but wore glittering diamond rings over their glove-covered fingers. Yet, the tall, lean, yellow-haired and blue-eyed young man found more favor with the ladies, especially with a certain very nice young girl, than did his dark-skinned rivals with curly, black hair, mostly young farmers, and the tutor got invitations to attend other balls at other places. On his way home he felt a little disturbed; it would not do to spend the night at balls and study during the day, and he resolved to have done with it and not to tell the Baroness of his escapade. But she was told, of course, immediately after her return home. What she said to the tutor was worse than he had expected. It was to the effect that she felt greatly disappointed to find that she had failed in her efforts to educate a young man to at least so high a moral standing that he would know how to choose his company. The tutor made bold to reply that the company was good enough for him so far (he was thinking of the nice girl he had danced with so furiously), but he agreed with her that teaching, studying, and dancing in distant places could not go together. One item or the other must be cancelled, and of course it would be the dancing. The lady answered, "It is just what I was confident you would say."

Those ten months in Gurahoncz were a happy though strenuous time. The goal was that Arthur should, within this time, be prepared to pass an examination which would enable him to enter the Third Class of Gymnasium next year. That meant double work, in half the time required for the usual course of teaching in the Gymnasium. Arthur had never been to school at all, and had been taught by his mother, most haphazardly in the bargain. But he was a boy of rare intelligence and willingness, just the opposite of the former pupil, Hans. Lorz and Arthur became good friends and were inseparable, not only at work but during their hours of play. In this respect they had to rely on themselves, for the lonesome "castell" was devoid of all means of recreation.

In a corner of the old house, Lorz one day found an old rifle. Though rusty, it was complete in its essential parts, and promised after cleaning to be a good toy. The boys had to work for two weeks to procure all the things necessary for target-shooting. The shooting-range was found, after much prospecting, in a wide meadow, divided into two parts by a little rivulet and backed by wooded hills. The target was fastened to a low post in the middle of the meadow near the rivulet.

The tutor explained to his pupil all he knew himself about shooting at a target. In the Austrian mountains, especially in Tyrol, it is the national sport; every Tyrolese man is a capital marksman and very often a crack shot, and every festivity has its target-shooting. High prizes are given to the best shot, who reigns supreme for a year as "king" in his shooting company and is shown

to the people in gorgeous pageants. Even when he prays
to his God, the Tyrolese likes to hear the thundering guns
outside the church. Lorz explained to his pupil what it
means to national defense if every man is an expert rifle-
shot, and how in 1809, the Tyrolese peasants under their
national hero, Andreas Hofer, had defeated even Napoleon.

Arthur was less interested in the history of Tyrolese
national defense than in what the marker of the shots at
the target had to do. Sometimes, the tutor told him, the
marker is equipped as a harlequin who runs to the target
as soon as the sign has been given to him. His attitude
in front of the target means everything to the shooter. A
disdainful gesture cannot be misunderstood. A compli-
mentary gesture means, you did not miss the mark very
far. He marks the shot with his instrument and then
swings it around his head as many times as the number of
circles. If your bullet hits the center, a cannon is fired
off by machinery and the marker behaves like a mad-
man, jumping and yelling; sometimes he even stands on
his head, waving his legs.

Arthur wanted at once to be the marker. "Rather not,"
replied his tutor. "We'd better walk together to the
target after each shot. That will give us some exercise."
So they galloped after each bullet, sprang over the rivulet and checked the hits. This forced exercise left the
shooters breathing deeply. Since a target shooter had
better stop breathing at all before he touches the trigger,
Lorz decided to stay where he was and allow Arthur to
be the marker. The boy was to hide himself in a little
copse to the left, far away from the target. Not until
he had heard the shot, was he to move from his hiding-

place, and run to the target to check the shot. Things went on all right for a long while. Then the shooter decided to try to hit the center by extraordinarily deliberate marksmanship. He took long aim, holding his breath, trying again and again until the peepsight, which hid the world from him, showed its head in the center of the black of the target. Off went the shot.

When the marksman lowered his barrel, a paralyzing terror loosened his limbs; his knees began to tremble. He saw Arthur standing before the target covering it with his breast, and, in the same moment, tumbling to the ground as if hit by lightning. Terror-stricken, the shooter stared at the ghastly scene, then with a sudden effort rushed toward the place where the fate of his life was to be decided. The doomed victim of the terrible accident seemed to be shaken by the last convulsions. The frail body of the boy curled to form a bow, as if trying to rise, then collapsed again. The tutor clasped Arthur and lifted him from the ground. The boy was still breathing, or rather gasping for breath; his face had a bluish color and his eyes seemed to be protruding. "Arthur darling, are you hurt, tell me, oh tell me!" the wretched youth groaned. "Arthur—speak a word to me!"

To his indescribable relief, Arthur said in his slow and deliberate manner, "You hit the center! I didn't think it was so difficult to stand on my head."

"Arthur, are you hurt? Tell me!" his tutor cried again.

"I, hurt? But how? I don't understand you! I tried to stand on my head as the Austrian markers do when the center is hit." The marksman wept tears of joy as he clasped Arthur in his arms again. The boy had gone to

the target because the wait had been too long. Probably
he had taken another noise for the whistle of the bullet,
and had arrived at the target just after the bullet reached
its aim—the center. When Arthur understood the situation and what cruel torture his tutor had lived through,
he was deeply moved, and clasping his arms around the
neck of his friend, whispered: "Mother must never know."
And she never did know.

Isn't it curious that Arthur in later years became a
good rifle shot himself and that this art stood him in
good stead when he and his gallant wife defended the
Austrian Embassy building in Peking during the Boxer
uprising!

The two boys dropped this kind of sport and turned
to their books again. It was a pleasure to teach Arthur
and to learn with him. While the boy prepared his lessons, the tutor studied hard to prepare for the much
dreaded maturity-examinations by which the Gymnasium
had to be wound up. Whoever had passed this really difficult examination was ripe to go to the University to
study law, philosophy, medicine, or theology.

One word about financial arrangements. The fee of
the tutor for the ten months was to be three hundred
florin, less than a hundred dollars in cash, to be paid in
installments. Some months it was paid, some other months
it was not paid. In spite of this, the tutor very soon became a capitalist in comparison with Lady R, who lived
from hand to mouth. It was a matter of course that the rich
tutor should lend money to the lady of the house when
she was in dire need of it, which was a rather chronic
condition. At last the bookkeeping got so complicated
that the tutor never knew how much he had at the mo-

ment. He felt so attached to the tottering house and to its desperately fighting lady that he considered his small fortune as hers, and hers as his. These two items summed up were zero, anyway. But this did not trouble the tutor because there was always the hope that the estate might be sold to advantage. The sale took place at last, and the whole family left the castle, poor as church-mice. But that happened some years later, when the tutor had already become a student of medicine in Vienna.

At the end of the tenth month Lorz brought his pupil Arthur to the Gymnasium at Klagenfurt, where he passed a very good examination and was admitted to the Third Class, while his tutor, as a private student, passed the much feared maturity-examination "*cum laude*." When Lorz took leave of Arthur, he did not know that at their next meeting he would have to greet his one-time pupil as His Excellency, the Austrian Ambassador to China!

V

A STUDENT OF MEDICINE

AND now that Lorz is twenty years old and definitely a grown man, the writer can no longer escape taking full responsibility for him.

Although my teachers advised me to study philosophy and become a professor at the Gymnasium, I resolved to study medicine. In my choice I was much influenced by Lady R, who had been related to the late Professor of Surgery in Vienna, J. Schuh, the predecessor of the famous Billroth. She had told me much about the medical profession at the time of Professor Schuh, and provided me with a letter of recommendation to Carl Langer, who had lived formerly in Hungary and was now Professor of Anatomy in Vienna as successor to the famous Professor Hyrtl. Somewhat downhearted, I resolved to go to Vienna and at least try to study medicine. The prospect of study did not trouble me, but the problem of what to live on; my whole fortune was about thirty *gulden*. It was rather an undertaking to find one's living in the great Reichs-Haupt und Residenz Stadt, Wien, the famous Kaiserstadt an der Donau. At that time, however, it was pleasanter to live in the Kaiserstadt than it is now. Food and lodging were very cheap; thirty *gulden* could cover one month if carefully handled. In the meanwhile the question was not one of study, though the lectures on anatomy had already begun, but of finding a job.

54

I knew of certain offices where openings for private lessons were registered. I went there several times a week only to learn that there were no openings, or that the openings available excluded students of medicine, who were not liked as private teachers. I had, of course, made my salaam to Hofrath Langer, Professor of Anatomy and Referent to the Ministry of Instruction in things medical, and had delivered my letter of introduction. Hofrath Langer found a temporary job for a poor young student. He bade me enter the title-pages of about a thousand books on anatomy in the catalogue of the Anatomical Library, but not before I had given proof of a calligraphic handwriting. I worked about two weeks and got about fifteen *gulden.* That was not much, but it was surely worth while to be known personally to the Hofrath Langer, as the future demonstrated. But this time good fortune did not intervene to help me out of the deep hole I found myself in. I could get no lessons, and the money dwindled in spite of the utmost frugality.

One day hope loomed large. I was informed that a high Austrian official who lived in Constantinople wanted a tutor for his son, who was to be prepared for the Gymnasium. Here was salvation at last! The relatively big salary could be saved; next year I could make a new attempt to begin the study of medicine. I ran to the agent who was entrusted with finding the right man, only to learn that an arrangement had been made with another student just an hour before. As fate would have it, I met the sister of this lost pupil many years later as a patient.

I used to take my meals in a kind of establishment called *Volksküche* (people's kitchen), and there became acquainted with one of the customers, a *Dienstmann* (public servant), who used to stand on a certain street-corner soliciting small errands, such as carrying parcels, love letters, etc. This man apparently took a fancy to me when I told him of my desperate and useless efforts to get a job. "Why," the man said, "I know of a job which is good enough for me. As my assistant you will easily make your living and save something for a later attempt to study." I pondered this possibility of keeping the wolf from the door quite seriously, and promised the man I would tell him when I was ready to accept the offer.

In my great plight, I remembered the day when I had left Weidenau, sitting on the box of the carriage at the side of Godfather Kluss, who had a brother in Vienna, a high official in the Ministry of Education. To him I went with my credentials and told him of my life since that memorable drive. Sectionsrath Kluss was very affable, and was delighted to hear me tell of his peasant brother.

"Can you help me in any way, Herr Sectionsrath?" I pleaded. "I am down and out, at the end of my rope. If I have to give up my plan of studying medicine, nothing is left to me but to enter the Benedictine Monastery of St. Paul. Once it was my fervent wish, but now I have changed my mind. I should make a bad monk."

Sectionsrath Kluss said: "God forbid that you should do such a thing against your convictions. Let me first provide for the need of the moment. Sit down, I shall dictate for you a request for immediate assistance from the Ministry. This request will be decided at once through my intervention, and after tomorrow you will have at least fifty *gulden*. That is for the moment. Now about the future! In my opinion you are a worthy candidate for a stipend. Just now some Windhag stipends are available. We make a request, and you get together your credentials and references. I have some friends on the Board of Trustees of the Stipend, and I feel pretty sure you will get it."

To a desperate young man, all this seemed to be a dream too beautiful to come true. Yet it came true. I got the fifty *gulden* at once. My protector Kluss advised me to pay a visit of thanks to Sectionschef N who had met his request so favorably. Herr N. was an old man with snow-white hair and a ruddy, healthy face. When I had finished my thanks, the Sectionschef patted me benevolently upon the shoulder and said: "Never mind, young man, don't worry, fifty years ago I was in the same plight as you and got the same assistance from the Ministry, and just that rather difficult period of my own youth has become the most precious remembrance of my life. Good luck to your future." I felt my own eyes grow moist when I clearly saw the old man's glitter with a surreptitious tear, and the unforgettable audience was closed. Of decided importance to me was the fact that I really got a Windhag stipend; that meant three hundred *gulden* yearly for the next six years. Even the examination fees were to be paid by the stipend fund if the examinations were passed at the legal term. But these fees, according to an added stipulation in the granting diploma, were to be paid back to the fund when the stipendiary should become able to do so. Now it did not matter so very much when my written request to be relieved of the payment of the so-called college money was refused by the dean on the grounds that the request had been delivered several minutes too late, that is, after the closing of his office-hour on a certain day. "I shall teach order to these young fellows," he said, or practically crowed. This brutality on the dean's part meant a loss of twenty *gulden* to me, and I felt like leaping at the ruthless old man's face. Don't make a youth revengeful! He never forgets an injustice meted out to him and will wait quietly for the hour of retaliation.

In spite of this mischance, the sky was blue now and all care forgotten. It seemed as if I had already finished my studies, since this had become only a question of time and was no longer a problem in itself. What I earned in addition by giving a private lesson, which I got in the course of the next few months, made me a carefree, even a rich man. My year had only ten months, since the vacations did not count as months of spending but of saving, for I continued to give lessons at the summer homes of my pupils. Now at last I could settle down and begin work in earnest, because I had the wherewithal for existence. My favorite study was anatomy, and after a few months I was able to teach my colleagues, who had neglected their studies, the secrets of human osteology. By good chance, Hofrath Langer, strolling through the dissection rooms, overheard his former catalogue-writer communicating his knowledge, as far as he himself knew it, to his wholly ignorant colleagues. Langer said to the self-appointed teacher: "It seems you have some gift for teaching. Take up anatomy very seriously; make yourself useful in helping my assistants, pass an excellent examination, and in two years I will nominate you 'official' teacher, as demonstrator of anatomy in my institute."

From that time on, nothing existed for me in the world but anatomy, and I worked day and night.

After the first medical examination, I was appointed Demonstrator of Anatomy. As it was an appendix to the professorship of the University, this new dignity brought a second stipend of three hundred *gulden*. My task was to repeat with the students the lesson of the day as delivered by Hofrath Langer and to help them with their anatomical specimens. I also gave private lessons in anatomy. Two of my private students were not students of medicine but were both Doctors of Philosophy who wanted to acquire some knowledge of anatomy. One of them, a fair and elegantly clad young man, paid for his friend's lessons. This friend was a man with a dark complexion, black short beard, and dark eyes. He wore a broad-brimmed, black slouch hat on his black hair, and a flowing dark coat; he looked more like an artist, a bohemian, than a Doctor of Philosophy. I called my distinguished scholars "the fair one" and "the dark one" because it was impossible for me to keep the dark one's name in my memory. This name, as pronounced by its bearer, sounded like the hiss of a sword-blow. Later on the whole world learned to spell, pronounce, and remember the name of this man, who was destined to become the founder and first President of the Czecho-Slovakian Republic— Thomas G. Masaryk, who to this day loves a broad-brimmed slouch hat. About forty-five years later, the former demonstrator of anatomy reminded President Masaryk of his anatomical studies, and how cruelly, in spite of the knowledge he had acquired, he had operated upon old Austria. And the President answered him: "Beg pardon, sir, old Austria was a corpse before I took the knife in my hand!" And it does seem true that old Austria as a state had fulfilled its historical destiny and was

ripe to disappear as an artificial congregation of diverse
nations with divergent ambitions.

But medicine does not mean anatomy alone, and I had
to find time to visit the clinics. At the beginning of my
clinical studies, I wanted first of all to know: What is
cancer? In my ears rang the remembered answer in unison
of a class, heard as I, not yet a schoolboy, was strolling
around the schoolhouse: "*Das ist der Krebs*"—*Krebs*
meaning in German both "cancer" and "crab." The little
boys in the school recognized not only "*der Krebs*," but
knew also how many legs he had. "*Der Krebs hat acht
Füsse*," still rang in my ears.

And the savants didn't in the least know what cancer
is. Is it the disease? Is it a symptom of disease? And
they don't know up to the present time! Studying medicine, I felt very much disappointed, and did not take
much interest in internal medicine, when I compared the
facts shown up by the pathologist with the poor ways and
means of combating them. Nature has its own methods,
and you cannot do much, if anything at all, to lead them
toward another final goal. It seemed all so discouraging
to me. Anatomy, I thought, would prepare me rather for
surgery, a branch of medical science then just beginning
its great progress. Financial questions no longer bothered me, and I could have given up my private teaching in
a very distinguished family whose head was a newspaper
man. But this family was my only resort in the city, my
only connection with the living world after my day spent
with the dead. Moreover, I liked my pupil Heinrich even
though he was rather a lazy fellow.

Heinrich's mother, the lady of the house, deemed it
very necessary to improve the social education of the still

rustic young instructor. Mrs. H was a very beautiful and a very accomplished lady, a lover of music, art and travel. From her, the demonstrator of anatomy learned to appreciate music, pictures and old architecture, which abounded in Vienna, and the pleasures of travelling, especially in Italy. She played the pianoforte and the young man sang Schubert *lieder*. He worshipped the lady as a superior being and the lady paid for this worship with plenty of delicate food, declaring him an unripe and underfed youth who had first to finish his growth before he should think of becoming a professor of anatomy.

My life was rather a hard one, for I was busy from morning until late into the night. Coming home at nine o'clock, I would prepare my tea and sit down to study till the stroke of midnight. I had not time to spend the money I had at my disposal. In vacations, I travelled, following all the advice given me by that expert traveller, Mrs. H, except in the matter of hotels. I spent so little money on my trips, which were made mostly as a pedestrian, that Mrs. H could hardly believe that I had really been in Naples, Rome, and other important places of Italy, as well as in Switzerland.

The affluent student was even able financially to aid his poor father, who, at fifty-six, became paralyzed in both legs. He had to have a rolling chair which he propelled with his hands and which was of course beyond his means. Had the poor man lived longer, his old age would have been brighter than it was. My mother had died some years before my father, swept away, as it were, by smallpox within a few days.

During the last year of my medical studies, I did my military service. By happy chance I was not marched off

to Bosnia, which was to be annexed by Austria—the first
nail in the coffin of the old monarchy!

The years went by without any excitement, and at the
end of the quinquennium (five years) the examinations
were passed without much ado. The choir-singer was now
a *Doctor Universæ Medicinæ*, but still far from being a
grand gentleman.

I had worked for four years in the dissecting-room and
had become quite an anatomist, *"ein Messeranatom"* as
the anatomists were called, who worked more with the
scalpel than with the microscope. Hofrath Langer invited
me to join his institute for good as one of the official assistants. Considering my skill and application, he said—
Professor Langer was then a personality of great influence and power in the Ministry of Instruction—he felt
sure that docentship and professorship were within easy
reach and could be attained in no time. This, a professorship of anatomy, seemed to be the goal at any university.
But the thought that I would have to spend my whole life
within the walls where *"mors gaudet succurrere vitae"*
(where death rejoices to support life) was unbearable.
Anatomy was all right and interesting enough, but I considered it only as a preparation for surgery. I was loathe
to cut in dead tissue; I wanted to work on the living
body. Professor Langer knew more about me than I
thought; he seemed to be really interested in me and
wanted to keep me on his staff. "I know, Doctor Lorenz,"
he said, "that you are interested in a young lady whom
you courted so fervently at the ball at the house of Mrs.
H. That would not matter if you were my assistant because my assistants are not bound to celibacy as are assistants at the clinics. I should not object to your mar-

riage!" I was dumbfounded and cursed the garrulous friends who had betrayed me. But even this last bomb could not persuade me to become an anatomist, and so I refused the offer, though I knew that the protection of Professor Langer had been lost for all time.

The decision meant a great deal to me because my stipend had come to an end and I had again to plunge into cold water to swim to another goal against many competitors. My provisional aim was the clinic of surgery. As an anatomist of some reputation, though in a narrow circle, I had the preference over others and was readily accepted at the surgical clinic of Dumreicher. At that time old Dumreicher was very sick; he died within the year. His successor was Professor Eduard Albert, who came from Innsbruck. Albert was a very energetic man, eager to make a great name, an ambition the more difficult because Billroth was his rival at the second surgical clinic. It was to Albert's great credit that he shone by his own light at the side of the genius Billroth. Of all my teachers at the University only these two men, Albert and Billroth, made an everlasting impression upon me.

Albert began his work at the clinic by firing half of the staff. Any surgical apprentice who did not show that he was heart and soul devoted to surgery was fired. Any one who failed to write scientifically on a certain question assigned to him by Albert was fired. Young Doctor Lorenz, however, apparently was found unassailable on account of his anatomical knowledge, which had disclosed itself occasionally, and on account of a pamphlet which he had written on some species of hernia which Professor Albert was interested in. I felt very much flattered when Professor Albert made my pamphlet the subject of a lecture in the Vienna Society of Physicians. I lived in the hospital, and the Clinic of Surgery was my world. In emergencies I was always the first one to be ready to handle the case, and Professor Albert approved of many of my sometimes extraordinary suggestions.

My colleagues unanimously designated me the next clinical assistant. This was, and still is, the most coveted position for any young doctor, especially if he aspires to a professorship. To be assistant at a clinic meant to be the responsible representative of and substitute for the Professor, to whom his students gave the title of *"senex"* —"old man." Assistantship was really the first rung on the academical ladder. There were only two more rungs to ascend, namely to become Docent, and, at last, after many years of toil, after having been tested to the quick to the heart's content of the faculty, and after having written articles, pamphlets, and books on your science— Professor Extraordinary. As such you were eligible to be chief of any surgical clinic. *Vox populi vox Dei!* When the next opening came, I was made assistant at the surgical clinic. I felt sure now that nothing could deter me from reaching my goal. At last I had found the missing glove! I knew that I was a very good teacher, and my courses on operative surgery and on surgical diagnosis were always more than crowded. I had not time to count the money I earned, let alone spend it. My happiness seemed to be complete, the more so because Hofrath Albert changed by and by from a superior difficult to please to a most amiable and benevolent adviser and friend.

But on one occasion I had the bad luck to draw the full wrath of my teacher upon my innocent head. It was

Professor Albert's custom to begin each semester with an impressive speech delivered to a large audience. This time he had chosen for his subject the wonderful progress of modern surgery in recent decades. He spoke of the great advantages of narcosis, discovered by American surgeons. He himself had heard patients whimper and cry under the cruel knife, when the only means of shortening their pain was to operate as quickly and as accurately as possible. He extolled the merits of Professor Esmarch, whose fame was greatly enhanced by the fact that he was the husband of a member of the imperial house of Hohenzollern. What an advantage it was to be able to operate on the extremities without losing a drop of the patient's blood—thanks to the Esmarch bandage! But all this was slight in comparison with antisepsis, the invention of the great Lister. With the danger of infection excluded, there seemed to be no limit to the field of the surgeon's knife; it could reach the very source of life. The glorious present and the unimaginable future of surgery was all due to Listerism. (Professor Albert liked to hear himself speak as a priest in the pulpit, or an actor on the stage.)

"And now," he concluded, "let us begin our work, which is to prove the truth of what I have said."

Before the operations began, it was my task as assistant to introduce to the audience some interesting cases who had come for consultation. I had found a charming little girl about five years old whom I considered a most interesting case, though—as I had to learn to my sorrow—she proved not at all suitable for the occasion. In a state of nature, the girl was made to stand upon a table, exposed to the eyes of the whole class, and also, of course, to the scrutinizing eyes of the teacher, whose grim face (he

looked like a Hussite leader in his slavic goatee) was
growing purple with rage. If his eyes had been daggers,
his unfortunate assistant could not have lived one minute
longer. But why, for God's sake? The child was so lovely,
laughing at the unfamiliar aspect of the crowd. It was
true that in spite of her feminine charm, she showed a
peculiar deformity in her whole attitude; her buttocks
protruded and her abdomen as well, while her lower back
was hollow and her knees bent, with her arms reaching
down far below her knees, like an ape's. When she took
a few steps her body wabbled from side to side, like a
duck's. Professor Albert had, of course, made the diagnosis from afar. Interesting as the case might have been
on another occasion, it was just as ill-suited to the present moment.

The whole staff was aghast at the fury of the boss.
What had happened to him? At last Professor Albert
quieted down and in a timid voice, a voice quite strange
for him, said: "Pride goeth before a fall. . . . Boastful-
ness deserves to be kicked in the neck. I have just finished
extolling to you the progress of modern surgery, and
now it comes to pass that the first case I present to you
shows the helplessness, the inefficiency, the utter inability
of modern surgery to cure that lovely child. Old Hippocrates knew and even described this condition. For
twenty-three hundred years medical science has tried to
help these children; it is still trying. All efforts have been
in vain. Not long ago the famous French surgeon
Dupuytren tried it again, only to fail again. He declared once more that this congenital condition is absolutely incurable; that it cannot even be improved."

The condition we were looking at was that of congenital

displacement of the hip-joints. I had witnessed this unforgettable scene abashed, and unaware of the future
which destined me, exactly me, the abdominal surgeon of
that time, to take up the difficult task of curing a condition which had baffled all efforts through twenty-three
centuries—and to succeed at last. The incident was soon
forgotten, but it emerged ten years later out of the unconscious mind—to stick forever in my memory.

VI

JUDGING MY TEACHERS

Here I might pause to consider some of my teachers critically—with due gratefulness, yet with some pardonable doubt as to their Godlikeness.

Students are the best and most unbiased judges of their teachers. They appreciate their merits, but do not overlook their faults. They remember their personal peculiarities, which cling to their memories longer than the lectures do. How learned young doctors would be if all the lessons they had gone through were to stick in their minds as tenaciously as the funny stories which, like legends, adorn their memories of their teachers! As apprentice to the Anatomical Institute of Vienna, I happened to be studying medicine at a time when the world-renowned beacons of medical science had just retired from teaching, but were still living and working—men like Oppolzer, and Skoda, who introduced auscultation and percussion as a means of diagnosing diseases of the chest. Skoda's fame cannot be belittled by the fact that old Hippocrates, the Father of Medicine, knew and described many symptoms which Skoda found to have been similar procedures three hundred years before Christ. But Hippocrates, you realize, knew everything and any treatise on medical science might well begin with the much-used words: "Old Hippocrates already knew. . . ."

Many funny stories were told of Professor Skoda. He

was consulted not only by people from all over the world, but also, of course, by the members of the Austrian imperial family. The Spanish etiquette of the Court prescribed that every visitor should come in full evening dress, even in daylight. The tail-coat was indispensable, but Skoda had never possessed such a thing. He always donned a walking-coat and went to court in his usual costume. When he entered the ante-room of Her Imperial Majesty, the valets would tell him that they dared not admit him to the room of Her Majesty because only a person attired in a swallow-tailed garment could be admitted to the room. "Oh! Is that so? I did not know it—excuse me, please. It's all right—I'll go home and send you a tail-coat from the next tailor shop,"—and he would leave the room. He behaved recklessly everywhere. Once he was invited to dine with a noble, aristocratic family. One of the dishes was fried sweetbreads, which the lady of the house regarded as a great delicacy. Skoda examined his portion like an anatomist, found out what it was, placed his knife and fork upon the table, and said: "Thank you, I never eat glands." Of course, at that time neither Skoda nor anybody else knew anything about the glands and their hormones, or Skoda might have deigned, if not to eat them, at least to discuss the merits of sweetbreads. That question, by the way, medical science does not know much about even at the present time.

Then there was old Rokitansky, the founder of pathological anatomy. He had no laboratory; he worked in a mere shed, and so the more brilliant were his discoveries, which made the medical school of Vienna famous all over the world. Many funny stories which were told about him cannot be printed.

Another famous physician at that time was Ferdinand Hebra, the founder of dermatology. He was a short, fat man with protruding eyes which were reinforced with thick glasses. He had to bring objects near to his eyes, but he overlooked nothing. Very ambitious and rich, he took it much to heart that his discoveries (among them, the parasitic character of a skin disease called scabies) should not have qualified him to be made at least a corresponding member of the Academy of Science of Vienna. He used to rant about the theoreticians who walked above the clouds and ignored any man who did practical work. I was his student, and often used to marvel at the way the plump little man would pull his patients about—often big fellows who could have thrown him off like a tiresome fly —in order to demonstrate to his students half-hidden symptoms in interesting cases. Once his students witnessed a very funny episode. A man came into the lecture hall to find Professor Hebra, saying that he had missed him at his home. It was evident that the man belonged to the better class of society. He greeted Professor Hebra very cordially, but Hebra did not respond with equal familiarity. He only said, "Sorry, I don't know you. Anyhow, take off your clothes." The visitor did so and Hebra examined him carefully all over, in his near-sighted way. When he came to his back and to the end of the spine, Hebra joyously turned the visitor round, shook hands with him, and said: "Now I recognize you! Glad to see you!" Many famous physicians remember the case better than the individual.

Hyrtl, the anatomist, Professor Langer's predecessor, was a remarkable man, known all over the scientific world not so much for his anatomical discoveries as for his invention for injecting the vessels of any organ with a special, hardening mass; the soft parts were destroyed by corrosion, and thus the wonderful tree of the vessels would come into view. Hyrtl was the only anatomist in the world who ever made money out of his dissections; he sold his corrosion specimens to all the anatomical museums of the world. As he had no family of his own, he used his large fortune to found the Hyrtl Orphanage, in Moedling, near Vienna, which certainly serves to preserve the memory of the great humanitarian. Hyrtl was also a famous orator who preferred Latin to any other language; he spoke Ciceronian Latin, which in his opinion was the language of the angels in Heaven. He did not like Greek. Funny stories were told of him by the hundred; two of them seem to me worth telling:

In an examination, Hyrtl gave the candidate some of the little bones which form the wrist-joints. Though they are very similar, they can be differentiated from one another, and many students make a hobby of telling them apart by the mere feel of them. Our candidate happened to be one of these specialists; Hyrtl seemed surprised by his prompt answers, and wanted to make sport of him, to gratify his own sense of humor.

"Now, what about the sex?" The candidate was not perturbed and gave an answer; he had at least a fifty-fifty chance.

Hyrtl continued: "What about the age?" Now the odds were greater, but the candidate guessed without much hesitation.

Hyrtl said: "Not so bad, surely better than I could have guessed myself," and then he added, "But now, what about the name and the last address of the former possessor of these little bones?" Roars of laughter from the audience followed.

Another little story concerns a candidate who seemed to be all-wise about the anatomical conditions of the thyroid gland.

"Excellent," commented Hyrtl. "But what about the function of the thyroid gland? Do you know anything about that?"

The candidate answered contritely: "Only yesterday I still knew it; today I have forgotten it."

"What a pity," said Hyrtl. "You, the only man in the world who knew it!" At that time the thyroid gland seemed to be good for nothing, not even for cooking like the sweetbread.

Hyrtl was an outspoken adversary of his colleague, Ernst von Brücke, professor of physiology. He hated the man as a professional dog-torturer when he learned that Brücke made experiments in the consequences of starvation and for this purpose kept dogs in cages without feeding them. Hyrtl tipped the keeper freely and saw to it that the dogs were able to stand starvation experiments for any length of time. Ernst von Brücke was a disagreeable, red-haired Prussian, whom the students did not like at all, though his fame as a scientist was world-wide. But what do students care about the fame of their professor if he is the poor and helpless sort of teacher who repeats his lectures word-for-word for thirty years?—and that was the case with this famous explorer. Just as deeply rooted in the scientific world was the fame of the pathologist Solomon Stricker, whom many students, including myself, hated like Judas Iscariot. He may have been not a really bad man, but we were loath to see him slaughter dogs for

THE YOUNG DOCTOR ADOLF LORENZ

PROFESSOR BILLROTH, FAMOUS VIENNESE
SURGEON

MY ADVISER, PROFESSOR EDUARD ALBERT

no purpose whatsoever. Ernst Bamberger, professor of internal medicine, was the finest diagnostician of his time, although the knowledge of the human blood, intensely studied by his assistant, Professor Neusser, was then still in its beginnings.

But the medical star at that time was Theodore Billroth, the founder of the Rudolphinum, a model hospital for the training of surgical nurses for the emergency of war. Neither Billroth, of whom I have already said a few words, nor his protector, Rudolf, Crown Prince of Austria, of doleful memory, ever saw the war which they prepared for as humanitarians. Bearded Billroth was of splendid appearance, endowed with a gift for fascinating every one who came in contact with him. As a surgeon, he was an artist; as the initiator of new operations of unheard-of procedures, he was a genius. He worked fourteen hours a day, yet knew how to lead the life of a *grand seigneur* who likes free and lavish spending. The young students and doctors used to rank him beside Rubens, the painter, diplomat, and prince. He died poor, and his widow had to depend on a pension given her by His Majesty, the Emperor Franz-Joseph. His students considered Billroth a very mediocre teacher. As a surgeon he could be reckless, many thought even heartless. He had few friends in the profession, but the great composer Brahms was his intimate and he was very much liked by Crown Prince Rudolf.

Eduard Albert, of whom you have already heard, had neither the brilliance nor the technical skill of Billroth, but was far superior to him as a teacher. His auditorium was always crammed to the rafters, while Billroth often spoke before almost empty benches. Albert was admired more as a scientist, philosopher, historian, mathematician, and even poet, than as a surgeon. He was what we call a "polyhistor"—a man who can ride upon any kind of saddle. He could be proud of not being outshone by a man like Billroth, whose pupil, Anton von Eiselsberg, preserved the glory of his school through three decades.

Now they are all gone, or have long since stopped teaching—great names like Nothnagel, the famous internist; Arlt and Fuchs, the no less famous oculists; Pollitzer, the well-known ear specialist. Though the old Vienna medical school has died out and young successors, not as famous as yet as their predecessors, have been called up to continue its glory, the Vienna medical faculty is flourishing and is still the shrine which attracts many followers of Hippocrates from all parts of the world, for Vienna is unique in the world as a place of teaching. *"Vindobona docet"* (Vienna teaches) should be stamped on the escutcheon of the city.

One of the old guard is still at his glorious work of curing the brain attacked by the most insidious fiend of humanity, the spirochæta, by means of malaria treatment —one of the outstanding medical triumphs of this century. Julius von Wagner-Jauregg has more than deserved to be awarded the Nobel prize. As a student, I was a colleague of Wagner's and went with him through the ordeal of several examinations. As a young doctor, Wagner happened by mere chance to land at the psychiatric clinic.

During my service as the assistant at the clinic, I attended an international medical congress at Copenhagen. There I saw Pasteur, who had just won world fame. As a young physician, I listened to his lecture with half-ears only. The short, stout, uncouth man was not even a physician, merely a chemist. What could he have to say? His hearers could not yet grasp the importance of his discovery, and rather made fun of him when, every half-minute, he would thump the table with his fist and bellow, "*La rage! La rage!*" sputtering his saliva all over the table. "Is not Pasteur himself infected with '*la rage*'?" asked the stupid bystanders—and among them, to his great chagrin today, was the present writer.

On one such occasion, I also met the famous old Virchow, the expounder of the principle *omnis cellula ex cellula* (Every cell out of a cell)—a principle, by the way, which is forever beginning to come into discredit. The founder of cellular-pathology was so old and seemed so fragile a dwarf that he looked like an unsheathed mummy. Yet the ugly old man could not forbear basking in the fading sunshine of his fame, and liked to ride on the shoulders of young admirers. Learning to my astonishment that the wizened rider was Virchow, I heard another man say, "No, that is no longer Virchow, it is only his stuffed skin, which is used now as a symbol. The real Virchow is long since dead."

It is really sad for an old man to outlive his fame.

VII

CALAMITY CREATES A "DRY" SURGEON

M Y happiness lasted about four years, only to be followed by a calamity as unforeseen as it was terrible. Young Doctor Lorenz, who meanwhile had been appointed Docent of Surgery, fell into an abyss out of which resurrection seemed impossible. So far as surgery—my profession—was concerned, I was suddenly no less disabled than an artist would be who had lost both hands in a terrible accident. At the moment when I was admittedly nearly at the top of my profession, a malicious fate declared me absolutely unfit to continue my surgical career, and required me to turn my back on surgery. At thirty years of age, and in spite of brilliant successes, I was doomed to begin anew somewhere, at the bottom. Good luck had turned into bad luck. The second glove, so recently found, was again the missing glove.

It was all because I had chanced to be born in the so-called "Lister era" during which carbolic acid reigned supreme. The surgeons at that time all but drank carbolic acid. They literally bathed in it, inhaled it, washed their hands in it, and lived in the sickening, suffocating fog of the carbolic spray. This last really was the worst of all tortures. Let alone the fact that you could not see anything while a good spray was on, hissing like an irritated viper, it made the skin pale as a corpse and macerated it until there was danger of gangrene. The time had not yet come when the German surgeons unanimously cried *"Fort mit dem Spray!"*—"Away with the spray!"

I became its victim. I had stood slow poisoning through four years: then my whole system revolted. But that was not the worst of it. My hands, from one day to the next, were covered with big, repulsive blisters which left the skin raw and bleeding. No possibility of washing such a skin, no possibility even of touching a surgical instrument. As a surgeon, I was like a man with no hands at all. A scientific furlough devoted to a book on the pathological anatomy of flat feet helped to finish the book but not the carbolic eczema of my hands. On the contrary, it grew worse at the slightest irritation, and developed into a regular idiosyncrasy against any antiseptic, whether carbolic, sublimate, or iodoform. I was to learn that I was absolutely unfit to be a surgeon in the Lister era. I was so desperate as to curse the holy name of Lister. God have mercy on the sinner!

Nothing was left but to resign my post and with it my future, my career which had begun so promisingly. Anatomy was taboo for me, as I well knew. For a while I planned to become what was called "*Ein Wald-und-Wie-senarzt*" (A doctor in the woods and meadows), and began to mend my knowledge in other branches which I had heretofore neglected. Hofrath Albert was very sorry to lose his promising assistant, but could do nothing but accept my resignation. He tried to console the desperate young man who had fallen from the bright heights into nothingness. In his incisive way, he said: "Well, if you cannot stand wet surgery, try dry surgery." He meant, of course, orthopædic surgery, a branch of medicine then still in embryo.

And so, against his will, Doctor Lorenz was forced by

necessity to become an orthopædic surgeon, and had more-over to be his own teacher. With the money saved from his lectures he hired an office, put in some gymnastic apparatus, and hung out his shingle: "Specialist in Orthopædic Surgery." To justify the title, he sat down and wrote a book on the pathology and therapy of lateral deviation of the spine, which was highly praised by certain German rivals. But in spite of this, he felt that he had been switched off from the main road to a side-track. His aim had been to become a great clinical teacher, like Albert or Billroth, and, of course, a famous operator, preferably an abdominal surgeon. Instead, he found himself a teacher of gymnastics. His hopes of putting an end to his poverty had to be dropped once more.

Thanks to the influence of Hofrath Albert, he got a travelling stipend to visit various clinics in other countries. Berlin, London, and Paris were the places where he hoped to see and learn something in orthopædic surgery. But there was nothing to see or to learn. Practically no orthopædic surgery existed. In London he saw some ridiculous attempts at correcting congenital club-feet. That was all. He hurried home, and at the invitation of Hofrath Albert took up orthopædic surgery at his clinic. The fallen Lorenz was contemptuously called the 'plaster Docent,' but he did not mind that, because he felt that plaster was a good material to build up his name with.

In his private practice he had for the most part to treat children, and he badly needed an assistant. This assistant was to be that same nice girl whom Professor Langer once had mentioned as a lure to bind him to his institute. The young lady belonged to a very good family. She was twenty-four, of medium height, very healthy, of rich coloring. Her hair was auburn, her complexion rosy, her cheeks like red carnations, her teeth white and slightly prominent, her lips very red and luscious; sometimes her eyes would look as green as a cat's. The doctor called her his "color-box." She was very energetic, and was just as poor as her lover.

"Why shouldn't we marry after seven years of courtship?" she asked him. "I'll be a better assistant to you than any of your plump colleagues, who never will learn how to handle your young girl patients." What she said was true, and in the next fifty years she was Doctor Lorenz's most helpful assistant—and will be his assistant for as many more years as God may grant her.

So the wedding was arranged. Just at that time the young doctor was very hard up, having spent nearly all his cash for his instruments. The question of buying the wedding-rings gave him some qualms. His bride naturally insisted on a nice golden wedding-ring. For himself he ordered one of brass, which he felt would glitter like gold and would do very well for the ceremony. "What is a ring good for," said the bridegroom, "if as a surgeon you never wear it? Besides, who will notice it?" But somebody did. During the ceremony, the sexton, while he held the tray with the rings, was obviously comparing them, making them clink slightly on the tray, and weighing them in his hands; finally he shook his old head, having evidently grasped the situation. The bridegroom felt sure that the sexton would make some sinister prophecy as to the duration of a union which relied on brass, and hastened to make him take a brighter view of the situation by a better fee than could be expected from the wearer of a brass wedding-ring. The bridegroom was very sorry that the brass ring was lost later on, for it would have enabled him to prove that the happiness of married life does not depend upon golden or preciously jewelled wedding-rings.

A honeymoon of just seven days was allowed the young couple. That happy time was spent at the summer cottage of Mrs. Lorenz's family in Altenberg, a little village on the Danube about twenty kilometers above Vienna. Opposite the cottage stood an old, ramshackle peasant house with a beautiful garden at the rear. The top of it commanded a magnificent view of the fertile Tullnerfeld, a wide plain surrounded on the left by the beech-clad hills of the Wiener Wald, foothills of the Alps, while the blue band of the Danube adorned the view on the other side. Whoever sees the Danube in late spring or summer will scoff at its "blue" color, which is really just as yellow as the Mississippi at New Orleans. But let him believe an old dweller on its banks that in fall and winter it is really beautiful blue! Mrs. L, who knew all the peasants of the village, remarked occasionally that the owner of the house was heavily in debt and must sell it, and that it would be a nice thing to have that beautiful garden. This time Eve, by way of change, praised not the apple but the garden in which it grew. "How can we think of such a thing," her husband retorted, "while we are living from hand to mouth and will be for a long time to come?" Mrs. L admitted it was just a silly dream.

The second week after the wedding, the orthopædic practice had to be commenced. My experience with the first private patient might have carried foreboding for a superstitious mind. A little girl of about five years had to have a plaster corset, which was to be put on in slight

extension. When the child grew aware of the preparations, she thought she was going to be put on the gallows,
and fled from the room and out of the house. But later
patients stayed, were helped, sent others, and in a short
time the private practice was flourishing—not to be wondered at, as I was the only specialist in my branch in the
great city. Among my first patients was one who did not
at all belong to orthopædic surgery. Our building was
also the residence of my former teacher in obstetrics and
gynæcology, and in the dead of night I was called in to
see the old professor. I found him in his bed, totally unconscious with his right side paralyzed and his face drawn
to the left. It was a severe stroke which might prove fatal.
I did not long deliberate what to do, and bled the old man
rather thoroughly, until he opened his eyes and looked
around bewildered. At that time bleeding had gone quite
out of fashion, and was looked upon as an obsolete procedure; I knew that the Faculty of Internal Medicine
would condemn my deed, but the patient proclaimed me
the savior of his life. In due time, the convalescent, a retired millionaire, out of his overflowing thankfulness sent
a tiny little silver goblet as a present to my newborn son.
When I thanked him rather effusively, he protested that
the goblet was not so very costly after all!

My life as a doctor was even more strenuous than when
I was a hard-working student. The forenoon was devoted
to Professor Albert's clinic, the afternoon to private practice, the evening and part of the night to writing pamphlets on orthopædic questions. By and by I had learned
to love the discipline which offered so many open problems.

Children with tubercular bone and joint diseases were
my most frequent patients. I could not treat them in my

wards because I had none. The clinic wards were taboo
for tubercular patients. How, then, were they to be treated
in the only way approved at that time by the medical
fashion of the day—by the "American traction method,"
which involved bed treatment? Theoretically speaking, the
traction method was the ideal way of protecting a diseased
joint from pressure of one surface of the joint against the
other, since by means of very intricate contrivances the
surfaces would be distanced from each other. This meant
that motion of the diseased joint should be allowed, as it
was without friction, the ultimate aim being to avoid final
stiffness (ankylosis) of the joint when the disease was
cured. This theoretical supposition demanded very complicated and carefully supervised bed treatment, a thing
which was impossible to carry out—let alone the fact that
confinement in bed and room was not a good way to improve the general health of the tubercular child.

At that time it was quite a venture to discard the
American method as unfeasible. It was necessary first to
demonstrate that not pressure, but, exclusively, motion of
the diseased joint was to be avoided. Every-day experience soon proved that a child with hip-disease could walk
and even jump around all day long without any pain, but
as soon as it fell asleep, the slightest movement of the body
caused terrible pains, with the dreaded night crying. It
was clear that pain was avoided during the day by the
spastic contraction of the muscles, which prevented any
movement of the joint. As soon as the muscles fell asleep
with the child, motion became possible and the least suggestion of it was a source of acute pain. I resolved to
imitate nature, adding to the muscular fixation of the
diseased joint an artificial fixation by means of a well-

fitting plaster-cast which had to be left undisturbed for many months, sometimes a whole year—a so-called "*Dauerverband*" (permanent bandage). How to keep the skin clean and healthy? By giving it a "dry wash" several times a day with a "scratch bandage" inserted between the skin and the lining of the plaster-cast. In such a cast the children lost their pain and could even walk, and in mild cases nothing else was necessary. The treatment had become very simple and effective. The children could even go to school with their casts on; instead of being bed-ridden, they could enjoy open air and sunshine. The effectiveness of the sun-treatment and the X-ray treatment was at that time not yet known. Nowadays the tendency is to neglect the mechanical treatment and to rely almost entirely on air, food, and sunshine. But this does not alter the fact that, so long as pain prevails, a fixing plaster-cast is by far the best means of relieving it. In my lectures I used to say: "Give my children good food, with their bandages on; they will be all right without special sun treatment because they can enjoy open air and the sun as far as he shines for all creatures." I had great success with this treatment, and my name spread. The treatment is still in use, as the best and most effective.

A very interesting problem for me was that of doing away with the terrible pains which the poor children who suffered from tuberculosis of the spine (spondylitis) had to endure. All available appliances were inadequate. It was my happy thought that for these children the hardest bed would be the best. So I made them beds of stone, the so-called plaster-bed, which is nothing but a well-uphol-stered plaster mold taken from the back of the patient. The child lies in his plaster-bed like a watch in an open case, or like a tortoise in its shell when turned upon its back. In this plaster-bed the child was bedridden, to be sure, but he could enjoy open air and sunshine in his perambulator. The pains were relieved to such an extent that the children didn't mind even if the perambulator was rolled over rough pavement. When I lectured, I would call the bed of stone a real pain-killer. To impress my students with the importance of this simple appliance (it could be classed with Columbus's egg) I used to say: "In case, on the Judgment Day, I should see that the scale with my good deeds rises because of the weight of the scale with my bad ones, I am keeping the heaviest plaster-bed I ever made ready to be thrown upon the rising scale. If that would not help, I can't be helped at all!"

The plaster-bed and the plaster spica are now known to surgeons the whole world over. I was very proud to see that cases which had been kept under heavy drugs, without relief, were made painless and later on actually cured by so simple a procedure, which acted like a magic wand. It was a solace to know that those victims of the World War most to be pitied, the ones who had been shot through the spine, could be and were relieved of their terrible pain by the plaster-bed. By this simple means they could be made fit for transportation to the *Hinterland*, where they would find proper treatment. One of my own patients told me of the excruciating pain he endured when transported in a cattle car with his spine shattered by a bullet. In captivity in Russia he found a Viennese surgeon who fixed his spine with a plaster-bed, and from then on transportation was painless. He was sent home and recovered, and for years he travelled with his plaster-bed because he could no longer tolerate soft beds.

And so it was not without profound reason that I put such great stress on my plaster-bed! Of course, it could not cure tuberculosis of the vertebræ, but it could improve the general health of the suffering children, permitting them to enjoy open air, better appetites, and quiet sleep, no longer disturbed by pain. Improving the general health is the best means of curing tuberculosis of the spine as well as of any other organ of the body. The chief aim of my work was not to invent new operations, but rather to do away with dangerous operations, substituting for them simple mechanical appliances. Except in very rare cases, the plaster-bed makes osteoplastic operations, such as transplanting a piece of bone from the shin to between the split spinous processes, superfluous.

VIII

BUILDING THE "FATHER-HOUSE"

Y practice grew and soon I was better off than if
I had stayed at the clinic as an assistant. Whenever I went to Altenberg with my wife, it was
chiefly to admire once more the beautiful view from the
top of that garden which was to be sold with the peasant
house. On a fine day in the autumn we became aware in
the clear atmosphere that the last outstanding sentinel of
the Alps, the mountain Oetscher, 2000 feet high, was distinctly visible about in the center of the famous view.
That decided the question. The garden must be bought
before another lover of nature should discover the jewel.
House and garden were to be had for about three thousand *gulden*. When the bargain was closed at the no-
tary's office, the peasant was informed that he had contracted more debts than he realized, and that when all his
debts were paid he would walk out of his property naked
as his forefinger. I could not bear this thought, and paid
the peasant, in addition to the price agreed upon, just the
amount of the forgotten debts, so that the seller was not
more disappointed than he knew he should be.

My wife and I were very proud to own even so small a
piece of the earth. The one-storied house upon it had two
rectangularly united wings. The house had not been
meant originally to be an abode for human beings; only
one room and a beamed kitchen had been allotted to them.
The rest belonged to the cows. These inhabited a large,

vaulted chapel—you might have called it—lit by four tiny
windows. The cow-stable constituted the larger wing of
the house; properly appointed, it could have served as a
refectory in a cloister. The house, especially the cow-
stable, was very solidly built of stone and could easily
sustain a second story. We derived an unknown pleasure
from planning the reconstruction of the peasant house
into a snug and comfortable villa. The cow-stable was to
be transformed into a kitchen. Thoroughly cleaned, the
vaulted ceiling painted white, floor and walls covered with
white tiles, the little windows enlarged, a big hearth on
one of the smaller walls lit by large windows, nice white
furniture, shining copper pots, tea and coffee cans on the
shelves—so, in spirit, Mrs. L saw her new kitchen. When
it was finished it almost excelled her fancy. The compara-
tively enormous kitchen called for a dining-room of the
same size above its vaulted ceiling. So it came about that
the reconstructed house was devoted chiefly to cooking
and eating, while for sleeping purposes only two small
rooms were left, just as in the case of the peasants. A very
large veranda with glass windows made up for the scarcity
in living rooms and bedrooms.

During the building, I would have liked to help the
bricklayers mix the mortar and sand, and watch every
brick being laid, but I had to renounce this pleasure. My
work kept me in the city. Late every evening, however, I
would come with a lantern and inspect the progress of the
day, which seemed to have been performed by magic
hands, as if by the famous *Heinzelmännchen* of the legend,
who this time worked in the daylight instead of in the
dead of night. The roof of the house was covered with
slate. I felt rather proud when the house was finished thus

far, and did not mind the fact that my money was also spent, to the last farthing. I had accomplished at least what, in my opinion, every man should have accomplished at my then age, namely begetting a child and building a house—the latter item being by far the more difficult part of the task! This house had to be the *vaterhaus* of my boy, to whom, little as he was, I tried to explain the meaning of it. When the roof was not yet finished, on a rainy day I carried the little boy Albert on my arm to a certain nook in the house which was already waterproof, and tried to convey to his mind the idea of protection which the "father-house" was to give him against cold, wind, and rain. Food, clothing, and other needs were another matter which the boy would have to solve for himself later on. In the meanwhile, of course, papa was ready to give him all he wanted. But you should never make a promise, because you never know. . . .

One evening in spring, I felt very nervous and ailing all over. All of a sudden I shook with a high fever, though nobody yet knew why. It was only the next morning that I felt a stinging pain at the end of my right forefinger. There was no wound, and with difficulty I remembered a little scratch which I had suffered the other day when handling a rusty iron orthopædic brace. I knew now all about what was to come: phlegmonous inflammation of my finger, of my hand, of my arm, and so on. I felt my finger and hand swell from one moment to the next.

Fever and pains increased; next evening the patient nearly lost consciousness. A surgeon from the clinic was called in. Diagnosis: severe phlegmon. Therapy: immediate deep incision into the finger. For the hand and forearm, poultices, fixing bandages. The fever rose and rose. Prognosis was very doubtful. Rumor had it that the doctor's arm was to be amputated or he would die. These prophecies were withheld from the patient, who in his somnolent condition was haunted by two visions. One was about a very impressive case which he had observed when he was still assistant at the clinic. A workman, young and strong, had entered his ward with the diagnosis "blood poisoning" through severe phlegmon of the right hand, with beginning lymphangitis. The patient got worse and worse in spite of all medical efforts; the next morning gangrene of the hand had set in. The patient was told that his forearm had to be amputated to save his life.

"No," said the young man. "But you will die," the doctors warned him. The young man said only, "Yes, but I won't be a beggar then." When Doctor Lorenz visited his patient in the afternoon, he found him worse and half-conscious. When he entered the ward in the evening, around the bed of the young man all the patients of the ward who could leave their beds were kneeling—praying. The patient was in agony. . . .

The second vision that haunted the fever-ridden doctor was of a less disturbing character. He saw the slater sitting on the roof of his new house, filling the gaps between the spars not with slates but with banknotes. The patient shouted in his fever that the slater should stop taking banknotes instead of slates, which, in the end, were the same thing. The trouble was that the doctor in his fever-dreams was haunted by the thought that he had become a debtor, that he would never be able to pay for the last slates. If he were to die he would leave his widow and his son with nothing but debts and an unfinished house.

In another anxious dream he felt himself at the bottom
of a deep well. All round him was blackness; far up at a
measureless height glimmered a spark of daylight. He
struggled, exerted himself, reaching up with his arms to
get at least nearer to that hope-inspiring spark. But he
fell back hopelessly. He was prepared to die. Too well
he remembered the fate of a dear friend of his who had
contracted an erysipelas from a patient and had died,
just at his own age.

But my time had not come yet. I recovered slowly and
was so utterly burnt out by the obstinate fever that I collapsed when I first tried to stand on my feet. It was Easter
week—Passion Week,—which would end in resurrection.
When, in the village church, I heard the priest sing
"Christ has Risen!" I thought that, as far as my prospect
of life was concerned, the song might just as well be applied to myself.

To regain the usefulness of my hand as soon as possible,
I adopted the Oriental custom of playing with a string of
small ivory balls, and felt myself conqueror when I was
able to wind my watch with thumb and forefinger. When
my incisions were nearly healed, the virulency of my infection was shown by the fact that Mrs. L got an abscess
on her left arm; probably she had pricked herself with a
pin when arranging my bandages. These times of dire
disease were not pleasant, and were made the more disagreeable by the pouring in of additional bills from the
builders, for a hundred things which had been forgotten
in the estimate. "You should not have built the house
before you had the money," Mrs. L said with some bitterness because her weekly housekeeping money had to be

reduced. I replied that I found it nice to have the house one year sooner. But the builders must be paid immediately, and were we going to have to starve? Mrs. L tried to avoid this emergency by buying meat and vegetables in the suburbs because of the lower prices. I told her that these long walks might do her good, but the gain would go to the shoemakers. Anyhow, we managed to pull through, though for a long time we again lived from hand to mouth.

To avoid further additional bills from the builders, I tried to do some of the work myself. For instance, painting the doors. Had I not watched the men painting the window frames? Had I not watched my father varnishing carriages? And I began painting with flourishing brush, pipe in mouth, and scoffing at the professionals because they did their work with apparent laziness, as if they had no intention of ever finishing it. Instead of imitating their easy-going method, I worked furiously to show what a man could do if he was bent to his work body and soul. The final effect of my boasting was disastrous. The brush dropped from my hand, sweat stood on my forehead, and I all but fainted, just from moving the brush up and down. I could not move my hand up and down for a week. Craftsmanship once more impressed me as something precious, to be acquired by hard training of the muscles, provided you had the necessary skill. From that time on I regarded artisans not only as my equals, but often as my superiors as far as skill was concerned. The only difference between my work and theirs was the preciousness of the material on which they worked.

It was not long after I had finished building my house that I had occasion to assist the architect in reconstruction work of quite a different type.

The number of my patients had been increasing from day to day, and it became impossible to accommodate them at Professor Albert's clinic. I had to move into new quarters. Although Professor Albert had never interfered with his pupil's work, this exodus was the first beginning of the independence of orthopædic surgery from its mother, general surgery. The old quarters of the kitchen of the Allgemeine Krankenhaus in Vienna had become inadequate, and it had been moved to new quarters. The old kitchen was good enough to accommodate orthopædic surgery. The room available was a big vaulted hall, like all the wards in the hospital. The architects of Emperor Joseph II, who built the hospital, had been careful not to waste their efforts on accessories to the wards such as tea-rooms, day-rooms, baths, etc., but they lavished themselves on what is the most precious and most expensive comfort in a building—on spacious halls with high, vaulted ceilings and very large windows. The wards of the Allgemeine Krankenhaus are really baronial. They profited from the baroque period of Viennese architecture. There is really no hospital in the world which can equal, let alone excel, this old Viennese hospital for spacious, well lighted, and well ventilated wards, however inadequate the accessories, which conform with standards of about one hundred and fifty years ago. The construction of the old house is of the greatest solidity. Architects of experience say that no modern building could have stood so many alterations, such as borings for ventilation shafts, breaking walls to put in additional windows, etc. A time came when this venerable old house, which hundreds of thousands of patients entered to recover or to die and leave the premises by the back door in their coffins, this old hospital in which more than ten generations of physicians studied their noble profession, this structure in which medical science was created by men whose glory will never fade, this venerable, austere, but nevertheless lovely old building, with its beautiful gardens in the great courts, was doomed to be wrecked. The World War broke out and saved the precious relic of a glorious past.

The large kitchen-hall was to be divided by thin walls into a waiting-room, a bandage-room, and an operating-room. A small but very high room was destined to be study and library of the new proprietor. A very important part of the new orthopædic institute was the former kitchen larder, which served as a dark-chamber to develop photographs and as a lumber-room for braces and bandage material. This rather dingy place was my workshop for the next twenty years. Small and inadequate as it was, it aroused the animosity of the general surgeons, who were opposed to any further specialization of general surgery. No matter what improvement of my institute I demanded at the Ministry of Instruction, my wishes were always disregarded, probably on the advice of my adversaries. To get an X-ray plant, in time, I had to plunder my own pocket. It was with the greatest difficulty that I could wring at least part of my expenses out of the stingy ministry. They cried "Hell!" when I demanded an assistant with some salary. For myself I dared not ask even the smallest compensation for the loss of my precious time at the hospital—I had so many other demands to pester the ministry with. This policy was wrong, as we shall see later on. After a short time the place was too small for the many patients who wanted treatment. But not another cubic inch of space was to be had. The new institute must not have any beds, lest it present even a fair semblance of an orthopædic clinic. The new institute must be kept down by allowing it only ambulatory treatment. When I protested and declared that I could not be held responsible for any accident caused by the necessity of throwing my patients from the operating table into the street-car, I was allowed *two* beds to permit my patients to recover from the anæsthetic. There must be no orthopædic surgery at all at the Faculty—that was the war cry. How foolish!

IX

DEVELOPING BLOODLESS OPERATIONS

In spite of all adversities, my institute prospered. I now had free hands, and began to study and to perform operations which hitherto I had not dared to think of because at Professor Albert's clinic carbolic acid was still the trump-card. For me it was still "taboo" as much as ever. So I had to work out my own method of antisepsis, clandestinely, because the mere thought of resisting a reigning fashion in medicine, especially in surgery, was a crime incomparably greater than refusing to follow a fashion of costumes created and dictated by sartorial kings. If it had been known that by my new treatment I lost three cases out of 200, I should have been called a murderer and put into prison, although other surgeons who had remained true to the Lister method had had more then 10 per cent mortality by the same operation.

I chose alcohol as an antiseptic long before it was officially introduced into surgery. Alcohol is a very effective germ-killer, as any one knows who suffers from a bad stomach. Why should it not work the same way in the treatment of wounds?—I argued. I was true to alcohol as an antiseptic for the next forty years. I was really of the opinion that not only blood, but also alcohol is a quite particular juice of very special qualities, a fact which was recognized by Americans much later when they made prohibition a law. Of course, everything has two sides, and a good thing always has an especially good and an especially bad side; it needs a wise man to choose the good side and to avoid the bad one.

The operation mentioned above was the so-called open reduction of congenital hip dislocation. The condition can easily be understood by any layman. Nature sometimes is very willful and treacherous, even to an unborn child. For some unknown reason, the socket which has to contain the head of the femur—the thigh-bone—does not grow properly and becomes too shallow to harbor the head of the bone. The latter slips out of the socket, and the child is born with a more or less dislocated hip. If the head has not been entirely thrown out of the shallow socket by the thigh muscles at the time of birth, it sits too loosely in its place, certainly not in the center of the cavity, and is liable to further displacement by muscular power as well as by the weight of the body later on, when the child begins to stand and to walk. It is, of course, an upward displacement which evidences itself in a shortening of the leg. The child often refuses to stand, and learns to walk later than normal children, with a peculiar, swaying, yielding limp. The deformity of the hip causes subsequent deformities of the spine. In bilateral hip luxation the deformity becomes very conspicuous later on. The abdomen protrudes, as do the buttocks. Hip and knee joints are slightly flexed. The whole posture seems to imitate a zig-zag line. Worst of all is the inability to walk any distance. In later years, when the body-weight increases, walking becomes painful and even impossible.

Congenital dislocation of the hip is a questionable privilege of the so-called fair sex, the ratio being eight girls to one boy. The cause of this peculiarity has not yet been made absolutely clear. It may have something to do with the difference in the growth of the basin in males and females. A further peculiarity is the fact that children born with hip luxation are usually extremely beautiful, and are otherwise in splendid health. It seems as if nature, to make a mock of herself, rejoices in marring her most beautiful work in order to deny it perfection. It should be an alluring task to make a mock of nature by restoring the beauty denied by her, that is, by curing congenital hip luxation—let alone the fact that it is the most frequent of all congenital deformities. Many surgeons, the best of them, had tried their skill, from old Hippocrates to the present time, and all of them had declared congenital hip dislocation not only absolutely incurable, but not even capable of improvement. Even if it were possible to reduce the ball into the shallow socket, what would be the good if the head could not be kept in its place?

But the younger generation was not deterred by the hopeless opinions of the old one. They tried and tried to solve the problem, at any cost. Listerism had enlarged the field of surgery in a measure never before dreamed of. What could be more logical than opening the hip-joint, deepening the shallow socket with a sharp spoon, cutting out the thick cartilaginous layers, modelling the head of the thigh-bone into the proper shape if it was deformed, and resetting the ball into the deepened socket? Many surgeons worked at the idea. I developed and carried out an operation by which it would be possible to complete the task described above without the severing of muscles, because these had to be left intact as the motors of the artificial joint. This method became the preferred method everywhere.

But I was never content with my work. I lost three children by septic infection—I had not yet realized that opening a big joint, like the hip- or knee-joint, involves a much greater danger than opening the abdomen. Was I justified in exposing little children to a danger which threatened their life if their deformity, which was not even a disease, had nothing to do with the question of life or death? In other words, is it permissible to correct a deformity which is completely harmless to life by an operation which threatens life? My answer to this question was: "No, never! There is no vital indication in orthopædic surgery." My life became a torture. As I operated on more than two hundred cases, there was practically no care-free day for me, for if one child was beyond the danger-point another or two others had to be carefully watched, to make sure that they would get safely beyond that point. The memory of a dear young mother tearing her hair in despair over her dead child would never leave my mind.

These exorbitant exertions of soul and body were bound at last to tell on a man who worked regardless of his health. One fine summer day my stomach said: "I am no longer of the party. I'm taking my vacation and won't work any more!" The stomach is a great power which can crush you to pieces. If you dare to hurt His Majesty, His Majesty will take a terrible revenge on you. From this time on I was never entirely free of stomach troubles. But at the begining of this trouble my physical condition became dreadful. I couldn't digest anything but a little bit of Westphalian smoked raw ham and soda biscuits, with oranges, and became a walking skeleton. My good friends whispered that I was getting tuberculosis of the lungs and had better go south. I did so, not on account of tuberculosis, but to change my surroundings and forget everything concerning home, hospital, and patients. I came back from Egypt not much better than when I left, but I feared to consult surgeons, who at all times are ready to open their patients, to see what is the matter with them.

At last I went to a physician who was known as a crazy fellow but a good stomach specialist. The crazy fellow gave me a crazy prescription: "Never wash, never get in contact with water! Just wipe your face off with a wet towel!" The good stomach specialist gave me an excellent prescription. He said: "Your stomach is all right, but your nerve power is spent. Stop working entirely." When I answered, "I can't. I should prefer death to stopping work," the stomach doctor put in: "All right, work then, even work hard, but stop your work at two o'clock. Lie down, rest a while, then eat your measured portions of meat and vegetables. Then undress, go to bed, drop the curtains, and think that there is nothing more for you to do in this world. You will sleep an hour or two. Then get up, and do some easy work at your writing table. But if you go on taking a bath every day, you will never get well, but die of consumption."

I obeyed my physician except where the washing question was concerned, and improved considerably by adopting the regimen prescribed. The old rule was proved true: Work on an empty stomach, rest on a full stomach. You can only feel really happy with a hungry and expectant stomach; a full stomach is a nuisance and makes you unfit for work. The gourmand Viennese people will never agree with this plain truth, but go on dividing the working hours by the heavy mid-day meal, about which they are very particular.

By and by I got back my strength. I badly needed my muscular powers because the bloodless operations especially required much exertion. At that time I did not yet know that the cure of congenital dislocation of the hip-joint would be made possible in a bloodless way, because it seemed to me as yet impossible to pull the upward dislocated head down to the level of the socket. I had first to find out the means of overcoming the resistance of the contracted soft parts. The treatment of congenital as well as of paralytic club-feet gave me ample opportunity to study that question.

Any layman can easily understand the problem of club-feet, whatever their cause. A club-foot can be compared with an eagle's claw, in that it has a convexity on the outside and a concavity on the inside. In a limb continually held in such a claw-like attitude, the muscles at the concavity will relax, while the muscles at the convexity will be stretched. The relaxed muscles adapt themselves to the crooked attitude of the limb and become shortened, that is, contracted. If you try to straighten out the claw, these shortened soft parts (muscles, ligaments, etc.) will resist. If you overcome their resistance by an adequate effort, the claw can be made straight, but the aroused elasticity of the soft parts will perforce try to restore the original crooked position. No matter what appliance (brace or bandage) you may use to keep the claw from doing so, you will see pressure of the recoiling claw

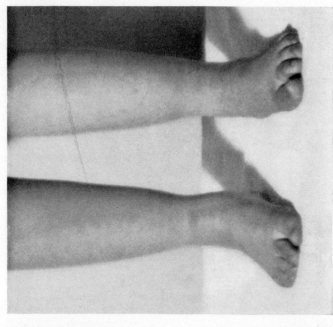

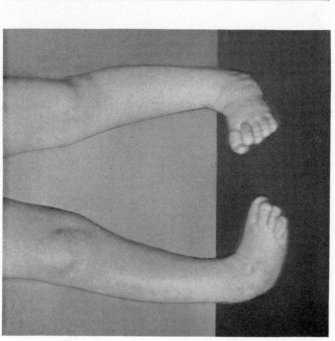

CONGENITAL CLUB—FEET

Left: Before correction. *Right*: After correction by Lorenz bloodless redressment method

PROFESSOR ADOLF LORENZ IN 1902

The photograph taken by the young man who was seeking his missing glove

against the appliance intended to maintain the corrected
position. In the case of a club-foot, if this pressure is not
immediately relieved there will be sloughing and gangrene, because the club-foot is not of horny substance like
the eagle's claw, but of living flesh and blood. Gangrene
caused by pressure made the whole treatment a failure.
You had to wait weeks and weeks before you could try
again, with danger of the same mishap.

To pursue the parallel, it must further be supposed
that the claw itself is as elastic as if it were made of steel.
Your task then is not only to overcome the resistance of
the contracted soft parts, but the elasticity of the claw
(foot) itself. The force by which the combined elasticity
of the soft parts and of the claw strive to reassume their
former position if impelled into a straight position is considerable, and explains the disastrous results of the pressure of the straightened-out claw against any retaining
appliance.

All resistance against correcting a deformity used to
be overcome by the so-called French *"redressement forcé,"*
in which one or two mighty efforts straightened out any
contracted limb, say a club-foot, and fixed it in the corrected position by an appliance, preferably a plaster-
cast. I recognized the danger and the futility of such a
procedure and introduced into orthopædic surgery what
is called the German "modelling redressment." It consists of hundreds of successive applications of measured
and moderate force, to be continued until the corrected
limb shows no tendency to recoil into its former crooked
position, and can be held in the corrected position without resistance against the retaining appliance. The difference between the French and the German redressment

is that the former arouses and the latter destroys the elasticity of the soft parts as well as of the limb itself. The German modelling redressment must be thoroughly studied, because it is not without dangers either, but these dangers can easily be avoided. A limb which has undergone a modelling redressment is expected to swell in reaction to the insult. Ample room must therefore be provided in the plaster-cast by rich upholstering. A circular bandage is not allowed. Any plaster-cast must be split immediately, or better still, a strip must be cut out in which the skin is laid bare.

A very unexpected advantage of the modelling redressment is the absence of pain after its performance. The explanation is simple. Tissues whose elasticity is annihilated are not the source of pain that tissues kept in severe extension are.

Applying my method, I was able to declare that no club-foot, either in children or in adults, of whatever origin (congenital, paralytic, accidental, spastic, etc.), could resist the modelling redressment. The treatment is perfectly bloodless and yields results not yet attained by any other method, because the bones are left alone. It gave me great satisfaction when I could declare that all bone operations recommended in cases of severe club-foot, such as extirpation of single bones, or wedge-shaped bone excisions, are not only superfluous but are really mutilating operations because they shorten the foot which is short anyway, and are liable to cause deformity later on.

I found my greatest pleasure in doing away with all severe operations in orthopædic surgery. The modelling redressment proved to be the clue to further successes. The knowledge of this method made it easy to correct

completely any paralytic contraction, or even to over-cor-
rect it, as is of advantage in cases of paralytic knee-contracture. By holding to the principle that the first and
essential task in treatment of deformities caused by infantile paralysis is the perfect restoration of the normal shape
of the limb (made possible by the modelling redressment),
I got far better results than could be reached by those
surgeons who relied on tendon transplantations and hoped
that the transplanted muscles would more or less restore
the normal shape of the paralyzed limb—a hope, which
was, of course, in most cases futile. I was called uncom-
plimentary names because I ventured to say: "Restoration
of the normal shape of a paralyzed limb is of greater
importance than any tendon transplantation." I never
neglected tendon transplantations, but always declared
that their indication is very restricted. It is an every-day
experience to have patients walk on a totally paralyzed
leg, even without any supporting brace, provided all
joints are in normal position, and the knee preferably
a bit over-straight. You can successfully treat paralytic
contraction without tendon transplantation, but surely
not without modelling redressment, if there be any contraction, however slight.

All successes in my practice were due to simple principles. The crowning work of my life was founded on my
method of modelling redressment. Without this experience I could never have ventured to handle a dislocated
thigh of a child in a way that could possibly bring about
the reduction of a congenitally dislocated head of the
femur into the socket—at least not in cases which were
beyond the first childhood. While performing open operations on the dislocated hip-joint, I had always medi-

tated on the possibilities of reducing the head in the socket
without opening the joint. The socket was always in existence, though often very scantly developed. My plan
was to stretch and lengthen all shortened soft parts by
means of the modelling redressment and then force the
head of the bone into its proper place. My endeavors
showed that the task was feasible but to no purpose as
long as it was impossible to retain the head in the shallow
and otherwise defective acetabulum.

Very tedious experiments proved that, except in very
rare cases, it was necessary to give the thigh certain extreme (so-called ultraphysiologic) positions in order to
retain the head of the bone in its proper place. In bilateral hip luxations the necessary position of both thighs
was comparable to the legs of a squatting frog. I came in
conflict with my conscience, which asked me such questions as: "Art thou allowed to torture nice little girls in
such a cruel way, thou who pretendest to be soft-hearted?"
But I would feel reassured when I asked my little patients:
"Girly, show me your knee, point with your finger at your
knee, but without looking at it." And the children always pointed to where the knee used to be, which means
that they felt the knee to be in its former and normal
position. The modelling redressment had done away with
the tension of the stretched and lengthened parts, so that
there was no pain.

The chief question, which could be solved only by long
experience, was: What now? How long must this extreme
position of the thighs be maintained? This question was
of especial importance in the cases of bilateral dislocation
because any possibility of walking was excluded as long
as this extreme position of the thighs was kept unchanged.

In unilateral cases, the possibility of moving about could
be procured by means of a very high shoe, put like a stilt
under the foot of the leg operated upon. By what means
could it become possible to stabilize the new position of
the head in the socket, regardless of the time necessary
for this purpose? Experience showed that when this extreme position of the thighs had been maintained for some
months, say for six months, it could be made less severe
without imminent danger of re-luxation, as was the case
immediately after the first re-position. This increased
stability was caused by the adaptation of the soft parts
to the new position of the thigh. Those same soft parts
which previous to the operation were lengthened and flac-
cid had become shortened and contracted, and prevented
the head from re-luxation at the slightest attempt to diminish the exaggerated position of the thigh.

Of course, this stability could never be sufficient to resist the weight of the body, which always works in the
direction of re-luxation. The question was: What about
later on? In this matter I favored a prophetic supposition: Suppose the head of the bone is forcibly held in the
socket by whatsoever means. Must not the growth of the
socket then be influenced by the pressure of its normal in-
habitant? Has not the growth of the socket been irregular, as it were lawless, because so long as it was empty
it grew in thickness yet shrunk as a cavity? Will not the
walls of the socket, after the re-position of the ball, grow
around its prisoner, encircle it and give it a reliable bed
to stay in for the remainder of the patient's life? When
the patient begins to stand, will not the upper rim of the
acetabulum, on account of its increased function as
weight-bearer, become stronger and grow to be a shelter

to the head of the femur, a roof, so to speak, to its cave-
dweller? In the course of time all these suppositions
turned out to be true; by X-ray pictures they were proved
equally true thousands of times many years after the operations. It goes without saying that an assertion as to
the curability of a disease or of a deformity does not
mean that all cases, without any exception, can be cured.
There are certain difficulties which are insurmountable.
But even such cases can at least be improved.

And, since this narrative is not meant to be a treatise
on orthopædic surgery but the story of the life and work
of a physician, further details are out of place. The
medical phase had only to be explained as far as any
intelligent reader can easily understand it.

I was sufficiently immodest to confess that I felt very
proud to have done away once more with a very serious,
nay, the most dangerous operation in orthopædic surgery.
I was at first scorned and laughed at. When, at a congress of German surgeons in Berlin, I spoke of my method
and its results, the president of the congress, the famous
—and, as a critic, much to be dreaded—Geheimrath von
Bergmann, rose and before I had finished my speech, exclaimed in a fury: "We have heard enough, you will have
to prove your stupendous assertions this very afternoon at
my clinic in the presence of the members of this congress."
It had the sound of a sharp military command, and I
answered in the same military tone that this was just what
I had come for. It was very easy to prove what had been
asserted. Before an eager audience, there was demonstrated a thing never before heard of: the physical symptoms of the re-position of a congenitally dislocated hip-
joint. The present generation may laugh at this fact,

but at that time it was a revelation. I was so much the more happy over my success, because it did away with not only the danger, but, at the same time, all other inconveniences, such as, for example, stiffness or even ankylosis of the artificial joints. But this last was not the worst sequel of the open operation. The deepening of the socket with a sharp spoon removed, at least partially, just those parts of the pelvic bones which attend to the growth of the basin—for future mothers, a terrible sequel to an operation which, in the last analysis, had not been absolutely necessary. It is known that even bilateral dislocaton of the hip, left alone, is by no means a hindrance to normal childbirth.

In the course of time the bloodless method came to be adopted as the method of choice in the medical world. It is a matter of course that many of the youngsters know all things about the method far better than the old man himself. But if they study attentively the books which I wrote on the subject, they usually admit that the originator of the method had somewhere already mentioned their new discoveries. Of one thing I am pretty sure, namely, that my method will not be rediscovered after an oblivion of fifty years. And there is another thing I am really very glad about: my happy thought has made it possible to blow away the dark cloud which shadowed the future life of all children who are afflicted by cruel nature with congenital dislocation of the hip-joint. The task of curing them is so much more attractive because the patients, as has been said already, are mostly healthy little girls of rare beauty. After being cured, they cannot help becoming real "beauties" later on. An army of beauties throughout the whole world has been made perfect by the bloodless operation, and other armies of little girls of all nations will be made perfect beauties by my life-work. All these I have the right to claim as my patients. As an admirer and adorer of women, I feel happy to have been destined by fate to spend my life mostly in the service of womanhood.

X

ROYAL RECOGNITION

THOUGH I did nothing but work, and was quite indifferent to titles and honors, the faculty at last acknowledged, though unwillingly, that I had brought about great progress in a new branch which strove for independence, and gave me the title "Professor Extraordinarius." And when my fame spread, and patients flocked to Vienna not only from the European continent but also from overseas, the authorities found out that the work of the Professor was of some economic importance to the city of Vienna. In due acknowledgment of these merits, I was asked by the Minister of Education whether I preferred an Order or a new title. I implored him: "Let me alone with Orders and titles and give me wards for my patients. I can't do with two beds." But wards cost money, and a new clinic for orthopædic surgery was deemed undesirable by the leading surgeons. Instead of costly wards, I was given an inexpensive new title. I was made Hofrath, "Counsellor to the Government," instead of Chief of Clinical Wards.

The most disagreeable part of it was that I had to give thanks for what I did not want, and my thanks had not to be given to the authorities but to His Majesty the Emperor himself. There was still another thing which stung me. For the Ministry, the gift of the title was inexpensive, but it cost the titled a lot of money. Due to my new title, I had to order a costly uniform. Trousers made of fine,

dark green cloth, adorned with broad stripes of gold
braid at the sides; a coat with dozens of superfluous glittering buttons; a sword hanging on gold-covered straps
and beautified by golden tassels; a rich, long overcoat,
and, most important of all, a triangular headgear from
the top of which flowed to all sides a glittering stream of
long black, blue, and green feathers which had once
adorned the buttocks of a gallant chanticleer. But that
was not all. A request had to be sent to the Imperial
Chancery for admission to an audience with His Majesty.
It was most graciously granted.

When I, the new Counsellor to the Government, entered the big anteroom to His Majesty's audience-cham-
ber in the magnificent Wiener Hofburg, I found it
crowded with people, most of whom outshone me by far in
exterior splendor. There were high officers, clergymen,
high officials, and a very few civilians in frock coats. The
wall at both sides of the door which led to His Majesty's
audience-room was studded with very tall, extremely good-
looking young men in brilliantly colored uniforms, holding halberds of threatening size and sheen. Examining
the crowd, my eyes met those of a little old man, clad
in the gold-embroidered uniform of a Minister. It was
His Excellency Mr. X, who for many years had been an
ex-Minister, living on his pension. I had treated him for
a long time, and had asked only a nominal fee, in consideration of his financial circumstances. Glad to know
some one in the crowd, I greeted the Minister with a
hearty "Glad to see you here," whereat the little man,
taking in the official degree of the accosting Counsellor
to the Government, granted me a gracious nod of the head.
I had forgotten that this anteroom was a world foreign

to me. I remarked to the ex-Minister that my Counsellorship would end after the audience, and that I would be glad to be once more just Professor Lorenz, the only title which I appreciated because it was earned by hard work.

There was a complicated formula of thanks for the nomination which I had to deliver to His Majesty. The Emperor asked: "What is your profession?"

"I am Professor of Orthopædic Surgery," answered the Counsellor.

"Is that so?" said the Emperor Franz Josef. "But, what is orthopædic surgery? I have never heard the name!"

"It is a new branch of surgery, Your Majesty, which has its cradle in Vienna, as far as Austria is concerned," answered the Professor.

"But what does it mean, what does it work on?" retorted His Majesty. Instead of a scientific definition, I ventured to say, "It works on the lame, to make them able to walk."

"That is much," said His Majesty, "and certainly very important for war surgeons." The audience was closed with His Majesty's typical formula: "I was glad to nominate you!" Then you had to retire "crayfishing," with face toward the Emperor, stepping backward and performing bows, while the adjutant watched your exit lest you miss the door.

The Emperor never shook hands with any one if he could help it, and never asked the name of a visitor because this would have meant a degradation of his Apostolic Majesty. He may have made exceptions in his private audiences and with the high-born Austrian aristocracy. I felt pity for the venerable old man, who seemed to be of the opinion that the Austrian Empire must go to pieces unless he himself attended frantically to the most petty affairs which just as well could have been left to subordinates. I went home convinced that I had played the part of a Counsellor to the Government for good. I felt that my fine new uniform was inevitably destined to be eaten by the moths—but again, you never can tell!

Decades had gone by, and in the fierce struggle of life I had quite forgotten the quiet days when I was a choir-singer at the St. Paul Monastery in Carinthia. One day I got a letter from a friend of my uncle, Father Gregor, who at that time was administrator of the cloister's vine-yards at Marburg, in southern Styria. The letter informed me that Prelate Augustin had breathed his last, and that a new prelate was to be elected. There were, of course, at least three candidates, among them Father Gregor and Father Eberhardt, who had been my foe as the boy who had a free place at the Gymnasium. Father Gregor objected strongly to being a candidate because he had reached his seventieth year, in truth because he loved his very quiet and independent life in his pretty, little castle at Marburg. He towered six feet and some inches, was healthy as a squirrel, and looked scarcely older than fifty-five. But he was undeniably lazy, just as he had been when he was a student. The monk-friend of Father Gregor asked me, in the name of many of his brethren, to try to convince my uncle that it was his duty to accept the great honor which his brethren were willing to confer upon him.

Next day I was on my way to see Father Gregor in order to make clear to him, if necessary, what it meant

to become a successor to former Prince-Abbots of St.
Blasien. Father Gregor had never in his life been ambitious; perhaps that was the reason why he deserved to
reach such high honors.

"Suppose," I said, "that the Gymnasium of St. Paul
had had eight classes at the time I was student; I should
then have entered the cloister and today I should be a
rival candidate, to whom you gladly would give the precedence. I assure you," I added, "it would have cost me
much less trouble and sweat to become a prominent figure
in your cloister than to become what I am at present, a
widely known specialist."

Uncle Gregor laughed the laugh of wise men who appreciate and enjoy life in their own way, but he yielded
and accepted the candidacy.

Some months later Father Gregor was the new abbot
of the Monastery of St. Paul. I was of course invited to
attend the magnificent ceremony of the benediction or installation of the new abbot by the Prince Bishop of Gurk,
with the assistance of certain other prelates and of all
brethren of the order. To make my humble contribution
to the gorgeous celebration, I resolved to put on my new
uniform of Counsellor to the Government. I had thought
to impress the Benedictine monks with its splendor, but
soon I became aware that I was a somber spot when the
priests appeared at high mass, followed by the hierarchial
apparition of Abbot Gregor, whose natural tallness was
increased to superhuman dimensions by the high tiara
which covered his head. The whole clerical assembly
sparkled with gold and silver. The most costly adornments
of the treasury of the cloister were brought out to do
justice to the importance of the ceremony.

Somewhere in the liturgy of the high mass, the ceremony of the oath of allegiance of the brethren to their new abbot was inserted. One by one the monks approached, knelt down, and kissed the white, gold-buckled slippers of the abbot, who then raised each of them to his breast and embraced him. I watched eagerly and intently for Father Eberhardt's turn. When he kissed the new abbot, something like a feeling of revenge pervaded my mind. "This for the stroke with the iron rod across my face," was my innermost thought. Beat a hound when he is very young and he will never go near you again. Degrade a child by a rude and unjust punishment, and he will hate his torturer for his lifetime. Be careful with children, you can just as easily win their love as their hatred!

After the ceremony, the new prelate retired to the prelature, and there received the homage of his nephew. Entering the large, high-ceilinged room, I clearly recalled the day when as a poor boy and choir-singer I had been introduced to Abbot Augustin by my uncle. From his picture on the wall, the late abbot looked down with friendly gaze upon the visitor to his successor. Abbot Gregor stood in the middle of the room; the prelate's golden chain with the golden cross adorned his neck and chest. On the fourth finger of his right hand sparkled the much-admired emerald which had made such an unforgettable impression upon the choir-singer. I took my uncle's hand, kissed the green stone, and said with some emotion: "I thank Your Grace for all you have done for me! Without your help I should not be where I am. In your hands I gladly deliver my thanks to the Monastery which made it possible for me to commence my studies. I know very well that with my poor alto voice I never was able to repay the benefits granted to me. I am almost in the mood to say that I am sorry not to have devoted my life to the Monastery!"

The prelate replied: "I should say you had better not be sorry. What could you have done as a monk for humanity? It's better that you became a great healer than a monk, even if he were an abbot!"

I had never been called to attend the Emperor as my patient, as had some of my doctor-friends, but I had the honor of attending the Emperor's grandchild, the lovely little Archduchess Elisabeth, who complained about her feet.

I came to the Hofburg in my everyday dress. An old lackey of the Archduchess Stefanie, the mother of little Elisabeth, wondered at my plain clothes and said to me: "When I was a young lackey, nobody dared to enter the inside of the Hofburg even by day if not dressed up." I told him the story of old Professor Skoda and his frockcoat, which I related earlier in this book.

Archduchess Stefanie behaved quite informally and gave me her hand to kiss. She looked me over attentively and said: "Why, it is curious, you very much resemble my father" (King Leopold of Belgium). I could not help laughing at this revelation, nor could I tell her Imperial Highness why I laughed so irreverently. A remembrance had struck me like a flash. Not long before, when in Paris, I had been about to return to my hotel in the dead of night, and, feeling that a cup of black coffee would be a good thing before going to bed, I had entered a brilliantly lit coffee-house on my way home. I had not known that this coffee-house was a special gathering place of the

Parisian demi-monde. When I sat down at a little table to order my coffee, I found myself surrounded and heartily welcomed by many fair young priestesses of love, who screamed: "Voila Popol! Bon soir, Popol! Where have you been so long, Popol?" I was sorry to have to tell the merry crowd that unfortunately I was not his Majesty Popol, with whom I had nothing in common but tallness and a long beard.

Quickly returning to the present scene, I marvelled that this blooming and beautiful lady should be the daughter of the rather fearful-looking Popol.

Just as nice as the Archduchess Stefanie, then the Crown Princess of Austria, was her little daughter Elisabeth. Had she been a boy, this child would have been destined before long to be the Crown Prince and even the Emperor of Austria, for as long as Austria had yet to exist.

The little girl had to undress, which she did somewhat reluctantly. When her shirt had come down to her waist and her mother bade her drop it entirely, the dear little girl looked up at her mother so beseechingly, so ready to burst into tears, that I stopped the peeling procedure and earned a look full of thanks, never to be forgotten. When the lovely little girl was dressed again she took me by the hand. I had evidently won her heart, and she showed me all her dolls and playthings. "But I can't find my skates. Where are my skates?" she asked.

I interposed: "But we are in July now, it is a long time before you will want the skates."

"But fancy," the princess replied, "my pond in Schönbrunn frozen over, and me without skates." Such were her sorrows at that time. The future had other, some-

what heavier ones in store for her. In a corner of the big
playroom, the doctor saw a full-sized portrait of the Empress Elisabeth in the imposing imperial regalia, really
the picture of imperial majesty incarnate. "This is my
grandma," the little princess said to me, stopping a moment before the big canvas. "Isn't grandma nice? But I
see her very seldom," she added.

I wondered whether the Empress was visible at all, even
to the members of her family, let alone the Emperor. Certain it is that she hid herself from the people, who knew
her only by her rare pictures, dating from her youth. She
hated to be photographed, always fearful of seeing the
first signs of age appear in her beautiful face. She lived
for her wonderful hair and for the flawless line of her
body. The great beauty of Empress Elisabeth was a
most extraordinary inheritance in her family, whose female
members were by no means famous for their comeliness.

As disease is no respecter of families, I found that I had
a rather serious case to treat in the family of an archduke.
Here I found no exclusivenes, no haughtiness, no cere-
monial aloofness, but was treated as I would have been in
any other well-bred family. Whenever it was necessary,
the archduke served as my assistant, and the lovely little
girl-patient with a significant name became my life-long
and dear friend.

XI

I RIDE MY HOBBIES

As my practice grew, I earned a lot of money which I mostly spent buying pictures, furniture, and "stones." As far as pictures were concerned, I preferred the showy and decorative specimens to those of modest appearance but extremely high prices. I never paid for the name of the painter, or for the age of the picture. Yet I gathered a very nice collection without asking what its market price might be. It was also my pleasure to buy dilapidated old furniture with fine inlay, so-called Maria-Theresa chests of drawers, and have them restored to their former splendor. To throw away old things and substitute new ones for them was against my religion, or I would have pulled down my peasant house to the deepest foundation stone, instead of remodelling the old den into a very comfortable abode. Another hobby of mine was collecting "stones," not precious stones, of course, but preferably carved marble statues, and the like. I used to speak of this as my "stone age." Whenever I visited Italy, I brought home old statues—a Proserpina, a Hermes, a Faustina, a Roman imperator, in pieces, to be restored; Venetian lions, and quite a collection of marble busts from the Posilippo, some of them really beautiful specimens. Mrs. Lorenz used to ask me, "Herr Professor, are you going crazy?" and I, unperturbed, used to answer: "Wait and see!"

Mrs. L became really anxious about the state of her husband's mind when one fine day carloads of stone arrived in Altenberg—four small and four gigantic stone columns without bases and without capitals. There were, furthermore, two great caryatids in wooden coffins—called by some visiting children the "two dead women." It was quite a heap of stones to be deposited in the garden, which had recently been enlarged by the addition of two other adjacent lots extending up the hill. Stones won't rust, I used to say.

One of the houses which had been acquired with the gardens was wrecked to enlarge the place near the villa; the second was thoroughly repaired and cleaned, for a guest-house.

But the greatest surprise for Mrs. L was yet to come. When the little river called "Die Wien," which flows stubbornly through the western part of the city, was to be vaulted over, two bridges became superfluous—the Tegethoffbrücke, named after the Austrian admiral who had defeated the Italian fleet at Lissa, and the Elisabethbrücke, so-called to commemorate Elisabeth's entrance into Vienna over this newly finished bridge, as the future bride of the Emperor. The railings of both bridges were pierced, exquisite works of marble—the one with a rectangular and the other with a circular design in the center of each component piece. In addition to the railings, the Elisabethbrücke was flanked on each side by about a dozen colossal marble statues, representing most Viennese heroes of the time of the last siege of the city by the Turks, and prominent men at the time of Maria Theresa. These statues, homeless after the wrecking of the Elisabethbrücke, after some wandering found their final resting-place along each side of the avenue in front of the magnificent city hall of Vienna. But they no longer were linked by the beautiful railings which were clamored for but had been lost. Nobody knew anything about them, or they would again have found their original place between the old marble heroes.

It was not until many years later, on one of my stone-hunting expeditions, that I found them covered with rubbish and half buried in the soft ground of a garden in the exterior suburbs of Vienna. A stone-carver, long since dead, had bought them for a song because he liked carved stones. They had since been forgotten. "Who could make any use of such bridge railings nowadays?" said the owner of the place. "I can," said I, and a bargain was struck which satisfied both sides. It was a very expensive business to transport the railings, many carloads of them, to the far-away garden in Altenberg, where the marbles were destined to continue their sleep. To Mrs. L it was not quite clear that her husband had not gone crazy. But I asserted that I hadn't. "Aren't carved marble stones just as nice to look at as rubies or diamonds or emeralds, let alone their market price? Wouldn't the Aldermen of Vienna be glad to buy the stones for double the price I paid for them?" I said. But I wouldn't even breathe to them the knowledge that I owned the railings so long sought for. I couldn't help it that stone carvings were my hobby.

Fine horses also became my hobby, and every day seemed to bring me nearer the ideal of my childhood, that of becoming a grand gentleman. I began driving horses, but later on renounced this pleasure for riding on horseback. This sport brought me into connection with the stable-master of his Imperial Highness the Archduke Francis-Ferdinand (who later was to be the heir to the throne and the first victim of the World War). A fine English hunter was to be sold out of the stable of the Archduke at a certain price which was to be final. Everybody knew how grasping the Archduke was in money affairs, and the question was: Why did he wish to sell the beautiful horse? Horse-sellers are never to be trusted, even if they are Archdukes! I found the horse faultless. It was some years later that I learned from the Archduke that the chestnut horse had always been so shy as to be frightened by his own apples. But, otherwise, the horse was good, much too good for this inexperienced rider. That was proved when on a fine autumn day I mounted the hunter and cantered across the shorn meadows of the Tullnerfeld. The horse was very lively because it had not been out the day before. In one respect, however, the noble horse behaved like any common horse without a pedigree: he turned homewards in a fury. When his rider failed to stop him at once, the horse ran away, stretched out his long neck level with his body and flew across the turf like a race horse. I had lost my stirrups almost at once, but held fast to the reins. There were water-ditches which I would never have dared think of crossing on horseback, but I was over the ditches before I could finish my thought. By and by I felt his breath grow short, and knew it was merely a question of minutes; I saw myself flung on the ground, or perhaps against some tree. By a happy chance, a newly ploughed field lay across the horse's path; he could not manage the soft earth, and stopped no less exhausted than his rider. He went home very slowly.

"No, sir, that won't do," I thought to myself. "Your bones are too precious to be broken by this noble horse, and your horsemanship is not good enough for such a racer. I wonder how the thickset Archduke would have stood this escapade." But it was a fine thing to ride that horse, and I could not make up my mind to give him away. He was not vicious, only wilful because he had not enough to do. But riding proved to be a somewhat risky sport for a surgeon who had to rely on his hands. It found its end in a very usual riding accident which you would find very disagreeable if you yere a hard-working surgeon. And yet, for my life I would not have missed that accident, because it brought a revelation to me.

It was an evening in late fall. During my vacation I had broken my horse by hard work to more decent behavior. I was riding along my customary trail in the woods on the banks of the Danube, which was running high, so that many ditches through the woods were filled. Crossing a meadow which seemed to fume with white wreaths of fog, I felt myself thrown backward on my horse, who had abruptly halted his trot. At the same moment, he turned round to run away, and threw his inattentive rider to the ground at one side. Falling on my shoulder, I felt a crack and knew that I had got what no horseman can escape, a fracture of the collar-bone.

But that was not all I learned in those moments fraught with happenings. Not far from me I saw something white, moving aimlessly around, and thought it streaks of witch-fog dancing and whirling in the light evening breeze. But no, it was something solid, something straggling, which spread long, wide arms and glided noiselessly into the thicker fog of the farther background. Still lying on my back, in spite of my discomfort I began to laugh, and laughed until the growing pain stopped me. I had seen again what had caused me such a terrible fright nearly forty-five years before in my grandfather's field, on a dim, foggy autumn evening—something flowing and

grasping with long white arms to catch me, which had
made me run so that my heels beat the drum of my buttocks. I had seen a ghost again! It was a big stork, a bird
unknown in the region where it had once frightened a boy.
Now it made a man with a broken collar-bone laugh. Was
the horse to blame for doing what the little boy had done?

But the adventure was not yet finished. The runaway
horse had first to be found. He was grazing at some distance. I tried to mount, but found it impossible; so I put
my right hand and forearm between the buttons of my
waistcoat, took the bridle in my left hand, and walked the
horse and myself home. Not so easy a thing as it would
seem, for I had to wade through brooks and water-ditches
up to my waist. Every jerk of the horse made me wince.
At last I decided to leave the horse alone, and he followed
me, not out of pity, but because he was going home to the
manger. I was still far from home when I met some people
with torches; it was growing dark by now, and Mrs. L
had sent them to look for her husband. When I got home,
Mrs. L welcomed me with: "Herr Professor, now at last
won't you stop riding?" I said: "Maybe I will, but I
would not have missed that accident. 'Grandma, Grandma, I have seen a ghost!'" They thought me crazy, but
Mrs. L remembered the story which I had once told her.

Since horseback-riding was so dangerous to my bones,
why not take up motorcycling? Your seat is lower, the
machine does not shy and run away, and you can choose
your speed. So reasoning, I bought the best machines to
be had at that time, one for myself and one for my son,
Albert, then a lad of eighteen. Albert was to be the groom.
I had made wide excursions as a bicycle-rider, and found
no difficulty in mastering the motorcycle. The only dif-

ficulty was getting started. As there was no starter, you had to adjust the gas and ignition and then run alongside the machine, bent sideways, since you had to hold on to the handle-bars. As soon as the first explosions took place, you had to remember that the machine would run away, dragging you with it. To prevent this, you had to jump with an elegant swing of your body into the seat. Woe to you if you landed there on your stomach!

Once in the seat, however, the world was yours, and all would have been right but for the bad Austrian roads. On an extensive tour into the Austrian mountains, the two motorcycles were caught in a thunderstorm which left the roads like the bed of a mountain river. When, after the heavy rain had ceased, we started again, I knew that my fate would be sealed before long. The front wheel slipped and I was hurled into the gravel. This time no bone was broken, but my left hand was awfully bruised; it meant a two-weeks' handicap. We took the boat down the Danube. When we reached home, and Mrs. L saw her husband with his arm in a sling, she said: "Herr Professor, are your bones really so cheap as that? Next time it will be your skull if you won't get sense!"

"Right you are," I said. "I toiled on the bicycle, I am risking my skull on a motorcycle, I deserve now to risk my life in a motor-car!"—and I bought the finest automobile to be had in Vienna at that time. It was at the beginning of motoring in Austria, and my purchase was considered a rather wanton feat. But the car never had the same charm for me as the motorcycle, and I used to envy my boy Albert when he started on a long motorcycle tour. A good motorcycle between his legs and a little money in his pocket make a young chap feel like ruler of the world.

I felt sorry to be excluded from the sports of the young.

One experience which might easily have ended fatally proved that I no longer belonged among the young men. As one of them, I had been at home in the Danube, and had crossed and recrossed it swimming, at a time when this sport was very little if at all in vogue, and the banks of the Danube above Vienna were lonely. I had long since given up such pranks, and restrained myself now to swimming in the deep rushing waters at some little distance from the bank. Unexpectedly, at the end of a dam which projected somewhat into the stream, I found myself caught in a whirlpool, and felt the sucking of the restless waters. I grew anxious and did just the opposite of what I should have done: I struggled against the waters, which tugged at my arms and legs. I was soon exhausted and my breath got short. In that moment I felt myself lost, but more ready to damn my carelessness than to recommend my soul to God. With only one eye above the surface of gurgling water, I saw something like a blue-green serpent shoot across my vision. It was the so-called heavy water which was passing by the whirlpool without partaking in the dance. It flashed through my mind that my salvation was in the direction of the open water. With a last effort, I strove toward the outer periphery of the whirl, and suddenly felt myself thrown away from it at a tangent. I let the heavy water carry me away, while I rested quietly on my back to regain my breath and quiet my throbbing heart. Then I easily made the bank, enriched by experience. Never fight against a whirlpool, because it is stronger than you. Keep to its outer border, that is all. The whirlpool has a tendency to throw you out rather than to suck you in, unless you behave like cattle which obstinately try to get back into a burning stable. I did not immediately tell Mrs. L of this experience—I felt ashamed because my wife was by far the better swimmer, and would chide me for my lack of sporting knowledge. When I told her later on and she scolded me, I consoled her by pointing out the fact that I was not a devotee of hunting, and there was no likelihood that I would ever be brought back from the hunt shot dead by one of my friends.

I had tried hunting in my youth, and later. The Tullnerfeld abounded with hares, and in the woods on the banks of the Danube there cackled more pheasants than I care for as a horseback-rider. When I once saw a hare shot through the spine, dragging his paralyzed hind-legs along the field and screaming like a child in great pain, I said to myself: "No, sir, that won't do. You are to heal the broken spine and cure paralysis, and not to break the spine to produce paralysis—even in a hare. You are no killer."

I remember only one occasion when I really wished to have a gun in hand, so that I might shoot the pheasants which squatted in the grass without rising, and then did so with the noise of an airplane (which did not exist at that time) before the horse trod them to bits. I needed a very quiet mount not to shy at the prolonged explosion. Yes, I could have shot a pheasant, the incarnation of beauty and stupidity. Ugliness combined with intelligence is a special kind of beauty, but beauty combined with stupidity is bare ugliness. The beauty of a girl who is stupid is marred in the eyes of a man who is not equally stupid.

In my middle age I was rather restless. I had always

wanted to travel and see the world. When I had the time
to indulge this desire, there was no money at my disposal,
and when I had the money, there was no time available.
Nevertheless, I succeeded in seeing the Sudan not long
after the Madi had been defeated by the English. I wanted
also to explore the Sahara Desert, but could not get farther than Biskra. There were no automobile routes at that
time. Twice I visited Sweden and Norway, and twice I
had the good luck to see, or rather not to see, the North
Cape, always veiled in a thick fog. When the first tourist
excursion to Spitzbergen by the Hamburg-American Line
was organized, I was of the party. At that time Spitzbergen was quite unknown, though excursions to Sweden
and especially to Norway had been made fashionable by
the German Emperor. The big steamer *Columbia* (which
was sent to the bottom of the sea by the Japanese in the
Russo-Japanese War) landed quite a considerable company of would-be Polar explorers on the ice fjords. There
was no year-round city on the shores of Advent Bay at
that time. A polar-bear hunter was the only living human
being met by the tourists.

The whole company was set ashore, and every single
member was told that he would run the danger of being
left behind on the island, to die a miserable death, if he
were not back on board at five o'clock sharp. There were
some "powder-baboons" among the tourists—professional
killers whose most ardent wish was to shoot an unsuspecting reindeer. I found some graves of men who had died
here in an attempt to winter in Spitzbergen, and I had the
luck to shoot a tiny bird, which was not at all shy—with
my camera. When the steamer's deep voice echoed in the
still, partly snow-clad mountains, it started a run of tour-

ists to get to the boats. When all were aboard, noses were counted. Two were missing, the powder-baboons. The captain, dear old Captain Vogelsang, ranted and swore, but had to wait. As in foggy weather, the steamer's siren droned at short intervals. At last the hunters came along, running for their lives. The captain vowed he would throw them in irons, but was glad at heart that they had come back. Why were they late? Their excuse was that they had seen reindeers and had followed them. Had they killed one? Apparently not, but they had at least shot at them and had certainly wounded one of the beasts, because they saw it fall and get up again after the shot.

"I should not like to be in your skins," I said to the bragging hunters. "The poor beast will die a miserable death. The reindeers of Spitzbergen have souls, and the soul of your victim will follow you, wailing and nagging at you in your dreams; you will have restless nights!" The prophecy came true. Not only the two powder-baboons, but nearly all of the tourists were so awfully shaken by the pitching and rolling of the ship in the stormy North Sea that sleeping and eating were out of the question, and even breathing became difficult.

From Bergen, in Norway, I had brought home skis at a time when these sporting instruments were scarcely known in Vienna. Certainly I was one of the first ski-runners in Austria. My Norwegian skis had no special bindings, and it was hardly possible to steer them. The ingenious bindings which make the shoe and the ski one unit without interfering with the movement of the foot were mostly contrived by Austrian ski-champions. But it was not decreed by my fate that I should quietly enjoy the fine, white sport. I must needs go up to the Rax, the two-thousand-and-more meters high mountain, favorite of the Viennese in winter and summer. I must needs ascend its highest peak, the Heukoppe, and try the descent on skis. The smooth beginning led to a disastrous ending. It chanced that while I was running fast, one of my skis slipped underneath a flat bough of creeping fir, the outer end of which was buried in the deep snow. My run was stopped abruptly, and the luckless sportsman was thrown down the steep slope, head over heels, in a dangerous "salto mortale." I was bruised and shaken all over, but no bone was broken. When I had gathered up my belongings, scattered in all directions, I said to myself: "No, sir, this won't do; this is something for the youngsters. Your bones are too precious to be broken against the rocks of the Rax," and I left my skis in the Karl-Ludwig house for any one who would have them.

Today every schoolboy in Austria is obliged to learn skiing, as well as swimming and dancing. When I came home from my ski expedition without my sporting instruments, my wife said to me: "Herr Professor, will you never get wise? Will you never admit that you are getting old, very near fifty, with your beard gray all over? You need your bones for working, to provide for your old age. As yet you have done nothing in that line." So far Mrs. L was undoubtedly right and I ruefully gave in. It was time to think of approaching old age.

XII

IMPORTED BY AMERICA

IT must not be thought that in those years I devoted my
time exclusively to sport. Only once in a while did I
go to excess in this respect. On the whole, I was always
devoted to my work. I used to call the Orthopædic Ambulatory in the Allgemeine Krankenhaus my most expensive
sport. To avoid the humiliating "going abegging" to the
assuming and pretentious bureaucrats in the Ministry, I
paid for my own instruments as well as my assistants'
out of my own pocket. I had not only many patients
but also many students, mostly Americans who came to
Vienna for post-graduate work. One of them, Doctor
Dexter Ashley, later became a prominent man in orthopædic surgery. I gave my lectures in English, as well
as I could. My students always assured me that they
understood pretty well what I said, but better still what I
did with my hands. I was not the first who tried to teach
in English; Professor Ernest Fuchs, the famous ophthalmologist, preceded me.

At that time, the many Americans who came to Vienna
were not yet organized as the American Medical Association of Vienna, which was founded on Thanksgiving Day
in 1903 at the meritorious instigation of Doctor Ravold of
St. Louis. Though extinguished by the World War, it
was feared forever—*quand on meurt c'est pour long
temps,*—the Association came to a new and prosperous
life immediately after the war had ended. Up to the present time, more than six thousand American physicians

have been numbered as members of the Association. Every year a book is published containing two to three hundred pages filled with all the advice possible regarding courses in various branches, all of them delivered in English by a staff of 200 well-trained teachers, professors, docents, and assistants. The number of courses in 1927–8 was 489. No other medical faculty in the whole world can offer a greater choice as far as teaching is concerned. All the teaching is concentrated in one place, so that daily journeys to distant places, such as are necessary in London or in Paris, are dispensed with. And the clinical material is abundant as it is in scarcely any other large city of the world, because Viennese patients are not so very particular about being examined by students if the latter behave in a friendly way and say, *"sind Sie so gut"* or *"ich danke Ihnen."*

It is a significant fact that membership in the American Medical Association often links the members in friendship through life. Professor Ernest Fuchs relates that when staying in Boston in November, 1921, he was invited to attend the dinner of the Viennese Dining Club, which was to celebrate its fiftieth anniversary. In 1871, twelve young Boston doctors studying in Vienna became friends and resolved that each one of them in turn should invite the others to a monthly dinner. Thus, twelve times a year, through fifty years, the happy remembrances of Vienna were revived. Among the diners in 1921 was one of the founders. Deceased members had been replaced by other Boston physicians who had studied in Vienna.

Of course, it is not only the remembrance of common study, made so comfortable in Vienna, but also the memories of youth which bind old members of the American

Medical Association of Vienna together. Young men are, of course, more appreciative of the comforts and attractions of Viennese life. These need not be enumerated. There can be no doubt that the place has an attractiveness of its own. The city cannot be compared with London, Paris, or Berlin. It is much smaller, but much nicer. Not imposing, but inviting. Not awe-inspiring, but *gemüthlich*. And so are the Viennese people, and so is the Viennese landscape—not grandiose, but beautiful and *gemüthlich*. Are not the vine-clad hills surrounding a great part of the city a sight to see? And the beech forests of the Wienerwald, twenty minutes distant from the Stefansplatz? And in two hours and a half you can be on mountain tops 2300 meters high. Music, theatres, and art need not be mentioned as attractions for worshippers. Let us consider only the more substantial comforts to be enjoyed by American doctors in Vienna. Is Viennese cooking not excellent? Viennese water is the best in the world, coming directly from the mountains. Teetotalers can revel in it. Excellent beer and good light wine tempted many an American away from prohibition. As many American doctors bring their wives with them, the beauty of Viennese women should be mentioned only to the bachelors.

Vienna isn't what it was before the war. Vienna is a noble lady still in mourning dress, but deliberating how to enliven her dark clothes with a bit of color. The *genius loci* has, nevertheless, something bewitching, and many foreigners succumb to it. From this *genius loci* the American doctors and Americans in general can learn something worth more than any other knowledge. They can acquire in Vienna a bit of Viennese philosophy of life. Work, work hard if need be, but never forget that you are a human being and not a beast of burden destined to die in the harness. In the long run it is cheaper to rest once in a while and to take life easy than to break down prematurely through overwork. Nervous breakdown is not so common in Vienna as in American cities.

There are prophecies that the American Medical Association of Vienna, though flourishing at present, will die of consumption when the post-graduate work at the American universities now developing will be at its height, as no doubt it will be some day. Furthermore, it is said that the young American doctors will stay at home, because it may be expected in the near future that American medical science will gain the undisputed leadership because many geniuses, with unlimited means at their disposal, are working at high speed. The prophecies may come true, but the young American doctors will nevertheless come to Vienna, just as they did before, because in Vienna they find that the teachers and the material on which to study are of a quality not to be excelled elsewhere.

Vienna, the Vindobona of the Roman Emperor Marcus Aurelius, as a center of science and culture will always be a teacher to humanity regardless of political alignments. There is still another factor to be taken into consideration. When the young American doctor has finished his studies at home, he will want to go abroad to see the old country which he has heard and read so much about. He will pass by all the big places to stay in Vienna. It is not only useful but even necessary for young American doctors to see countries which are not standardized—yet. Their stay in Vienna will be their most precious remembrance.

Nearing my fiftieth year, I had been repeatedly told by

my wife that I was getting to be an old man. "Then I should be at the height of my life," I had answered. But how could this be true, if I couldn't even manage to get rid of my down-the-hill neighbors at Altenberg, whose dilapidated house spoiled the beautiful view commanded by my garden. The neighbor down-hill was not only a nuisance in this regard, but was also the keeper of the village inn. On Saturday and Sunday evenings his guests were free to make a hideous trumpet concert in the little garden of the inn below the very windows of my study. Rumor had it that the innkeeper encouraged his guests to do their best in this regard. He speculated on my weakness for getting rid of a neighbor whom I could practically hug through the windows of my study. And the innkeeper was right in his speculations. I simply had to have the inn and garden to get a dignified entrance to my own house. I had bought my three peasant houses at reasonable prices, but this time a shrewd seller put screws on both of my thumbs. I had to pay four times as much as the old shed with its strip of garden, the breadth of a suspender, was really worth. To quench my wrath over the seller's mirth, there was nothing left for me but to run a battering ram against the brittle walls of the house. One single wall of it was lowered so as to complete the new fence. I was happy now. No more trumpet concerts and drunken singing below my study windows. This time not even Mrs. L scolded me for having squandered my money uselessly.

"But this must be your last prank, Herr Professor, or you will be a beggar in your old age!" said she.

"I think I have time enough to worry about that," I said, opening a letter with a very foreign-looking stamp on it. Chile, Magellan's Strait. "Do you know where

Magellan's Street* is, Mrs. L?" I asked my wife, who promptly answered in the affirmative. "Was it not thereabouts that Johann Orth, the refractory and unruly former Archduke of Austria, went to the bottom of the sea in his sailing vessel?" Mrs. L protested vehemently when I ventured to opine that the accident was very unlucky for the Archduke, but very helpful to an Austrian lady's geographical knowledge. She composed herself, however, when I reminded her of a theatre evening very, very many years ago. The comedy concerned a very famous Doctor Claus and his servant; the latter had dared to prescribe to a peasant patient from the country in the doctor's stead, and was nearly crazy through fear of what might have come of his counterfeiting. "I was still a student at that time," I continued, "and a certain young lady at my side, Miss Emma, whispered in my ear: 'When you as a doctor become as famous in our Gärtnerstrasse as this Doctor Claus seems to be in the whole city, then we could easily get married.' Isn't it curious," I went on, "that I am quite unknown in nearby Gärtnerstrasse and so well known in Magellan's Street that some nice people are coming from there to Vienna with a little girl, afflicted of course with congenital luxation of the hip-joints." And the girl came and the whole affair was joy from beginning to end. The name of the girl came to my memory again when a well-known member of her family was recently killed in an airplane accident.

At that time I really had an international practice. But it had not yet happened to me to be called to see patients outside my own country.

---

* The German word *Strasse* may mean either "street" or "strait," making possible a play on the word which of course is lost in English.

My secretary, Mrs. L, one day brought me a cablegram which asked me to come to Chicago to treat the little daughter of an industrial king, whom for brevity's sake, we shall call "the king." The little girl was afflicted with bilateral luxation of the hip-joints and had already been operated upon by an excellent specialist, with unsatisfactory results. I did not like the case from the beginning. The age was rather advanced, the anatomical conditions certainly unfavorable, or the excellent, surgeon would not have failed. The simple fact that the child had already been operated upon impressed me most unfavorably. All these reasons made me rather disinclined to accept the invitation. But then and there my secretary announced a quite different opinion. She not only pronounced an affirmative, but determined the fee due me. Under the circumstances, I felt ashamed for my manager, but the same manager asserted: "Herr Professor, you know excellently well how to spend your money, but you are utterly at a loss and blush like a young girl when it comes to asking for it as compensation for your services." I was sure that the king would find the proposition unacceptable and took some pleasure in the prospect of my over-confident secretary's getting a lesson. But she did not get that lesson, for shortly afterwards she produced another cablegram which declared everything satisfactory. Mrs. L had her triumph and succeeded in convincing me that the fee, though nice enough, was by no means exorbitant if the losses caused by my long absence from Vienna were taken into consideration.

So it came to pass that I took a furlough from the hospital for some months and with my assistant, Doctor G. Mueller, sailed from Genoa for New York in the au-

tumn of the year of grace 1902. In Naples the boat made
a stop of some hours, just long enough for a drive through
the city to see old places again. It just happened to be
the 19th of September, one of the days when the blood of
San Gennaro becomes liquid in its reliquary, as it used
to do several times in the year. Drawn by the crowd of
visitors, both doctors entered the church and saw the
reliquary kissed by thousands. The darkened liquid contained in a glass case was very thin and mobile, as was
shown by the ready adaptations of its level to the various
inclinations of the reliquary as it was offered to the
mouth of each devotee and after each kiss was wiped with
a dry linen. A very nice way to spread disease, but then
—the saint would protect his devotees. I envied them
their faith. If I had had but one-tenth part of it, how
eagerly I would have kissed the glass case to gain as
my reward the firm conviction that my errand would be
a success.

The passage was not too smooth. Ordinarily that would
not have mattered, as I am not a bad sailor, but a small
piece of the breast of a *"faisan de Bohème"* which had
probably been shot in the woods of Bohemia a year earlier
made me so sick that I found myself doomed to oatmeal
gruel for the rest of the voyage when it had scarcely begun. I arrived in New York as empty as a blown-out egg.

Chaperoned by an adjutant of the king, I had to pass
the customs. A big chest with instruments which looked
like machinery aroused the curiosity of the customs-officer.
"Who are you?" he asked. "I am Doctor Lorenz," was the
answer. "Is that so!" said the officer. "You are welcome
to this country!" The adjutant remarked laughingly:
"See, Doctor, you are found out already." At the old

Waldorf-Astoria Hotel, a suite of rooms had been prepared for the newcomer. "I hope you will like the rooms as well as did his Imperial Highness, Prince Henry of Prussia, some weeks ago," said the manager. "I hope they will do for a night," was my mocking reply.

I felt much less satisfied when I entered the diningroom ready for a hearty meal after the protracted oatmeal gruel diet, and even more ready for a good glass of beer. But, lo, all the tables were covered with bottles and glasses filled with a colorless liquid which I had, though incredulous for the first moment, to take for water, and a little later on for ice-water. Rather a surprising revelation to a middle-European newcomer who might just as well have been a lake-dweller. As beer was not a refined enough beverage in those airy halls, I ventured to order a small bottle of wine; there were only big bottles to be had. I felt like a criminal when I poured some wine into the ice-water, but regained some of my lost poise after a while. That was at a time when nobody thought of prohibition. But evidently the trend was toward icewater, at least in the fine hotels. This trend may not have been obvious then to the New Yorkers themselves, but it certainly was very impressive to a newly arrived middle-European who had thought of himself as a very sober man, only to be revealed to himself in the Waldorf-Astoria as an alcohol addict.

After a meal which may have pleased his Prussian Imperial Highness but was far from being satisfactory to a critical Viennese gourmand, I took a stroll through the neighboring streets. There was then no danger of being run over by a flock of automobiles, four abreast. I passed a large shop, whose whole front was open toward the street, and looked in. The big hall was filled with red fire-engines. The officer came forward to welcome the hesitant visitor. Looking me over once more, he said, "How do you like America, Doctor Lorenz?"

I gasped, "How can you know me? I just left the boat."

"Isn't this your picture?" the officer said, throwing me an evening paper. "Who else in New York has such a beard as yours except some Polish Jews?" I had to admit at last that I was the doctor. In recognition of the fact, the officer promised me a spectacle. "Stay at my side," he ordered. Suddenly electric bells rang furiously in the background, and out from nowhere, as it seemed, emerged beautiful horses, entirely unharnessed; they put themselves each in his predestined place, while from the ceiling descended fully equipped harnesses which had escaped the attention of the visitor. A second later the big engines were whirled into the street while the horses' hoofs clattered a general tattoo. "This is how the New York Fire Brigades answer their calls," said the officer proudly. I thanked him for the show, never to be forgotten, and marvelled. It was the first proof of American hospitality offered me on the first and only evening which I spent in New York on that visit. There are many ways of being hospitable, and the proud officer chose the one which was possible to him.

The traffic in the streets was not so tremendous as to impress me very much. Quite new and consequently impressive was the traffic in New York harbor, with its hurrying ferry boats with levers moving up and down at their tops. They seemed to be gesticulating, exciting themselves to still greater haste. The famous skyline of the city as seen from the water seemed to me the incarnation of fantastic irregularity.

The Twentieth Century Limited took me westward. Then and there I learned for the first time the magnificence of American railway travel. And yet, after some deliberation I did not give the Americans too much credit for their railways, because they simply could not help building them as they are. A country of such magnificent distances had to have magnificent railways or contact between its parts would have been lost.

When I entered the king's house in Chicago I felt somewhat disillusioned. I had expected a palace, and found instead a "bourgeois" residence like a hundred others—very nice, of course, and very costly, but the greatest luxury of all, roominess, was lacking. The ceilings were rather low, and no room had half the size of my own dining-room in the rebuilt peasant house in Altenberg. The king was a very sympathetic middle-aged man, very affable and unpretentious. His wife, the queen, was a very elegant, rather dark beauty of a southern type, very lovely and charming indeed. I was anxious to be introduced to the princess, a girl about six or seven years old. She was called in, and did not at once enter the room, but looked suspiciously through the half-open door to see what was going on. Evidently she had heard something about a new doctor who had come to see her.

"Come in, darling, and shake hands with Doctor Lorenz, who has come a long way to see you."

With some difficulty the little princess came nearer, hesitating, shy, and full of mistrust. Reluctantly she held out her hand, ready to withdraw it any moment, and raised her lovely face to the somber, bearded man who, bearing not unjustly the nickname of Santa Claus from his English and *"Père Noël"* from his French patients, was for children an apparition always mixed with fear. Nevertheless, the girl decided at last to give me her hand. I took it and held it quite a while in my own, regarding the lovely child intently. I felt moved to the depths of my heart.

Had I ever seen such a charming and lovely creature? Her rosy face might have been an angel's. Her full-lipped mouth betrayed at certain moments when puckered an unchildlike firmness which melted away when she smiled and two unexpected dimples made their appearance on her blooming cheeks. Her nose was a little bit tip-tilted, which gave her face a somewhat roguish expression. Rebellious waves of rich, soft, auburn hair were always trying to hide one of her searching, deep brown eyes. I loved the child at first sight. Had I not loved her, I could not have pitied her so much. I ought to have regarded her rather as an impersonal object which I was called to work upon, instead of as a charming creature on whom I must inflict pains which I myself would feel not less than the child. I doubted in that moment whether I was hard-boiled enough to be a surgeon at all. At least, I resolved to cause the child as little discomfort and pain as possible.

The operation was easier than I had feared it would be, and promised full success. I felt a heavy burden taken off my heart. I remembered San Gennaro, whose liquid blood I had kissed—in spirit.

After about a week I thought I could leave without arousing any further publicity, but in this assumption I was quite wrong. I got many invitations to operate publicly in hospitals where crowds were waiting to see my performance. I operated privately on a five-year-old girl who was a friend and playmate of the princess. Her father being in reduced circumstances, I was, of course, glad to do the operation for God's sake. I had so much to do that I could not pay any special attention to that case; yet this girl, as I heard later on, was perfectly cured.

I could not escape a visit to the famous stockyards. When I left this place of horror, I felt sick, yet I learned a great deal. I had previously had not the slightest idea that profound science was the basis of many of those colossal American enterprises, be it meat-packing or automobile-manufacturing. The single fact that practically all parts of any slaughtered animal were made use of—except the breath, as they told me—filled me with due admiration. When I saw the offices with hundreds of clerks who worked as sedulously with the pen as I had seen other workers of the establishment work with hammer and knife, and when I penetrated at last into the "*sanctissimum*," the office of the boss who gave orders, dictated, telephoned and sent telegrams over private wires to all parts of the country, then I felt I had been right in calling him "the king." And his majesty interrupted his work with a smiling face, as if he had nothing else to do but welcome his rather intimidated visitor.

If there be really no other means of keeping life alive than by destroying life—animals eating plants or themselves and man living on both of them—then the wholesale, concentrated killing in the stockyards may seem preferable to a ubiquity of carnage. Keep away from the stockyards and you can more easily forget certain depressing facts.

While in Chicago, I had to pay a visit to Mrs. Misa

OPERATION BEFORE A GREAT AUDIENCE, CHICAGO, 1902

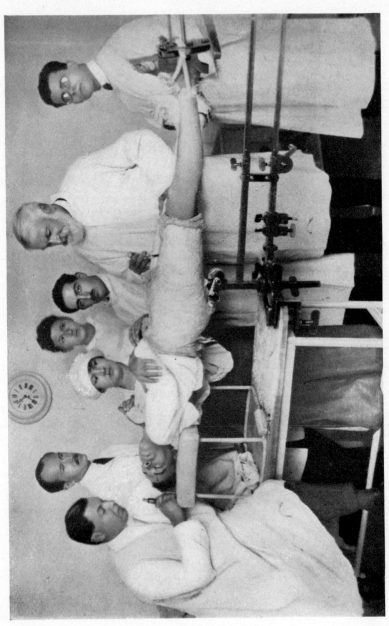

PROFESSOR ADOLF LORENZ OPERATING ON A SPANISH ARTIST WHO HAD
PAINTED A PICTURE FOR HIM

Here he is painting the painter

Bacon, who was that very lady with whom and her sister Helen and her brother Arthur, as children, I had inaugurated singing concerts consisting mostly of Carinthian songs, on many a winter evening before the fireplace of the dining-room in a lonely castle in far-away southern Hungary. As fate would have it, Misa had found her way from Gurahoncz to Chicago, being married to a well-known physician, while her sister Helen, as the same inexplicable fate would have it, had become the wife of a brother of Mrs. Lorenz and so my sister-in-law. Arthur had made a splendid career as a diplomat, and was at that time Austrian ambassador to Persia, in Teheran. Old memories came to life, and I felt quite soft at heart when Mrs. B opened her treasure-box and produced an old, dried-up hazelwood stick in the bark of which were incised the words: *"Was der Thau den Fluren, sind der Seele Lieder."* And besides the baton, Mrs. B produced the small, silken red-and-white band which was once the badge of the Singing Association of Klagenfurt. To save expenses, the band was real only at the front where it crossed the breast of the singer, while at the back, string had been substituted for the silk. This costly badge had been given in succession to the best singer among the pupils.

So dear are the memories of youth that the most trivial emblems connected with it become cherished treasures. It was pleasant to live for an hour in the distant land of youth, which in this instance was southern Hungary.

My carefree life in Chicago was of a sudden very disagreeably disturbed by a conspicuous headline in the newspapers: DOCTOR LORENZ TO BE ARRESTED. There was no prohibition at that time, or I would have

pleaded guilty in this regard! But I was really a trans-
gressor of the law without my knowing it. I was to be
arrested because I had no legal right to practise in
America. I had no license! As this deficiency could not be
made good at a moment's notice, and as I went on operating
in the hospitals, I could not help feeling in danger of
being put in prison for a while, at least to do the law
justice. That evening as I went home to my hotel, I was
aware of being followed by a gigantic policeman. The
law on two legs, I thought to myself. What else can you
do but submit to the categorical invitation of the representative of the law to follow him to the jail? I turned
into a side street; the policeman did the same. Now it
was clear that the man knew whom he wanted. I slowed
down, while the policeman stepped out and came nearer
and nearer. At last I nearly broke down when the heavy
hand of the giant came down upon my shoulder.

"Are you Doctor Lorenz?" the policeman asked, in a
not too friendly way, I thought.

"Sure," I answered. "I guess you want to arrest me.
Do so, please, without causing a sensation."

"I arrest you!" laughed the giant. "Who will arrest
you? Surely not while I am with you! I only want to
shake hands, and thank you for the kind advice and good
hope you gave yesterday to the child of a friend of mine."

"Oh, I thought you were going to arrest me because it
was in the papers this morning," I observed.

"If you really were to be arrested, it would not have
been in the papers," the policeman said, and instead of
my whole person, the blue giant arrested my hand for a
short moment in a rather painful grip.

To avoid serious arrest, I had to comply with the law

and pass the examination prescribed to get the legal license. If a man has heard nothing of chemistry, physiology, and pharmacology for the last twenty-five years; if furthermore, in the meanwhile, new branches have sprung up of which he has never heard at all; and if, last but not least, all these long years he has been absorbed in his own work body and soul, scarcely looking to right or to left, it is hard for him to pass an examination on a day's notice. I asked for a postponement: I would try hard in the interval to brush up my knowledge, which was not lost but had only sunk beneath the threshold of consciousness. I was told that only practical questions would be asked. The time of the examination was fixed. I felt a bit uneasy, even though, as a substitute for the famous Billroth, I had myself examined candidates in surgery. But it is a fact that even an examiner, if examined in turn by one of his dear colleagues in another branch, would surely get plucked. Though this gray old candidate was prepared for the worst, I reassured myself by the thought that even the severest examination could not possibly tear my head off.

The examination was as formal as possible, with quite a committee of examiners seated round a long oval table. All the examiners were very young, except a gentleman of about fifty-five, who had short white hair and a clean-shaven, ruddy face with blue eyes. The examiners and the candidate faced each other. I thought to myself: This distinguished, clean-shaven, white gentleman with blue eyes cannot and will not intentionally hurt an exceptional, equally blue-eyed candidate because he is not clean-shaven but adorned with a rather too long "pepper-and-salt" beard.

What will the first question be? thought the candidate, with the same vacant feeling in his stomach that he had felt twenty-five years before on similar occasions. Presently the examiner said, "Er-er-how do you like America?"

I was puzzled. An examination should never be a farce, I thought to myself, and answered as if freed from care, "Oh, very much indeed!" The examiner nodded his satisfaction. Second question: "What impresses you most in America?"

I answered: "American charity and American hospitality." The examiner smiled satisfaction. But I had been wrong in assuming that these questions had anything to do with the examination, for they were only a prelude to the real examination. In a very earnest tone, the examiner continued: "Now, please tell us something about your methods and how you came by them?" and, turning with a smile to the other gentlemen, said: "I presume the candidate will know more about it than his examiners!"

I then gave a short speech explaining the advantages of my mechanical treatment of hip-disease compared with the American method, and laid stress on my successful endeavors to do away with dangerous operations, substituting for them harmless, preferably bloodless procedures. I closed by emphasizing the fact that in orthopædic surgery there are practically no vital indications, and therefore operations dangerous to life should be avoided.

The examiners were quite satisfied and declared that the candidate had passed the examinations *cum laude*. When they congratulated the new-baked American doctor upon his success, I thanked them heartily for their courtesy and explained that the examination was absolutely the same that the candidate for the so-called Docentship had to pass in Vienna. On motion of some members of the medical faculty, I had been spared this examination, which was against the law. You cannot escape your obligations, and must eventually make up for any former sin of omission, be it twenty-five years later. Now the law had been complied with, and the new doctor could again breathe freely.

XIII

A HARD-WORKED TOURIST

AFTER my rather prolonged stay in Chicago, I could have gone home. But I felt an irresistible desire to see more of America, especially California. I went there not as a physician but as a simple tourist and sight-seer, but I had to learn that in the freest country in the world, I was doomed to be the least free man. The tourist was turned into a doctor again in Denver, where I stayed a very short time. My medical services were rewarded by a drive through the city and the suburbs, in the company of my hosts. We rode in a string of carriages, drawn by strong horses. The site of the city is so beautiful, its air so balmy and invigorating because of its five thousand feet elevation above sea level, the sky so deep and clear, that in my opinion Denver should be the "air resort" of the United States for all patients suffering from lung complaints. The tourist would have liked to make the easy trip up to the summit of Pike's Peak, but the physician was not allowed to do so. I was sent like a registered parcel to Salt Lake City, and after similar experiences in that city, to San Francisco.

From Salt Lake City I carried away the sweetest remembrance that a man of nearly fifty can be blessed with. A beautiful young girl, in her sixteenth year, the daughter of a physician, declared she had fallen in love with me. Of course she had not as yet the slightest idea of what love meant. She sent me flowers, love-poems, and souvenirs. The young creature simply had to have and to adore an idol, and she chose the old man because I had done some good work for some children. Sweet M may be a grandmother by this time!

In San Francisco, I had little time left me for sight-seeing; I must play the part of a physician in my usual performances. But one day I succeeded in escaping and made the excursion to Mount Tamalpais, without getting much of a view of the Golden Gate on account of the fog. On my way back I met on the Sausalito boat a society of ladies from San Francisco who were delighted to meet me, just as I was, of course, delighted to have met them. Some of these ladies proved to be true friends later on, when Viennese children and their parents lacked the fundamental necessities of life; they became helpful angels then. One of these angels died and I had to send my thanks to Heaven.

As the evenings were sometimes left to me, I indulged in my love for the theatre. In my box I was joined by some of my new acquaintances. There was a Norwegian doctor who brought greetings from one of my patients, a little girl, Maria H, in Bergen; a young lady who lived in Honolulu; an X-ray man from New York; a physician from San Francisco, and I myself from Vienna—and upon the stage, an artist whom I had seen in Berlin some time before. It was agreed that the world is very small, though it was not then thought of as an infinitesimal grain of dust, whirling around the sun, toward a goal which probably will never be reached.

On my way southward, I stopped in Los Angeles and stayed there for a while. It was the only place in America where I was left free of medical and social obligations. I basked in the sunshine and had a good time. Of course, I did not miss Mount Lowe, with its marvellous view. A Viennese lady, Mrs. J, who lived in Los Angeles, invited her fellow-countryman to her beautiful home and proved to me that she had not forgotten her Viennese cooking. The crown of the feast was an *Apfelstrudel*. Compared to an American apple-pie, the Viennese *Apfelstrudel* represents the culinary art in its highest development; the apple-pie shows it in its first beginning.

To honor their guest, some of my medical friends arranged a carriage drive through all parts of Pasadena, which was separated from Los Angeles by a good distance at that time. There were no automobiles to disturb the silence of the streets; the big carriage of the party was drawn by four beautiful horses. In this way the palaces and bungalows of the place could be inspected most comfortably. If I had had some foresight, I would have bought some lots on a modest site and saved myself many troubles afterwards. There was no Hollywood at that time, and yet Los Angeles was the same wonderful city it is today. It was then the city which I would have preferred to any other in America. I am not quite sure whether at present the air of its streets, which are more than crowded with motor-cars, befits a health resort of world fame. Without Hollywood, Los Angeles was certainly a quieter place thirty-three years ago, and harbored fewer disillusioned young boys and girls than it does nowadays. I left it reluctantly, with a faint hope that I might see the city and its beautiful site again in my life. Like San Francisco, the Los Angeles of that day was a city of women, wine, and laughter. As far as beautiful women and laughter are concerned, the place has certainly not changed, but the fate of California grapes was changed. Now they are again being used for their original purpose, turned into the poetical gift of a blessed country, California wine.

You may be pardoned by an American if you have been in Rome without having seen the Pope, but you must plead guilty if you have been in America without having seen the Grand Canyon of the Colorado River! In conformity, I left the main line at Williams and to my surprise was welcomed by the officials of the side line. How could they know? "Well, we read the papers even down here—we have expected you and we know your picture." No privacy for me—I had been found out even at Williams.

The conductor must have had a very good memory. About twenty years later, Professor Ernest Fuchs, the famous Viennese ophthalmologist, who resembles me as far as stature, face, and beard are concerned, when in Williams bound for the Canyon was greeted by the same official as Doctor Lorenz. When the mistake had been cleared up, the conductor excused himself: "Well, bearded old fellows are difficult to differentiate. Give my compliments to the Doctor anyhow!"

I would have liked to stay at the Canyon for at least a week. The crisp winter air was like a whip, not only to the lungs—you could not get enough of it at a breath—but also to the stomach, which cried for more when you were afraid you had already overeaten. The hotel was a primitive adobe building, made comfortable by a multitude of Indian blankets and rugs on the floors and walls. The cooking could have been worse and still would have been deemed excellent. Certain peculiarities of a certain place at the side of the house reminded the traveller of similar customs to be found in lonesome valleys of the Tyrol! To give a whole family the possibility of sharing in natural necessities of a very important kind, the long seat of the roomy apartment was provided with apertures of different sizes, the smallest of them made easy of access by some wooden steps!

The next day was set aside for a descent to the bottom of the canyon, to permit of at least a hand-bath in the gurgling waters of the Colorado River. But you never can tell. How it came about that a telegram from Chicago reached me in my seclusion at the edge of the Grand Canyon, I could never make out. But there was the telegram, saying that Northwestern University of Chicago had resolved to honor the Viennese doctor with the degree of Doctor of Laws; the ceremony was to take place on a certain day, and the candidate was expected to deliver a speech of at least twenty-five minutes. Fame, if ever so transitory, nevertheless has its drawbacks. Instead of descending to the bottom of the canyon, I had to be content with sitting on its edge, with my legs dangling above the abyss. Instead of enjoying the unique sight undisturbed by any earthly care, I had to suck out of my ten fingers what commonplaces I could gather to fill that endless time of twenty-five minutes without having a book at hand to steal from. I so far forgot myself as to curse the resolution of Northwestern University—but only for a brief moment. After I had recovered from the shock, I felt crushed by so great an honor and worked with my fingers instead of with my legs, but was just as tired in the evening as if I had gone down and up the walls of the canyon on my own legs.

I had to take a hurried leave and go to get the hood and the cape. Yet the gorgeous picture of the walls of the canyon and of the gigantic, multi-colored towers and spires striving to rise from its bottom to the level of its edges remains unforgettable in my memory. Nowhere on earth can you see the bowels of Mother Earth in brilliant sunshine, to a depth of about 2000 meters, as a result of the corrosive work of the Colorado River through the ages. The water gnawed and licked and nibbled and dissolved anything that could not withstand it, and in the course of hundreds of thousands or millions of years dug out the mighty cleft, with its sheer walls clad in glowing colors by the sun. And the water goes on doing its work and will for future millions of years, to astonish contemporary man, even though he has reached his highest possible degree of development. And all these millions of years mean nothing in the incommensurability of cosmic time or space.

On my way back to Chicago in the sleeping-car, I was awakened by some one who pulled my leg roughly and cried out: "Are you the man who got a million for an operation?"

It took me some time before I grasped the situation. "Oh, no," I answered, "I got two."

"But then," the reporter put in, "you pulled Mr. X's leg severely!"

"No," I said, "Mr. X didn't think that I pulled his leg, but you surely pulled mine a bit too hard."

"Oh, beg your pardon," the reporter replied, "I had to get some news out of you." Then he withdrew respectfully, as seemed due a man who was worth two million dollars!

Although I had become a legal medical doctor only after examination, Northwestern University of Chicago invested me with the degree of Doctor of Laws without an examination, and I felt unworthy of such a great honor. The investiture constituted quite an academical exercise. There was playing of the organ, prayer, and speeches. I had to answer the speeches with one of at least twenty-five minutes, which contained, I fear, many truisms and is scarcely worth preserving. The only item that clings to my memory is that I was clad in a black silken robe adorned with purple velvet, that I wore a peculiar hat, and that I looked more like an old Doctor Faustus than a newly fledged Doctor of Laws. After the ceremony I had my first experience with American handshaking. My poor right hand was grasped, pressed, squeezed, smashed, crushed by at least three hundred other hands, sometimes powerful ones which expressed the friendly feelings of their owners, until my hand hung swollen and nearly paralyzed from its wrist. When I began to wince and wriggle, I heard some one say, "Have mercy on the man who wants his right hand to squeeze other men's feet with."

I could not help thinking of the poor President of the United States, who is supposed to be able to stand tortures a hundred times worse. The good old custom seems to need reforming, at least so far as the President of the United States is concerned. He should shake hands without being shaken by the hand. This could easily be done if he simply touched with the palm of his hand the back of the hand of his visitor—a palm to the back of the hand, instead of a palm-to-palm handshake.

I had invitations from many hospitals and from many places in the United States and accepted them as far as time and circumstances would allow. Wherever I went, I was followed by reporters who watched all my doings. When I once caressed a nice little darky, the papers said, "He likes colored people." When I sometimes knelt down to save old people painful movement, the papers would extol me: "How humble he is!" Even my hands were unexpectedly caught by photographers. While one of them would ask to see my "wonderful" hands, his colleague would be snapping them with his camera, and the newspapers published the picture without my knowledge or approval. I had become a toy in the hands of the newspapermen and of local committees of physicians, who dictated to me twelve working hours a day without mercy, and totally deprived me of my personal liberty. Travelling from one place to the other, I would be met midway by a member of the committee of that other place who often transported me directly from the depot to the operating-room. There I would be welcomed by the yells of the students, for instance: "He is all right and more than all right—God bless him!" and so would begin my work. This popularity, for which I certainly did not strive and which was rather a nuisance to me, derived from the fact that I could afford to work regardless of fee. So my charity appealed to the people, who said of me: "He is devoted to the poor because he was a pauper himself who worked his way up from the plough." A picture in the newspapers showed me guiding a plow with my right hand, while in my left I held a book from which I was studying —and yet the furrow went straight.

If you are in Chicago, a visit to Milwaukee is indispensable. It must be confessed that my visit was devoted not so much to medical work as to the study of the Pabst

Brewery and its products, a program which in the end
proved to be more exhausting than difficult operations!
A garden party enlivened by German music, a dinner
party and speeches, made life more difficult than hard
professional work. The worst of all was a "smoker" of
dribbling wetness. There was no trend to prohibition at
that time in Milwaukee. I proved to be an infant compared with my younger and older colleagues as far as my
tolerance of "booze" was concerned. Thanks to my method
of sham-drinking whenever there was a "Here's looking
at you," I stood the wet exercise better than many a dapper worshipper of good beer and light wine. I was pes-
tered by reporters for my views on total abstinence or
moderation. When I said that I had to be careful not to
lose my English under the influence of alcohol, because
it was not so very deeply rooted in my brain, the reporter
wrote that I, coming from a country where wine and beer
were indulged in without thinking much whether they were
useful or harmful, was a fervent preacher of absolute
abstinence.

When my patients had been given proper care, I was
free to leave Chicago. I carried away with me a very
precious document in the form of a beautiful volume in
which was engrossed a resolution of thanks, presented to
me by the City Council.

Short stays in Boston and Baltimore were filled with
earnest medical work. The city of Boston appealed to me
very much, and I would have liked to remain there for a
while and enjoy its attractive environment. As the Austrian ambassador to the United States, Baron H, had
arranged for an audience with President Theodore Roosevelt, I had no time to lose in either of these places, and had

to leave for Washington. A long stroll through the beautiful city made me, as a foreigner, feel at home, at least as if I were in a European city. But I was very soon disillusioned in this respect at the beautiful Arlington Hotel, where I hoped for a splendid dinner. The dining-room was imposing enough, no less so the tableware and the table linen. Two giant, white-clad Negroes shoved a service table on wheels round the room. A huge, shining, silver cover which looked like a dome seemed to invite the guest to exuberant anticipation of its treasured delicacies, but when the big dish was uncovered and part of its contents, with heavy silver spoons and forks, was displayed on the plate of the expectant diner, it proved to be a hare ragout made from all the least appreciated parts of a hare which might have been killed a fortnight earlier. Much ado about nothing! A piece of bread and some ice water made it fully clear to me that I was not in Europe, least of all in Austria, where hare ragout, though served less ostentatiously, is a delicacy for which, as a matter of course, the back of the hare is always preferred. The Viennese are modest people in many respects, but certainly not as far as cooking and eating are concerned. The Austrian ambassador—a Hungarian gentleman—and his wife made the doctor forget the hare ragout of questionable character by Hungarian cooking which was as excellent as the most demanding gourmand could desire.

It snowed and rained for the first time that winter when, dressed as usual, I set out with the ambassador for the White House. The roads in the grounds were deep in melting snow, and the wheels of the carriage left deep ruts. At a slight ascent in the road the horses stopped and refused to make further effort; we had to leave the carriage and walk in the mud. In soaked boots, we entered through a small door at the back, which opened from the park. A man in simple, brown clothes led us along a maze of corridors, the walls of which were covered with books up to the ceiling. "The President is below somewhere and will show up any moment," the man said; then a door opened and Roosevelt came in with quick, elastic steps, the tails of his long coat swinging like the thick watchchain on his waistcoat. His trousers bagged a bit at the knees, like those of a man who spends much of his time at his desk. He greeted me with extended arm and shook hands heartily. Laughing, he showed a formidable set of teeth, like a tiger's.

"Are you the famous doctor?" the President asked, looking at his visitor through sparkling eyeglasses.

"If not so famous, then certainly a doctor," I answered.

"Just this morning Mrs. Roosevelt spoke of you. She said it would have been good luck if you had visited America at the time when one of our sons had knee trouble for a long while. How do you like America?"

"I should like it but for the strenuous life which you have to lead over here."

The President laughed at the "strenuous life," an expression of his own coining, and said: "That's what keeps the Americans healthy. As far as I know they have made you lead a strenuous life over here whether you liked it or not. Which country are you from?"

"From Silesia, a province of Austria," I replied.

"Silesians are known as very diligent and intelligent people," the President said ingratiatingly. "My ancestors came from Holland, driven from their country on account of certain religious differences, as happened often in those times. Some of them must have been sailors. I am much interested in all questions regarding the sea! I know that the Austrian fleet did very well at Lissa under Admiral Tegethoff. Well, we do not lack excellent admirals either, and the American fleet has shown what it can do. I wish you a happy return to your country, which I hope to see once more."

With another handshake, quite informally, the audience was closed. I remembered my audience with the Emperor Franz Josef, whom a humble subject scarcely dared to look at. To shake hands with any one of his subjects would have been an unheard-of thing. Roosevelt, the personification of democracy, looked more like a well-to-do citizen who did not care so much about outward appearances as did an emperor pole-axed by his own ancestral dignity. Years later, ex-President Roosevelt, returning from his African hunting expedition, and sojourning a few days in Vienna, wanted to pay a visit of courtesy to the Emperor. The question of dress was discussed. Roosevelt had no frock coat, and his rough-riding uniform was among his luggage; so he met the Emperor in some outfit similar to that in which I had seen him, and the old Emperor was delighted.

The next day in Washington brought me a big framed photograph of the President, with his signature and kindest regards. The picture has the most prominent place in my Viennese waiting-room, and many young Americans have profited by the occasion to make their salaam to "Teddy." When I visited the Columbia Theatre the following evening, I was greeted by the beautiful old Austrian anthem, played by the orchestra as soon as I appeared in the box. I bowed my thanks to the musicians, but in the depths of my heart I did not know whether to look solemn or to laugh, for all this seemed so preposterous.

When I came back to New York, I changed my former suite-de-luxe in the old Waldorf-Astoria for a simple room at the old Murray Hill Hotel, in the lobby of which I met a venerable but very lively gentleman who happened to be the father of the Chicago queen. "You offer good assurance to your family," I said to the nice old man. "How so?" asked the latter. "Because old age and health do not usually go together."

"I am not old," replied the old gentleman, "as long as I can enjoy my breakfast and run along." People get old the world over, but Americans will never admit it.

In New York I was a guest in many clubs and my colleagues vied with each other in the hospitality extended to me, so much so that I was glad to escape for a few days to Rochester, New York, where a friend had urgently invited me to come.

How calm and quiet was this place, after the turbulent city of New York which, even without motor-cars, merited the name of the "roaring city." In one of the hospitals I had a very amusing experience. I was asked to demonstrate the efficiency of my method in correcting the congenital club-feet of a fifteen-year-old boy; hitherto all endeavors to cure the boy had failed. I declared it would be too much for me to correct both feet at the same time because I lacked the special instrument which I had constructed to overcome the difficulties in such established cases. One foot would be a hard enough task for my strength, and it was only fair, I said, that the colleagues should share with me the thanks of the patient. They seemed to be sure that I would fail this time.

The operating table stood on a kind of stage, the boards of which had been newly varnished for the festive occasion. This floor was so smoothly polished that my feet slipped when I was most in need of a firm stance in manipulating the foot. I was in danger of falling off the varnished platform. My efforts became ridiculous, and excited some ill-advised spectator to laugh. A rug was brought, but on it the danger of slipping became even worse. Of course I hated to drop my work because of such a difficulty, and to the astonishment of the spectators I sat down, unlaced my shoes, stripped off my socks, and under the applause of the audience, who began to understand my intention, continued and successfully finished the work. I put on the plaster-cast, demonstrated all the necessary measures and precautions, and said to my colleagues: "I leave the patient today and probably will never see him again. I wager you will have no trouble whatsoever with the boy as far as the foot operated upon is concerned, and you will have no trouble with the other foot if you follow my prescriptions."

The evening paper had every detail of the performance and enlarged upon it. "He took off his shoes and like the Great Healer, Christ, cured his patients barefooted!"

In New York, I had invitations to inspect establishments, factories, warehouses, and what-not, but my time scarcely allowed me to accept all of them. In the palace of the Western Union Telegraph Company I was shown the marvellous technical equipment without much profit to me. Old Judge Dillon interrupted the lecture to say:

"All this is very remarkable, but the most remarkable thing in the room is this table. Around it I have seen represented more than a thousand million of dollars, but never a drop to drink." It was never quite clear to me whether the judge regretted or enjoyed the fact!

XIV

IN THE BANKERS' CLUTCHES

As I love to go to the theatre, I accepted with pleasure the invitation of a friend and his wife to see a play, though I had an invitation for the same evening to attend the annual banquet of the bankers of New York. I was quite sure that bankers did not interest me at all, and after an excellent dinner at the house of my host, I chose the play. When the performance had come to an end, my host remarked: "We are not through yet; now I'll show you a unique theatre, which cannot be seen any other place in the world—the annual banquet of the bankers of New York, which means one of the most remarkable social events not only of the city but of the whole country, on account of the after-dinner speeches, which often are of political importance and are delivered by the most famous orators anywhere. I am glad you need not miss the chance of attending the banquet as an onlooker. I've got a nice box in the Waldorf-Astoria banquet-hall. We are just in time to hear the after-dinner speeches."

I thought "Kismet! You cannot escape your fate," and accepted the invitation. Our little party arrived in our box, high up on one wall of the big hall, just in time to listen to a famous lawyer and orator. Spellbound, I looked down on the magnificent picture of the brilliantly lighted hall filled with thousands of men—or so it seemed to me— in evening dress. Black and white at the front and equally black at the back. Seen from the height, the multitude of bald shining heads was surprising. Hard-boiled bankers

as a rule are not youths but middle-aged or old men,
liable to loss of hair through excitement by day and schem-
ing by night. The tables were covered with thousands of
more or less emptied champagne bottles, while the streaming eloquence of the speaker was frequently and irreverently interrupted by the pop-guns of opening bottles. The
air was heavy with the haze of tobacco-smoke which rose
slowly to our level in dissolving wreaths. But the most
gorgeous aspect of all was the tier of boxes filled mostly
with ladies who wished and deserved to be admired not only
for their beauty, but also for their diamonds and pearls,
not to be seen in any jeweller's shop. Restless fans of all
colors made the tier look like a wind-swept flower-bed. It
was really a spectacle not to be seen elsewhere.

I was wholly absorbed in the unique picture when a
young man entered the box and delivered a message from
the president in the chair, which ordered me to come down
and be seated beside the president on the elevated platform. "Useless to remonstrate," I thought, "you have to
obey the order of the president." Fancy a dog which re-
sists with his four legs the leash of his forward-striding
master, and you can imagine me reluctantly following the
messenger who dragged me along by the leash of the presi-
dential summons. But it was not so bad as I had feared.
The president simply shook hands with me and bade me
sit at his side. Nobody seemed to take any notice. A very
eloquent speaker at the other side of the president was just
beginning to describe some of his impressions on a world
cruise from which he had recently returned. He said that
on his way round the world he had constantly been intent
upon finding out where the heart of the world might be
throbbing. Travelling westward, he had reached his last

stop and had not yet found the site of the world's heart. But when, one fine morning in London, he faced the Bank of England, enlightenment flashed through his mind. Here, upon the banks of the Thames, in the Bank of England, throbs the heart of the world. From here the invigorating stream of blood is pumped by the work of the heart into the arteries, reaching the remotest parts of the earth, and from there the blood streams back through the veins and is sucked in by the heart in its rhythmic efforts. Woe to the world, the speaker exclaimed, if the throbbing of the heart should stop some day! Woe to the world if it should even become irregular!

Like all the audience, I felt oppressed by the frightful thought that the heart of the world might stop throbbing, quite oblivious of the fact that my own heart, under the influence of more champagne than might have been healthy, was hammering away lustily. But the hush of awe did not last long; the crowd felt too happy to be depressed. It was leisurely digesting the excellent dinner, and enjoying strong cigars, sipping black coffee and more champagne.

But a crowd, even one composed of bankers, can never be relied on. At the moment it seemed like a purring cat after a good meal. In such a mood, a cat would not devour a mouse, but play with it just to frighten it a bit. In its most amiable moods, however, a cat remains cruel at heart, and I was doomed to learn the truth of this statement. When the applause after the speech about the heart of the world had died away, an ominous silence seemed to pervade the big hall, to be interrupted suddenly by a simultaneous cry from hundreds of throats, repeated like a college yell: "Lorenz—speak! Lorenz—speak! Lorenz—speak!!!"

And the ladies in the boxes, although they had not had a drop of champagne, joined the bankers in their own way: the flower-bed of fans and white handkerchiefs seemed to be swept by a hurricane, silently but imperatively summoning a thunderstruck man to the speaker's stand. I felt not only thunderstruck but wrathful, like one who has been caught unaware in an ambush. I wished in my heart that an earthquake might tumble the hall down and crush all the slightly and agreeably exhilarated bankers. There was no escape from a tight place, and I had to proceed to the stand while my brain searched desperately for a deliberating thought. At last it came, and I began reproachfully:

"Why did not you ladies and gentlemen allow me to be a humble onlooker at the feast? Why must you drag me down from my box into the glaring light of publicity? You cannot possibly expect better speeches than those which you have just heard, from a man who is wont to work with his hands rather than with his tongue. It seems to me that you yourselves do not know why you have done so. But, on second thought, I myself have found out your motive. You ladies and gentlemen simply want to know how I like America. I like it very much indeed!" Roaring applause! I felt that I had won, and I continued: "The ladies and gentlemen most probably also want to know what impresses me most in America, because even at my examination to obtain my license, the examiners asked me the same question. It is American charity and American hospitality which impress me most." Roaring applause again! "And then, another thing also impresses me very much. Americans don't like honorary titles, as they do in Europe. Honorary titles are mostly granted to men who don't know a thing about the matter which the title covers. for instance, I was appointed a Counsellor to the Austrian Government perhaps because I understand nothing of governing! And now I beg to be excused, so that I may avoid the danger of being nominated a Counsellor of Finance simply because I do not understand anything of finance. Thank you, ladies and gentlemen!" Frantic roaring applause. It was a narrow but a happy escape.

If the famous lawyer, specialist in the diseases of the heart of the world, were to come back from his world cruise today, he would have to say that the heart of the world has been transplanted by the World War from the banks of the Thames to the banks of the Hudson, and that it throbs lustily, though sometimes faintly, in Wall Street, despite the narrowness of that place.

I could not possibly leave America without paying a visit to Philadelphia. My stay there at the house of my friend Doctor Wilson brings back unforgettable remembrances. The lavishness of the hospitality extended to me could be surpassed only by its heartiness. The exclusive Union League Club opened its doors to me as a foreigner without asking my political views. It was there that I was introduced to a little old gentleman of very modest appearance who invited me to visit his workshop the next day—though, as he said, his line of work was somewhat different from mine. The next day this unpretentious gentleman revealed himself as the owner of Cramp's Shipyards, where the new U.S.S. *Maine* was being made ready to join the United States Navy. The old gentleman caressed the mighty steel-plates of the battleship with his frail fingers and said: "May she have a better fate than the old *Maine*." He explained the differences between the old and the new *Maine*. As a matter of secondary importance, his tiny hand pointed to the colossal steel ribs of three cruisers under construction. "They will look different in another month," he said.

My medical friends could not forbear telling me that the old gentleman had not been nearly so amiable with His Imperial Highness, Prince Henry of Prussia, when the latter had paid a visit to the shipyards some time before. "Why should he have been less amiable with the Prince?" I queried. "Because ships are 'in his line,' " was the answer.

Just as much out of my line of work was a visit to the mint in Philadelphia. I admired the precautions taken against possible theft or robbery. Polished corridors led down to a colossal steel door which weighed, I was informed, nine tons. The door had three seals which were broken by three officials. Then they put the electric machinery of the doors to work by means of three different keys, like magic wands, and the doors opened noiselessly. The deep vaults were resplendent with many electric lights, but all these lights were not strong enough to elicit the faintest gleam from the surface of the clumsy ingots of gold which covered the ground in heaps. Was this clay-like material really the shining gold which is said to rule the world? I was invited to lift one bar; I could scarcely move it. I would not have been able to carry away a bar worth about thirty thousand dollars. Could not the gold be stolen in spite of all the heavy steel doors? The officials said: "No. Modern thieves would never try to break in the doors, but would try to enter the vaults by a tunnel, but they would have a surprise before they were near the vaults!" As a souvenir, I was given a sample of every current coin in copper, nickel, or silver, and, in addition, a bronze plaque with McKinley's portrait on it.

When I left the building I found a great number of young ladies, employees of the mint, assembled in the hall, eager to shake hands with me. This was rather an agreeable exercise, for any one of these young girls was nicer to look at than the heaviest gold bar in the vaults of the mint.

Many agreeable hours were spent at the house of Doctor Wilson, called the "doll house," in Atlantic City. Although the house was small, it had a spacious porch on which many medical friends of Doctor Wilson convened in the evening to see the guest of their friend. It was quite an informal convention, without speeches and addresses. I was asked questions about Vienna, and especially about the medical faculty. Nearly all of the physicians assembled on the porch had been there, and cherished most agreeable memories of the time spent in Vienna. I let them indulge in their happy recollections and rocked myself pensively upon my chair. How quickly one forgets the customs of one's own country, I thought. It had been only a few weeks before that I had instinctively jumped off a rocking-chair when it inadvertently rocked backwards, whereas now I had learned to lean backward and still farther backward without the slightest nervousness or fear. But suddenly I swayed beyond the line of gravity, rolled over with the chair, and turned a backward somersault.

Everybody was eager to assist the fallen man in getting to his feet. "I hope your spine is not broken, so we would have to try your plaster-bed on you," Doctor Wilson exclaimed.

"No," answered the Viennese acrobat, "I only twisted my neck to the breaking-point, but it stood the test."

"But how could it happen?" put in another man.

"While you indulged in your Viennese memories," I said, "I was feeling proud of finding myself at ease in an American rocking-chair."

"But that was no rocking-chair you sat upon," exclaimed Doctor Wilson. "It was just an ordinary chair, which you used as a rocking chair."

Your vices follow you wherever you go. Many times Mrs. L had predicted for me just such an accident as punishment for the disjointed state of her chairs.

In accordance with my host's principle, pleasure after work, I had to see all attractions on both sides of the boardwalk, and the no less interesting view of the dense crowd along the sand. People everywhere want to be amused. Here they walked long distances, or danced curious dances, or descended to the bottom of the sea to see the fish, or looped the loop to get sick, or indulged in wine or beer in quiet nooks, with not the slightest symptom of drunkenness to be seen. I was invited to visit some of the newly finished palatial hotels, *le dernier cri* at that time, and admired the magnificent suites *de luxe* for the upper 400, the prices of which set my middle-European heart atrembling. In one of these hotels I was introduced to Mrs. Varina Jefferson Davis, the widow of President Jefferson Davis of the Confederacy. The old lady was very lively in spite of her seventy years of age.

At that time it was impossible for me to admire the beauty of American ladies who walked on the sand. Any modest evening dress is liberal in opportunities for guessing at hidden treasures, but the bathing dress of those times looked rather like the aviators' suits of today. The dresses reached from top to toe, and included stays as well as ruffles which had to be stiffened by mechanical contrivances to resist the flattening influence of the water. Only the arms were left free up to the elbow. How often do these two-legged ants crawling on the sand change their customs in clothing, eating, drinking, and thinking, while the mighty waves thundering against the shore roar their eternal and unchanging music! Is there another place on the shores of the seven seas where that living grain of dust, Man, can be more impressed by the eternal waters than at Atlantic City?

American hospitality showed itself at its best at a reception extended to me by Jefferson Medical College in Philadelphia. The students' band gave the reception a festive character; moreover, they had composed a new yell for the occasion: "Hip, hip, it's out! Oh, Lorenz! Hip, hip, hurray, it's in the socket!" At this purely social affair, no scientific discussions were to be allowed, although above the speaker was enshrined the bust of Marion Sims. After the president had welcomed and introduced me, he asked me to make a few remarks in reply. I was well prepared for the occasion, and since scientific matters were excluded, told my audience a story:

"About forty-five years ago a little boy not yet in school was searching for a toy upon the lumber shelf in his father's workshop. Among old straps of leather, shreds of cloth, and like refuse, he found a wrinkled, old black glove, obviously a man's. The boy put his fingers, his hand, and half his forearm into the abyss of the glove and ran so to his mother. 'Look here, Mother,' he said, 'I have a glove. I am going to be a great gentleman' (this was his typical answer whenever he was asked, 'Adolfla, what are you going to be?'). His mother said, 'My dear Adolfla, if you want to be a great gentleman, you must have at least two gloves. Your glove is only for the left hand. Not until you will have found the right glove, can you hope to be a great gentleman.'

"The boy felt rather discouraged, and forgot the whole affair. In later years, however, he often remembered the little incident very clearly and learned at last to understand its real meaning. Has not his whole life been a search for the second glove? Didn't he think at a certain time that he had found it, only to lose it again after a short while? He is not even quite sure whether hitherto he has always had the right understanding of what the second glove means! Today, however, he feels convinced that at last he has found the second glove, for today he is certain that he has won the esteem and appreciation of his medical colleagues. That, to him, means the second glove, on account of the fact that for a physician nothing on earth is more difficult to get than the appreciation of his colleagues."

The audience laughed and applauded the speaker in spite of the open jibe at professional jealousy—which cannot be helped because physicians must be artists and artists are jealous by nature.

My little speech must have been favorably commented upon by the papers and by readers, or I would not have got so many letters of congratulation. Two of these are still in my memory. A farmer wrote me very aptly that the second glove could not possibly be the same thing to all who were searching for it. To the doctor, the second glove meant the appreciation of his fellow-doctors. All right.

But he, the farmer, as a seeker for the second glove, was certainly in a worse condition than the doctor because the appreciation of his fellow-doctors was a thing which he, the doctor, could not see and, therefore, could not covet so ardently; whereas he, the farmer, not only could see his second glove with his eyes, but could grasp it with his hands and even with his feet, and yet, he could not get it. In a word, his second glove was that field of his neighbor's which happened to lie just between two of his own fields. He must have it or the eyesore would blind him in the course of time. But God was merciful! Hadn't he sent the Viennese doctor to these shores, and would not the Viennese doctor in the kindness of his heart understand that not only he himself but also other seekers of the second glove were to find it at last—and send him a thousand dollars for this purpose?

The doctor answered the farmer to the effect that the second glove could only be found by the seeker himself and never by another man.

The second remarkable letter asked: Would not the doctor help a struggling photographer in his search for the second glove by allowing him to take the doctor's picture? Of course, I was later glad to comply with this wish and was rewarded by the best pictures that had ever been taken of me. This photographer would certainly have found his second glove without the help of any other man.

The big Jefferson Hospital building at that time was, as far as I could see, destined to be a marvel among new hospitals. I was very sorry that later on I could not attend certain academic exercises at Jefferson Medical College. I would have got an honorary degree which was promised me. I was in the City of Mexico and could not reach

Philadelphia in time. I would have flown there, had there been airplanes at that time.

Leaving Philadelphia for New York, I was met at the depot by many young girls and boys who offered me souvenirs and asked for my signature. I got more pencils, pens, penholders, erasers, little notebooks, and other writing paraphernalia than I could make use of for years to come. Influenced by such an example, a middle-aged man came up to me, pulled out his gold watch and chain and offered them as a gift, saying "Take it as a souvenir." I remonstrated that I could not accept precious souvenirs, and decreed that the prodigal should keep his watch but should give five dollars to the poor, which he promised to do. Before the train started, the engine-driver, with his staff, in overalls, and other railway officials, came to shake hands with me. The engineer assured me that he found pleasure in the thought that my precious life was entrusted to him for a few hours, and that he would drop me safely in New York.

In my compartment, I felt a bit tired by so many unmerited honors—but could I not really think that I had found the second glove at last? Indulging in this and other agreeable thoughts, I felt ready for a little restoring nap when a newsboy entered the compartment and offered his illustrated papers. When I made my choice and asked how much I owed, the boy refused to accept payment because he was too glad, he said, to offer the famous doctor even so small a present. He hoped to be some day, if not a famous doctor, at least a doctor. As a poor student of medicine, he earned the money for his studies by selling newspapers on the express train during his vacations, a job that paid better than selling newspapers in the streets

Can anybody imagine how my heart went out to that nice boy! I encouraged him and assured him that men of his quality would certainly reach their goals. But I would accept his present only on the condition that the boy, in return, should free me of a ten-dollar gold piece which was rather a nuisance in my purse. It was difficult to convince the young man that he must have a "breeding penny" in his purse.

I had long forgotten this little episode when, a number of years later, a nice young man entered my office in Vienna and presented himself as the newsboy whom the "*Heckpfennig*" had helped so much to reach his goal of becoming a doctor.

Before I took leave of New York, I was invited by Mayor Seth Low to the City Hall to accept a very precious document, a resolution of thanks and appreciation from the Board of Aldermen, duly engrossed in the shape of a thick volume in a satin-covered case. The volume was taken off the desk that had been Washington's, or so I was informed, and given to me during a very elaborate ceremony. A friend who stood at my side whispered to me: "After what has been said and written, you may sleep quietly in the future. Should the worst ever come to the worst, the City of New York cannot but give you a place in its houses for the poor!"

XV

QUEENS AS MOTHERS

On a cold winter morning in 1903, I took leave of the New York skyline on board an English steamer bound for Liverpool. Off Queenstown, Ireland, I got two cables from London. One was from an editor who asked me to write at once a book on my American experiences—liberal royalties! The other was from a London office, asking whether a family living in Melbourne, Australia, would find me in Vienna if they sailed at once. I answered the first: "Impossible to write a book for want of time." My answer to the second was: Yes, of course they would find me, and I had had patients from Australia already.

I stayed a short time in Liverpool where I was the guest of a highly distinguished physician. I operated in Liverpool as well as in London on several instructive cases. In a London hospital I met a middle-aged lady who proved to be the sister of that awful boy Hans, my former pupil at Klagenfurt, whose flight by night had caused me so many troubles—or at least so I thought at that time. Without that flight, my life might have taken quite another turn. No, Hans had never finished his studies. The family had gone bankrupt; the father had died; the enterprising sister had married in London and was doing nicely as a milliner. She had found her second glove!

I felt as if I had gone off duty when I took the express train, Dover—Calais—Vienna. And when I reached the dear old place, the Kaiserstadt an der Donau, die K. K. Reichs-Haupt und Residenzstadt Wien, then in its full glory, I thought to myself: There are many fine places in America, but dear, old, quaint and quiet Vienna cannot be surpassed.

I was asked many questions by my colleagues, by the students, and by people in general. All had been a bright dream, and I had fallen back on my very modest academic position, which was in great contrast to my well-known name. I lectured on my adventures, and told the students that their American colleagues would very much mind having so many holidays during the semester. They would be likely to ask their teachers, "What do we pay you for?" No, hospital physicians in leading positions received no salary, and the hospitals were maintained by public charity. The physiological and chemical laboratories were equipped in a way to arouse the envy of any professor of any university. The anatomists were in constant lack of material, however, and what they had was preserved exclusively by low temperature. In horror, I remembered the sight of frozen corpses hanging by the neck from the ceiling of the refrigeration room. The big hospitals were generously equipped, but lacked the one and greatest comfort so liberally provided for in the general hospital in Vienna—roominess. That is to say, all had room in the general hospital except me, though by the hospitality of my brother-in-law, Doctor Frank, I could now boast of four beds. He has done so well with four beds, why should he need more? thought the authorities. I felt less disposed to lick the boots of the Minister, and I took pleasure in the thought that a signature from my hand had enlarged orthopædic hospitals in America. Anyway, I hadn't much time to spend in the anteroom of the Minister of Instruction. Patients poured in from all parts of the world, and I was very proud to welcome the dear little girl from Melbourne who was afflicted with bilateral congenital hip-luxation. This girl is now a happy mother and a dear friend of mine.

Then came a letter from Christ Church, New Zealand, asking me to see a grown-up girl with congenital club-feet, if, by chance, I should come to pay a visit to the Antipodes. What an exuberant fantasy! I said to myself that people living upon a small island seem to lose all conception of the vastness of our globe. But you never can tell. Shortly after the letter from New Zealand, there came another from Yokohama asking whether, on my way round the world, I would not stop there to cure a boy afflicted with congenital luxation of the hip-joints. "On your way round the world," I mused. This really had been my dream since boyhood. A dream never to be realized, of course, unless you have the time, let alone the money. But then it would certainly not be a performance to brag of. It would be quite a different thing to make a trip round the world, not as a sightseer, but as a physician invited to come to various places in a sequence which would take him round the globe.

But the gap between Vienna and Yokohama was too wide. Unexpectedly it shrunk to a manageable distance, in spite of a detour. I got a letter from Chicago inviting me to visit the princess once more the next spring. What had seemed preposterous when I read the letter from New Zealand had by now become feasible. As two of my brothers lived in Australia and as I had patients there,

Australia should be included in the medical round-the-world tour. Vienna, Chicago, Yokohama, Sidney, New Zealand! I did not stress the gap between New Zealand and Europe, because India was the next item in my travelling program anyhow. As if it were sunshine, I basked in the thought that a professional consultation tour round the world would be a record not to be beaten.

But I had to rest content with the thought that this world tour would have been possible but for an unexpected *force majeure*—the Russo-Japanese War, which tumbled down all my plans.

About a year later, the Japanese boy was brought to Vienna. He was only half Japanese, the father being German. Though not more than five years old, he knew all about his condition. When he was lifted upon the operating table, he stood there for a while, then stretched out his arms and shouted in a shrill child's voice, *"Banzai! Banzai!"* Two years later I operated upon the boy's sister. The girl was a perfect Japanese but for her German tallness of figure.

I had to work very hard to meet all demands upon me. Money poured in; I scarcely knew what to do with it—certainly I had no time to spend it. Had I been a counsellor of finance, I could not have done worse than to invest my money in state securities, because the state was the most secure, most reliable, the most conscientious debtor. And you need not worry about the interest. If you did not collect it, it was automatically invested in new securities; there was no trouble whatsoever about your savings.

Mrs. L was satisfied that her husband had begun at last to procure for his old age. "No, there is still time for that," I told her. "I am putting money aside to build a new house which will be something more than a hyper-dimensioned dining-room; it will be a house provided with all the contrivances money can buy."

"I am afraid," Mrs. L retorted, "that you are going to go crazy yet. Isn't our house adequate and homelike?"

"With one bathroom?" I put in. "I want a house like some I have seen in America, only more roomy!"

"God be thanked you have no time to carry out your crazy plans," said Mrs. L. "Here is a letter from Madrid inviting you to operate upon a real princess whose father need not take off his hat in the presence of the King of Spain!"

I resolved to include the Spanish visit in my trip to America, and to sail from Gibraltar.

My visit to Madrid was taken notice of by Queen Christina, who had just been suceeded by her son, King Alfonso XIII. There were rumors in the papers that the young King had inherited from his father the lung trouble of which the latter had died, and that the days of Alfonso's life were numbered. As the Queen knew that I was on my way to America, she may have thought me the truthful man ready to deny such groundless rumors in America, and so she invited me, through her private physician, to pay her a visit any time it would please me. "With pleasure," I answered, "if it pleases her Majesty. All right!"

But it was not all right. The Austrian ambassador to the Spanish court had also taken notice of the visit of an Austrian subject to the Spanish capital, and was watching my every step. A visit to royalty without the in-tervention of the ambassador would be nothing less than an outrage to the embassy. What else is an ambassador for, anyway? A free-hand visit to the Queen! *"Quod non"* —there was no such a thing in the world! I must write a humble petition that I be allowed to comply with her Majesty's urgent wish to pay a visit to her Majesty tomorrow!

"But will this petition be decided before tomorrow?" I asked. "I must leave day-after-tomorrow or miss the boat at Gibraltar."

"Let that be my concern," answered the diplomat, with a reassuring gesture.

That afternoon the Austrian embassy knew what it was for! It was kept busy getting back the petition, decided in the affirmative, and getting it delivered to the petitioner.

When I entered the gorgeous entrance-hall of the royal palace and looked round, astonished, I could understand the self-satisfied words of the first Napoleon, when he laid his hand on the lion at the staircase and said: *"Enfin je te tiens, lion d'Espagne!"* But I did not want the lion; I was out for the King of Spain himself! There were some courtiers about who knew what the foreigner wanted. One of them, apparently of a more external service, would hand me along to another courtier of more internal service. With each change, the warrior-like outer appearance of my usher would become less appalling. The halberd disappeared entirely, the swords became shorter, and shrunk at last into a symbolical leather-sheathed toothpick, while the final lackey was armed only with a frock-coat and spotless white gloves.

At last I was shown into the sanctuary, where I found Queen Christina sitting on a couch. I could not pay

much attention to the handsome appointments of the
room, because I found myself fettered by the intent eyes
of the Queen, a slim, middle-aged lady of very aristocratic
bearing. She welcomed me most heartily. She wanted to
shake hands with me, she said, but asked that I first strip
off my gloves, adding that she wanted not only to shake
hands, but also to see her visitor's hands. When I had
taken off the gloves, the Queen took my rather sturdy right
paw into her slender delicate hands, turned it round, and
said: "How wonderful a hand is yours!" I laughed: "It
is only a workman's toil-accustomed hand, with the sole difference that there are no callouses on it. The hand of a
surgeon must be strong, yet smooth."

"I was not admiring your hand," answered the Queen
smilingly, "but the work it has accomplished and will accomplish in the future, if God grant it."

The Queen told me a great deal about her charity work
and the difficulties she had to overcome. Turning to the
real object of the visit, she asked me to give the King, her
son, a looking-over. He had gone for a ride in the park,
which stretches behind the palace as far as the eye can
see, but he was expected back at any moment. The Queen
had scarcely finished speaking when his Majesty, the
King, made his informal entrance. He was perspiring and
dust-covered. "Excuse me, Professor," he said. "Had to
get out of the city for some fresh air, and had a nice ride."
When the Queen bade him take off his coat, he pouted
at his mother, who said, "But, Alfonso, you must!" The
King laughed and obeyed, cheerfully submitting to the
examination, and chatting most of the time either with
his mother or with his own physician.

At the end of a brief but very satisfactory examination,

I could not forbear alluding to the fact that his Majesty, the King, a very tall but strongly built boy, with the face of an eagle and the first down as a token of near-maturity on his upper lip, showed, in spite of all other kingly qualities, a tendency to stooping habits—like all tall men, I remarked consolingly. Had I not had to fight this habit myself ever since I could remember? But for a king this habit was absolutely unbecoming, though, of course, he must not be super-straight either. A natural, medium straightness should be the best attitude for his Majesty.

"Don't you see, Alfonso," interposed the Queen, "how right I am to admonish you to hold yourself erect?" The King was not pleased because he felt that the others were right.

I prescribed some exercises and massage of the muscles of the back. "By the way," I added, "I should advise your Majesty to dispense with suspenders; they drag the shoulders down by the weight of the trousers. I think a belt around the waist would be better." The King shook with laughter and could not stop laughing.

"Oh, no! Oh, no—not that!" he exclaimed at last. "No belt, by no means a belt," and he began to laugh again.

"What is the matter?" the Queen asked.

"The matter is," said the King to me, "that I am a good eater."

"Just as behooves a young and still growing man," I put in.

"Sometimes I feel I must undo the uppermost button of my trousers after a good dinner. I couldn't do that so surreptitiously with a leather belt. No, rather, I could not do it at all, because the trousers would slip down," and he began laughing again so hard that it took away his breath, and exclaiming at intervals: "Imagine a king at a reception with his trousers slipping down!"

All present joined in the mirth of the King, who was now in high spirits. As if he were dancing he jumped from one leg to the other and of a sudden, quite unexpectedly squatting, he clasped his mother's knees, lifted her off the rug, and danced with her around the room crying: "Mother, dear!" while the surprised Queen screamed just as any other woman would have screamed if her dance-partner had clasped her knees instead of her waist. Smoothly his Majesty let down her Majesty, and bowed to her very courteously. "Isn't he a naughty boy!" exclaimed the Queen, half angry and half amused, arranging her crumpled skirts. "Will he ever become serious?"

"It has been a unique spectacle, anyhow," I said, "to see the Most Christian King of Spain dancing with his mother, held in the air."

The King became very earnest, however, when he spoke of the American battleship *Maine*. In his opinion the Americans had blown her up to get a pretext for the war. On this question, I had no opinion at all.

I was given a picture of the Queen and of the King with signatures. When the King put his name under the photo, the Queen admonished him: "Please, Alfonso, write clearly, with ink, of course, and without blotting!" In the private rooms, Alfonso—it was long before his marriage—was still the boy and not the king. Before I took leave, the Queen introduced me to her daughter, an ethereal-looking young lady with black hair and a white face which was not enlivened by the tired smile on her lips. Her fate was a premature death, whose shadows then seemed already to loom in the background. When I left the royal palace, I knew that I had not only been given an audience, but had been admitted for an hour to the family life of the Most Christian King of Spain.

The same evening, a reception was given me by the noble family of my host. It seemed rather an exclusive party. Everybody knew of the audience, of course, and wanted to know every word the King and the Queen had uttered. The young ladies, some of them exquisite Spanish beauties, were all in love with the King, as a matter of course. One of the guests, a beautiful young countess, was especially eager to know all about the King. What did the King say, what did the King do after his examination?

"Well, the King grasped the knees of his mother"— and saying this, I grasped the knees of the young Countess and danced with her around the room. The Countess screamed as if she were going to be murdered.

"What did the Queen say about the behavior of her son?"

"Well, the Queen screamed, not less than the Countess did," I answered. In certain unexpected situations, all women behave more or less alike, they simply scream.

Having seen Alfonso as the playful boy in his mother's rooms that day, I had the good luck to see him as king the next day, when a great number of recruits had to take the oath of military service. Riding a beautiful black horse, he arrived at the place in the midst of an escort of horsemen. He looked like the young god Ares in his splendid uniform, of which a shining helmet was the most conspicuous part. Blasts of trumpets, beating of drums, shrieking of pipes and cries from the crowd greeted the King, who looked as earnest and as fearless as any grown-up Spanish king could ever have looked.

I was glad to violate a medical secret by spreading the truth by word and pen that the King of Spain was as healthy and good-looking as any healthy and good-looking American boy could possibly be, and that his prospects of longevity were no worse than for any other young and healthy boy. The future proved this diagnosis to be correct.

Queen Christina—lovely, affable, motherly, democratic, and endowed with the indescribable charm of a Viennese lady—is one of the pleasantest memories in my collection of queens. My oldest royal friend, however, was Queen Carmen Sylva of Roumania, the crowned poet. She was not only a real mother to her own family, but to all the families in her country, and especially to the poor children. She used to send them to me with a tag around their necks imploring my good-will and unduly extolling my art. When the little patients had been cured, I would send them back to her with my answer on a tag around their necks. Thus, in time, quite a *dossier* of letters, photos, good-wishes, and greetings were piled up in my desk. The old Queen was just as dignified as she was lovely and charming.

Her daughter-in-law, Queen Marie of Roumania, falls into quite another class of queens. She was not yet a queen at the time I met her, nor was her son Carol then a king. She brought little Carol to Vienna to consult me regarding a condition which, in the opinion of the doctors, was developing and which in time would necessitate an operation. I was summoned to the hotel where they

were staying and ushered into a room where Marie
awaited me. She stood in the center of the room and
answered my courteous bow with a very frosty, scarcely
perceptible nod of her beautiful head. Her attitude
greatly disgruntled me, because I saw before me not a
Crown Princess, but a mother, who wanted something from
me, while I wanted nothing from her.

Little Carol, then about four years old and a charming
little chap, was promptly brought into the room. He ran
to the visitor with outstretched arms and said: "You are
welcome, Uncle," or something like that, and wanted to
kiss me. I squatted down beside the boy and allowed him
to kiss his "uncle," I suppose to the great displeasure of
Marie, but I surmised that she had probably prepared the
boy to meet an unknown uncle of whom he was not to be
afraid.

At that time Carol was still very obedient to his mother,
certainly more so than in his later years. The charming
boy was also very obedient to the doctor and allowed me
to carry out an examination which neither children nor
adults like very much. I was able to assure his mother that
milder means than an operation would serve to arrest the
further development of Carol's condition. Marie seemed
gratified, and condescended then to reward me with a
lovely smile. But I was not satisfied with that smile—I
wanted my revenge for the haughty manner in which she
had received me. So, when I took leave of her, I planted
myself in front of her, drew myself up to my full height of
six feet and several inches, looked over her head, nodded
just as imperceptibly as she had deigned to nod, and left
the room. It is not likely that Marie took that silent lesson
to heart, but even a grandchild of the late Queen Victoria

of England should not allow her haughty manners to come to the surface when she is asking something for her child. Anyhow, I had my revenge, and have forgiven her, not because she is a queen, but because she was, and still is, a very beautiful woman, and beauty deserves some consideration.

But let us go back to my departure from Spain. The voyage from Madrid to Gibraltar was as complicated and uncertain as travelling by a special train from Paris to Cherbourg is simple and reliable, and it was only due to good luck that I reached the boat on time.

It happened that on board the liner I met an old friend who was a professor of surgery somewhere in Germany. The passage was rather rough. I was never so good a sailor as to feel quite happy on board an ocean-going steamer; on the other hand, my friend developed an unnatural appetite. "I congratulate you on your stomach," I used to say when the German professor would indulge in most indigestible dishes, the mere sight of which was nauseating to me. It was just Easter week and the weather almost calm. The German professor was full of pep. He rang the ship's bell one afternoon, singing "Christ has risen and nature will rise again!" The unfortunate man had no idea that the worm in his bowels was ready to begin its destructive work, and that he was doomed to die not long afterwards of an incurable disease in the same organ whose excellent functioning he liked to brag of.

This time I did not stop in New York, but went directly to Chicago to see the little princess. When the plaster bandage was changed, I was sorry to have to say that things did not look as promising as when I had left. I feared that the result would not be as perfect as I had assumed at the time of the operation. But pessimism not being my favorite philosophy, I still hoped for the best. Other more or less neglected cases did splendidly.

XVI

SOUTHLAND JOURNEY

AFTER a short stay in Chicago, I started for New Orleans to attend the congress of the American Medical Association. Only the International Medical Congress in Europe could compete with this congress, the members of which came exclusively from the United States. As in Europe, the drawbacks about such huge scientific gatherings were crowded trains and crowded hotels; the travellers not only crowded each other, but a great part of them were apparently doomed to starve. The train had become so long that in Carbondale, Pa., it had to be divided into two parts. Lucky were those who travelled in the first part, because theirs was the dining-car. The travellers in the second part, by dire necessity, were melted together into a communistic state or family. Whoever had anything eatable or drinkable put it at the disposal of the needy, and the American ladies did their best to make the various cold dishes attractive by serving them on the spotless white linen pillow-cases. Thus bad luck was the cause of a feast of fraternization.

In the dead of night, the train had to stop several times on a spur track in the swamps. A pale moon made the live-oaks and other giant trees, all richly covered with moss, look like men centuries old, whose flowing gray beards were stirred by the night breezes. Strange cries of unknown animals filled the air; it was enough to make the heart of any naturalist quiver with yearning to explore the night of the virgin forest. Wooden huts on high posts gave evidence that man was vying with the animals for possession of the swamps.

All the travellers were glad when Lake Pontchartrain came into view. At the New Orleans depot, I was informed that the chief of police wanted me. "Lorenz to be arrested"—flashed as an American memory through my mind.

"You don't want to arrest me?" I asked the high official.

"Oh, no, I want just to shake hands with you and assure you that I shall arrest anybody who may give you any trouble," the police chief answered, laughing. My personal safety as a foreigner in New Orleans was evidently a settled question. At the new St. Charles Hotel I was informed that I would not be charged one cent for my room. It was here that I made my first acquaintance with the "Father of Waters" when I filled the bathtub with a dark liquid—the water of the Mississippi.

The congress opened in the Tulane Theatre. Doctor Billings of Chicago made a remarkable speech on the organization and reorganization of medical studies, a subject which to this day continues to the fore in all universities of the world. I had the pleasure of being introduced to one of the most prominent among the leading surgeons of America, one of the Mayo brothers, who are a duality, two in one and one in two, so that they need not be differentiated from each other. I had been given the task of operating on some cases and lecturing on my methods, and could not bring myself to care much about the congress. If you want to visit a place, don't do it so long as it is cluttered up with a congress. I scarcely had time to walk over the low pontoon bridge to get a bit nearer to the mighty Mississippi. On the bridge, I was asked by a half-grown boy, "Do you know, please, how long this river is wide?" I answered: "You should know better how long the river is wide, and how to ask about it!" The boy stared nonplussed at the man with the foreign accent.

Though my delightful host took me along the magnificent Tulane belt-canal and other tree-lined streets in his swift buggy, informed me of the exact cost of each of the marble columns of the big Customs House, and showed me the French market and some other picturesque sites, I was sorry not to be able to see more of this most interesting city and of its attractive people. I had to be content to remember New Orleans as a city of gardens, magnolias, flowers, and wealth of every kind, receiving, as it does, all the riches of the largest valley in the world, from one of the greatest rivers in the world, on the mercy of which depend not only its wealth but its very existence. An excursion across Lake Pontchartrain on my host's steam yacht showed me its great possibilities for enabling the inhabitants of former swamp-land to get plenty of fresh air and recreation. The steam yacht entered a picturesque river, the banks of which were scarcely discernible behind the rich foliage of gigantic moss-covered trees, and stopped at a quiet harbor in the wilderness. Though the river is said to be inhabited by alligators, I did not have the pleasure of seeing one—any more than I saw a crocodile in the Nile above Wadi Halfa.

Among the social entertainments of the congress was an excursion down the Mississippi upon one of the huge steamboats with wheels of extraordinary height. I welcomed the trip as a much-needed rest. I felt dizzy after accepting the many, many invitations to "have a drink," though I had practised, undetected, my sham-sipping. As soon as the boat set out, I searched for a quiet nook and found an extraordinarily dirty third-class cabin, which seemed good enough for a nap. But negro minstrels followed me, dragged me out, and nearly killed me with their ragtime tunes, for which they wanted a liberal payment. Twenty years later, all the glorious remembrances of New Orleans were not so vivid in my mind as the oft-heard invitation: "Have a drink!"

Before I left New Orleans, I attended a *fête champêtre* in the city park. A nobler setting for an opulent spring feast could not be found than the lawns of the park adorned with gigantic magnolias in blossom. The place was brilliantly lighted and swarmed not only with the members of the congress, but with the society of New Orleans. No other place in the world can afford such an exhibit of beauties of a special, exotic type as New Orleans, at a moment's notice. This fête was really one of beautiful women, wine, music, and laughter. Doctor Billings, like an emperor, deigned to accept the homage of the beauties with olive skin and sparkling black eyes in a flowery tent built especially for the president of the congress.

A prominent member of the congress was both an ex-president of a long-past congress and at the same time an ex-governor of Maine, who thought it a matter of importance to celebrate his ninetieth birthday during the congress. He had come 2500 miles not to miss the occasion. I had the honor of being introduced to this remarkable gentleman, who looked his age but was very agile. When I dared admonish him to take better care of his health and stay at home instead of travelling 2500 miles, the old gentleman answered: "I should never have been able, even as a young man, to do your work, but as long as I can do any kind of work, I am not old—at least, I don't feel old, and shall go on celebrating my birthdays." He looked as enterprising as if he were sure of the whole of his tenth decade.

Though strongly urged by some friends to proceed to Havana, I preferred a land voyage to the City of Mexico. Once across the Rio Grande, I ceased to be a doctor and became a mere sightseer. It was the middle of May, and the strange landscape looked its best—which really did not mean so very much, in spite of the colorful blossoms of the cactus and the yucca trees and other strange-looking plants. In the middle of May, the Wienerwald can certainly compete with it in beauty. In Toluca the locomotive engineer, a stout, thick-set, straightforward American, insisted upon having me at his side in the cab, the better to see the finest scenery in the world. He had not promised too much. From La Cima on, the traveller obtains most beautiful views of the Valley of Mexico with its lakes, the City of Mexico in its center, and the grand, snow-clad volcanoes of Popocatepetl and Ixtaccihuatl in the background. German schoolboys used to make fun of the name Popocatepetl, and I had never dreamed that I would lay eyes on the lofty snowfields of the volcano.

The visit to Mexico was very interesting, but the cooking was marred by rancid fat, on which the indigenous seem to thrive, but by which a traveller coming from the United States can easily be poisoned. An incident also spoiled my high spirits as a newcomer. The Vice-President and Minister of Foreign Affairs of the Republic asked me to see his wife, who, he said, had put her last hope in me. The invitation could not possibly be refused, although the appeal filled me with the worst forebodings. I found a middle-aged, finely built American lady suffering from an inoperable condition. What could I do, a specialist who thanked God every day of his life for not having to treat that particular malady? Nothing but act as a professional sympathizer—and liar. Such an incident during a pleasure-trip could spoil the mood of a more hard-boiled man than I am. In my memories of childhood I heard again the children's unanimous chorus, droning out of the open windows of the school-room: *"Das ist der Krebs"*—and forty-five years later, science did not yet know what it was, let alone how to cure it. And will this question ever be solved?

The Vice-President wanted to introduce me to the President, Porfirio Diaz, in Chapultepec, but I declined on the grounds that I didn't want to disturb the old gentleman in his summer retreat, and, of course, tell him how hopeless was the case of my host's wife. On that lugubrious day, I unknowingly committed a crime: I bought a nice opal, the characteristic jewel of Mexico, as a souvenir for my little princess in Chicago.

After the execution of Emperor Maximilian, there had been no diplomatic relations between Austria and Mexico for a long time. It had been only recently that Count Hohenwart, as Austrian ambassador to Mexico, had re-established the broken connection. The dinner which the Count and his lovely wife gave their fellow countryman will always be remembered by me as the only blessing I ever received in Mexico as far as cooking is concerned.

An excursion to Cuernavaca brought me to Acapancingo, summer residence of the Emperor Maximilian. The house was dilapidated, but had never been more than a primitive damp-hole, provided with a swimming-pool in the foul water of which there seemed to lurk all the vermin of the tropics. In the small garden grew coffee bushes and mango trees. In spite of the great elevation of the place, the heat was suffocating. To stay here for any length of time must be hell, I thought, and in my mind there emerged like a glorious vision the white castle of Miramare, near Trieste, on the blue Adriatic—a wonder of architecture, surrounded by fairy gardens and enjoying a delicious climate. And from this earthly paradise, a harmless man had been driven by a woman crazy with ambition, who wanted to become an empress. To be haunted by the vision of her husband facing the rifles of his executioners was her punishment, relentless to the last day of her seemingly endless old age.

Being so near the tropics, and wanting to see more of them, I need only descend to the *tierra caliente*. Easy at heart, I took leave of the Cathedral of the Asunción de Maria Santissima, of the Zogalo Garden, the flower market and the Alameda, to make the descent from the Mexican plateau to the coast level. I easily withstood the temptation to visit Mount Orizaba, and enjoyed the unique scenery, admiring at the same time the remarkable engineering. This trip alone makes a visit to Mexico worth while. Drawn by two locomotives, the train dives into forests of tropical richness, through gardens of oranges, limes, lemons, bananas, pomegranates, sugar-cane palms, coffee plants, and trees of unfamiliar shape and unknown name; it threads many tunnels, crosses countless bridges across wild gorges, to arrive after a day's journey at the dreary place called Vera Cruz, the city where the vultures walk the streets or sit on the roofs of the low houses unmolested.

The hotel in Vera Cruz commanded a view of the pretty market-place, surrounded by quiet houses of definitely Spanish architecture. The middle of the place harbored a tiny garden with palm trees, in the branches of which tropical birds sang songs which were loud and disagreeable and utterly unfamiliar to the visitor from the north. But it did not at all matter, because the heat weighed upon your sweating body and covered it with a palpable coverlet of down, preventing any thought of sleep. The windows were black holes without panes. Not the slightest stir in the air. The high-tuned song of the mosquitoes could not alarm you under your net, and other accidental inhabitants of your room found you wide-awake. Rancid butter was pardonable under such conditions.

I paid a short visit to the harbor, in which, to my surprise, I found a big ship bearing the name of my young friend King Alfonso XIII. Here, where Cortez had landed in 1519, a Spanish ship, though it bore the name of a Spanish king, was a visitor no less foreign to the place than the sightseer from Vienna. It was a few days later that I was to meet again, not exactly the King of Spain, but one of his fiercest foes, though a confessed admirer of the King as well as of his mother.

After an uneventful journey from the coast back to the cooler plateau, I found myself really longing to go back to the United States. At the depot in Mexico City, I was introduced to the representatives of the Mexico Mining and Exploration Company, who asked me to come to their private car and share their meals, an invitation which was

gladly accepted. These gentlemen knew how to travel in
Mexico—private car, their own cook, and enough White
Rock water to insure them against poisoning. I immediately felt myself lifted to a higher standard of life. Mr.
M. C. B., president of the company, introduced me to the
most prominent member of the party, Rear Admiral
Schley, U. S. N., a nice old gentleman who greeted me by
saying: "We all know you better than you do us!" The
train had scarcely left the city when a tropical thunder-
storm broke loose with a flood of rain, a blessing to the
dried-up country. We all felt very safe in the mighty Pull-
man car.

I was very much interested in the unobtrusive old gentleman who, despite the fact that he was a Rear Admiral
in the United States Navy, was content with a one-dollar
watch. He told me that he was of Bavarian descent, but
that his mother was a Huguenot and that was the reason
why he never learned to speak German. Yet he had a taste
for German sauerkraut and smoked pork, he adored German music, and declared the Germans in America the most
valuable and distinguished part of the population. Forty-
six years he had served in the tropics, never sick, never
wounded. His chief feat was the battle of Santiago de
Cuba, in which he commanded the flagship. The *Cristóbal
Colón*, the last Spanish man-of-war to fly the war-flag in
the Caribbean, went down to the bottom of the sea before
his eyes at about the same place where Columbus had
landed. A bullet had torn off the flagstaff before she went
down, and Schley had given orders to raise the floating
pole to make some precious canes out of it as souvenirs.
Schley told me he could have destroyed the whole Spanish
fleet, which was at his mercy, but as a soft-hearted man

he stopped the fire as soon as the adversary was defenseless. Schley took the defeated Admiral Cervera to his flagship and put his wardrobe and his purse at the prisoner's disposal. "You have lost all but honor," he consoled him. Cervera embraced the Rear Admiral and said: "I have never met a sailor who was not a gentleman!"

"A pretty answer," commented the old gentleman to me, smilingly.

Cervera had the task of explaining to the Spanish government how it came about that seven hundred Spaniards and not one American had been killed. This explanation should not have been very difficult. If you have a gun of a wider range than your adversary, the latter is just as much doomed as you are safe and sound. Under such conditions a sea-battle need not be ventured, because the result is clear beforehand. Schley got a silver service, ten thousand dollars, and a seven-thousand-dollar sword of gold, destined to become valuable items of some museum, as Schley said, except the cash.

When Rear Admiral Schley put his signature in my notebook, he wrote with a pencil, and I asked him to repeat the signature with a pen. "I shall tell you why," I said, and related to the surprised Admiral my recent visit to the King of Spain and his mother, and how the latter had admonished her son to give me his signature in ink and not in pencil. The Admiral said he would be glad to know the King and Queen. How noble a woman the Queen must be—and the King, what a fresh, nice boy! "I am really sorry to have offended both of them so deeply and yet so involuntarily! Men are just tools to keep the history of mankind going!" I was sorry to take leave of the remarkable old gentleman when I had to leave the private car of the Mexican Mining and Exploration Co., which went to El Paso.

My own route led me to Ciudad Porfirio Diaz, where the name Lorenz on the train relieved its owner of any trouble of the sort not uncommon at the frontiers of the United States. When the train had left the Ciudad, it stopped after a while upon the open track, and the travellers found themselves in the States again. They were examined for their health, and were asked especially whether anybody had been in Vera Cruz. As I felt fit and fine, I forgot about my visit to Vera Cruz—and so it was concluded that nobody had been to that poisoned place.

Texas stretched endlessly to right and left and endlessly in front of the train, which rolled on day and night before it reached the approximate center of the state at Dallas. At the junction, Spofford, the train had to stop for three hours. A wooden shed was the only building to receive the travellers, and there was nothing to eat except eggs, ancient ham, and margarine—in the midst of a cattle land!

In Dallas I was received with utmost courtesy by the dean of the medical department of the University. Among the gentlemen to bid me welcome was an old man who, greeting me, produced a small photograph with the words: "Do you know the place?" Of course, I knew it immediately—it was the market-place of my native town, Weidenau. Mr. J had been born in a little village near Weidenau, in Silesia, and had come to the United States on a sailing vessel more than fifty years before. He was now the editor of a newspaper at Fort Worth and felt that he simply had to come to see a man who hailed from near his own birth-place, which he could never see again. Nothing is stronger than the memories of childhood!

Dallas as a city was much younger than its visitor, yet it had about 60,000 inhabitants. The United States at that time had about seventy millions. If the entire population of the United States were to live in Texas, the state would be as densely populated as Germany, for example. All the possibilities of America seemed to be concentrated in Texas—cattle, wheat, cotton, sugar, horses, and what-not. All was produced in abundance in Texas, which was big enough to be a kingdom in itself. If only the thorns of the cactus plants could easily be removed! All this may be changed by the higher development of agriculture and industry at the present time, yet the climate has remained the same. There is no real rainy season, and drought is the dreadful enemy. But there is water beneath the surface, and the agriculturists promised to bore as many holes in the ground as would be necessary to flood the land at any moment.

I had not come to Texas to have a good time. There were hundreds of children to see, coming from all parts of the country, and I worked very hard with good Doctor Rosser, who is now the head of the new and palatial Good Samaritan Hospital. The hospital of that day, a wooden structure in a beautiful magnolia grove, was surrounded by buggies and perambulators filled with ailing children. I worked in this old hospital like a mule, both forenoon and afternoon, on selected cases. I was glad that I was able to cure a boy with club-feet, who had been especially recommended to me by the Governor. I remember a very pleasant interruption of my work when a delegation of the women school-teachers of Dallas, all more or less beautiful young ladies in spotless white dresses, came to congratulate me on my work for crippled children. They watched

me work for a short time and then declared unanimously
that they preferred teaching the mind to straightening
the body.

Sunday came, to bring about another interruption of
the hospital work, and the question of divine service loomed
in the background. As a Roman Catholic, I was claimed
by Father X, who promised me an exceptionally splendid
high mass in the cathedral, the most conspicuous archi-
tectural monument in the city. Father X belonged to
the fighting category of Catholic priests and insisted
peremptorily on his right to drag me to his herd. But I
never liked fighting priests, and declined to be ordered to
attend divine service in the cathedral. Now I know that
I was entirely wrong in doing so; but Father X was not
less wrong in his peremptory behavior. If both of us confess our sin, we shall be forgiven.

My reception committee wanted to present their guest
to their congregation, and invited me to attend divine
service in a large wooden hall instead of in the monumental
cathedral. "We pray to the same God," I answered, "and
I have always been interested in the ways different people
pray to God, be they Mohammedans, Buddhists, or Christians." I did not have to repent my choice, for I never
heard a more eloquent and edifying sermon than that delivered by the Reverend Mr. M. I felt myself to be in a
family of friends who likewise were all friends with their
minister, and to tell the truth I liked the dignified, clear,
and understandable way of service better than the complicated ceremonies of a high mass, which will always be
enigmatical and incomprehensible to the laity.

Before I left Dallas, a festive banquet was given me,
attended by more than a hundred guests; the most promi-

nent persons of the city of course were present—except
the Roman Catholic clergyman. A speaker of remarkable
eloquence, Mr. J. T. T., expounded the riches of Texas, its
possibilities and its brilliant future—prophecies which
have become realities. Two features of my stay in Dallas are
unforgettable because they were unique. A reception was
given me by the ladies of the Elks' Club, in which I was
the only representative of the stronger sex and was therefore, as the Germans say, *"der Hahn im Korb"* (the rooster
in the basket)—a bit of good luck which not every man can
boast of. Extremely pleasant was my visit to St. Mary's
College, where I was taken by Bishop G. There were more
than a hundred young ladies ranging from sweet sixteen
to sweet twenty, blossoms not yet quite opened, budding
future beauties from all parts of Texas. They filled the
big hall with negative or positive, yet extremely feminine,
electricity. Whosoever denies the existence of such an
electric fluid would have become a believer had he attended
this reception. How many autographs had to be written!
But in return, some of the promising young ladies wrote
their names in my notebook. One of them, a sweet and still
unself-conscious beauty who wanted to display her German, wrote the following lines: *"Wenn Du wirst weit
gehen, Ich werde Dich im Herzen sehen!"* The man whom
you wanted to see in your heart is in the hope that in
time you saw the right man in your heart and that you are
a happy grandma by now.

When I left Dallas I felt sure I should go back some
day, but that hasn't happened yet.

At the end of May, 1903, I arrived in St. Louis. My
first impression of the city was black smoke and brown
dust. In the bathtub, the muddy water of the Mississippi

invited me to take a moorish mud-bath. After the busy days in Dallas, I was hoping for some rest in St. Louis. To my great surprise, the *St. Louis Globe-Democrat* printed on the front page three duly illustrated items. First, General Luke E. Wright, Vice-Governor of the Philippines, was being welcomed to his home in Memphis with kingly honors. Second, President Theodore Roosevelt had delivered a remarkable speech upon the necessity of annexing the Philippines. Third, Doctor Lorenz, the great Austrian surgeon, had arrived that day in St. Louis. The most modest man cannot get away from American reporters if the public has taken the slightest notice of him.

My days in St. Louis were just as crowded as in Dallas, but instead of a blooming magnolia grove, I had to work in gloomy hospitals. I was barely allowed time to see the preparations for the St. Louis World's Fair, as a guest of the great brewer, Adolphus Busch. The lovely Mrs. Busch was the sweetest hostess imaginable. How reliable a friend I had in her was proven many many years later when—Adolphus Busch was already brewing in Heaven— Mrs. Busch sent me a considerable sum of money for poor Viennese children as soon as the war had come to an end.

I had, as a matter of course, to visit the Busch Brewery. Nothing was to be seen but many big boilers, sparkling with copper and brass, standing in an enormous hall, the floor of which shone like that of a dance-hall, with not a drop of liquid anywhere! Nothing was to be heard but the subdued hissing and buzzing of seething water destined to become good beer. But Adolphus Busch did not regale his guest with his beer. Only the choicest Rhein or Mosel wines to be had in Germany were good enough. As a souvenir, the guest got a pen-knife which had a tiny little hole in the end of the handle. If you held the knife against the light and looked through the little hole, you saw, whom? Adolphus Busch himself! In this way, at some cost, he made himself the cynosure of the eyes of his guests. This curious word was a new acquisition in my English vocabulary, when I read one day that on some occasion I was the cynosure of all eyes. I had to be told what it meant. At least this cynosure didn't cost me a cent.

When I got back to Chicago, I found my princess doing very well, but was aware of a general feeling of uneasiness when I offered my little sparkling gift, the Mexican opal. Opals, it seems, are never to be trusted because they always forebode evil. The queen, as a collector of unset jewels, knew it for certain! When I took leave, it was agreed upon that after a certain interval the princess should pay me a visit in Vienna to get the proper after-treatment.

While still in Chicago, I was informed by my brother-in-law in Vienna that Mrs. L was now expecting another baby—at her age of forty-two and after an interval of twenty years since her first child, a rather risky situation. What was to be done—should I not return home as soon as possible? "No," I replied, and added that nothing was to be done for the present; let things take their natural course. I was much surprised at the announcement of the prospective arrival of the child, whom, by anticipation, I called "the American," because in some enigmatical way his embryonic existence may have been due to the influence of crisp American air upon his father.

As the gynecologist told me, a premature birth was likely, perhaps even an abortion; would not the latter be preferable to the former? Is no child at all preferable to a prematurely born child with questionable chances for the further development of soul and body? This question I had always answered for myself in the affirmative, as I always had much to do with children afflicted with congenital spastic paralysis, which is most often due to premature birth. It is a fact that brain and spinal cord are extremely sensitive to the slightest abbreviation of the intra-uterine life. It is as if the nervous system, before all other tissues, must be fully developed in the womb. Seven-months children are very often a questionable gift to their parents. They seem all right as long as they are little, but when they begin to stand or try to walk, and sometimes even sooner, a certain tenseness or spasticity of the muscles causes contractures of the joints and makes walking impossible. The muscles seem to be more under the influence of the spinal cord than under the command of the brain. Medical art can make these unfortunate children walk, but their mental development is always an open question, although such children are sometimes gifted in one way or another. When they grow up to maturity, they are often a nuisance to themselves and to the community. I had seen many hundreds of such cases, and now I foresaw the possibility of becoming the father of such a child, and had to decide my attitude in my own case, if it should become a reality.

My resolve was the following: Take all proper care of the new-born, as if it were a normal child. No incubator as an artificial womb, no extraordinary precautions of any kind. The new-born child must be fit to stand the extra-uterine life, or it had better die. Any one who has seen as many cases as I have will not call my view of the question cruel. Without a certain amount of vitality, the new-born should never try to live. With this resolve taken, I was ready to meet all eventualities. Of course, I was not quite sure whether my behavior would match my resolution in case the "American" should arrive too soon. Such children are often the darlings of their parents.

For the time being, I put the whole question out of my mind.

XVII

HAZARDS OF THE THEATRE

I HAD earned some final holidays, which I spent in New York. A friend introduced me to the family of George Gould who, in turn, invited me to his country-place at Lakewood, New Jersey. I did not admire the house of the millionaire, which, except for its dimly lit hall, lacked roominess and was more than filled up with trinkets. A staircase which led down to the lake had been a marble parapet, and Mr. Gould couldn't forbear drawing his guest's attention to that fact. But I bluntly told him that I was not impressed by such a trifle in the way of marble railings; as far as the latter were concerned, I could not only compete with George Gould, but in this one case I was the millionaire and George Gould the beggar. "Come and see my marble railings from the Elisabeth and Teget-hoff bridges in Vienna, they will celebrate their resurrection very soon," I said to my astonished host. On the other hand, I was much impressed by the guest-house and the sports-hall which were situated near the palace. There were provisions for all kinds of sports, and the boys of the family made diligent use of them. A steeplechase was arranged in honor of the guest. It looked rather dangerous when George Gould's sons, still mere boys, took the jumps at the risk of going off their horses. Mrs. Gould, who was watching the game, exclaimed aloud whenever a jumper seemed unsure of his seat. "I must say, I don't like it at all," she said when the pageant had come to an end without mishap. "I must say," Mr. Gould retorted, "I do like it very much." Father Gould was weather-beaten, and drove his car without hat, gloves, or warm overcoat.

There were lovely daughters besides; Edith Katherine promised to became a beauty, though she was only sixteen months old, while Helen Vivian had fulfilled her own promise. Mrs. Gould was intent upon showing her guest the splendor of the royal household. The table was a still-life picture, composed of costly laces, shining candelabra, massive plate, cut glass, flowers, and other paraphernalia. The clean-shaven lackeys had white periwigs and were clad in red, laced frock-coats, white trousers, white silk stockings, and low shoes with silver buckles. King Ludwig II of Bavaria could not have less exactly imitated his adored idol, "*Le Roi de Soleil*," than did Mrs. Edith Gould his dining-table.

All was royal except the food, which was not worthy of the ceremonies. It was an awful contrast. Yes, there was terrapin, but what if a man doesn't like it? And there were other dishes of unknown name and questionable flavor. I left the table hungry for a hearty, simple meal such as I was wont to have at my home. "If you ever come to Vienna," I said to Mr. Gould, "honor me by your visit and I will show you some marble railings and some Viennese cooking!"

George Gould came to Europe many years later. His wife had died on her golf-course, but he did not stop in Vienna; he went to the Côte d'Azur—to die there.

Lakewood was then a place more favored by the New York millionaires than it is today. They formed a great family. I saw a lot of them in big Gould Hall, and among them Mrs. Pulitzer, the wife of the newspaper publisher, to whom, a sick man, I must pay a visit. I found a gentleman not much older than myself, sitting in a large easy-chair, being read to by his secretary. The poor multi-millionaire was blind, and could not see his house nor his pictures, which he remembered very well. He even invited me to see the pictures in his New York home. The remarkable thing was that the unfortunate man was quite serene and seemed to be reconciled to his cruel fate.

Mrs. Edith Gould had been an actress before she married, and seemed to be pleased when I told her how much I liked the stage and its people. "You have had some interesting experiences with them, I know," said Mrs. Gould. "Would you mind relating some of them to me?" Complying with her wish, I told her the following stories:

The people on the stage must always have been informed of my presence in the theatre, because they at once took notice of it in one way or another. Very embarrassing had been my welcome by the orchestra in the Columbia Theatre in Washington, when they had played the beautiful old Austrian hymn, an honor which not even an ambassador could claim. Another time was in New York. I had seen the beautiful play, "The Crisis," and had admired the hero Stevens just as much as the heroine Virginia. I had been invited to the stage to pay my respects to Virginia and to other ladies of rare beauty. Mr. Hackett, the famous Shakespearian actor, had given me the book, *The Crisis*, which I had read twice with ever increasing interest. I always thought its author, Mr. Winston Churchill, one of the greatest American writers of the present time.

In Rochester, New York, I had had an agreeable experience. A love-scene was taking place on the stage; the lover had tried and tried to get nearer to his beloved, a very, very nice young lady, who always knew how to elude him. At last, he had to be content with inhaling the perfume of her hair, at a measured distance. When the curtain dropped, I was asked to come upon the stage. There I greeted the beautiful girl, congratulated her upon her performance, and said that I envied her lover. The young lady laughed: "Well, he is not so much to be envied, because he will never get what he wants—a kiss. He ought rather to envy you, because you can have it any time." So I kissed the young lady in the presence of the stage company and she confessed: "I have never been more honored." I said to the young lady: "I wish I were as young as you are; then you would feel much less honored, but certainly more thrilled by my kiss." It is much better to omit kisses by which young ladies feel honored; it reminds you too much of your old age.

Once I roused the anger of an actor on the stage. He was a negro performer in a vaudeville theatre. I was being shown over the new house, and, much against my own will, attracted the notice of the audience, who watched me attentively. The actor on the stage lost his temper, interrupted his performance, and harangued the audience: "Ladies and gentlemen, look here, I am the fellow." Nothing was left for me but to flee.

Sometimes the actors would extemporize in a harmless way, but sometimes in a less obliging strain. For instance, an actor had occasion to comment on the bad-looks of his rival: "Stand straight, so that Doctor Lorenz can see your crooked legs. Oh! What an ugly face you have; you should be operated upon by Doctor Lorenz!" Another time a young fellow was deliberating with his old father as to how he could get on in the world. After some thinking, the father said: "I have it, grow a beard like Doctor Lorenz and you'll make your fortune." Applause from the audience. In a theatre where a German comedian attracted crowds of people every evening, I had to pay for his applause. The comic sang a vulgar song with the refrain, "It was Mister Dooley"—the latter to be understood as a man who knew all, commented upon everything mockingly or approvingly, and was, so to speak, the public conscience. Every stanza of his song ended with "It was Mister Dooley." He never had lines enough; the audience always wanted one more. At last the droll man made signs that he had run out of verses and wanted to leave the stage. On his way out he stopped, pointed at his forehead, and began his very last strophe:

> "We have with us a noble guest.
> To please him is today my quest.
> As artists do, twisting the pegs,
> An artist too, he pulls the legs.
> But who taught him to pull the legs?
> *It was Mister Dooley.*"

Roaring applause from the audience.

In so far as the actor apostrophized me as an artist, he was quite right: I always wanted to be an artist, much more than to be what they called a "wise, learned man"; nor was the actor wrong as far as "pulling the legs" is concerned, for I have built an appliance by which a leg can be all but pulled out of the body, if you are foolish enough to try it. I knew, of course, the meaning of the slang expression "to pull one's leg," and I appreciated the wit. It was harmlessly meant.

On another occasion, I had been really embarrassed by

an actor. A scene in the play showed a man who was eulo-
gizing his partner because the latter had done so much to
improve conditions somewhere. "Leave me alone," answered the man praised, and, pointing to where I sat in a
box, added, "If I could do as much good as our distinguished visitor up there, I should be satisfied with life."
The audience applauded frantically, and the play was
interrupted. There were cheers and cries: "Doctor Lorenz
—speak! Doctor Lorenz—speak!" I remembered the
bankers' banquet, where I was caught unprepared, in a
similar situation. I did not say a word, but simply bowed
to the public. The cheers and shouts continued. The
situation reached a climax when the actor who had extemporized came forward to the footlights and said po-
litely: "Please give us just a few remarks, Doctor Lorenz."
But this time I resisted, though tempted to say: "Ladies
and gentlemen, you as well as I came here to see and hear
these excellent artists whose performance has been so badly
impaired by my presence; excuse me, and let them not miss
the opportunity to make their few remarks." A sweeping
gesture with my arms toward the actors on the stage stood
me in good stead of an improvised speech.

Mrs. Gould laughed at her visitor's stage adventures
and said that she could fill a book with her own experiences
as an actress. At that time I had no idea that, more than
a quarter of a century later, I should be trying to get into
closer relationship to the theatre as a playwright. It
seems very doubtful whether my play on the stage will
arouse as much interest as did my presence in the audience.

Before I decided to leave for home, I had to fight out

with myself whether to stay in America for good or to leave for good. Untold possibilities urged me to make America my home. But Vienna at that time was not such a bad place to live in either. And for another thing, I was wont to work hard, often harder than was good for my health, but I was not the fanatical sort of worker who alone can be successful in America. And even if I were successful, could I have a big, lovely garden and the fine house which I saw already in imagination—a house on top of two terraces which were to be lined with marble balustrades which would make even a multi-millionaire like George Gould burst with envy? If I worked like a beast of burden destined to die in harness in America, I would not reach my goal before I breathed my last. I calculated that in about ten years I would be dead if I kept on working as I had worked in America. I could not get rid of the Viennese philosophy of life which taught me not to consider myself a beast of burden, with work as the only object in life, but as a human creature intent on enjoying life. There is no better way to enjoy it than to take life easy at least once in a while, and use work as a spice to make your going-easy ten times pleasanter. You must have time to thank God for his sunshine which you are enjoying. I found it not difficult to decide to go rather than to stay, though at that time the immigration laws were no obstacles to foreign lovers of America.

I sailed on the North German Lloyd *Kronprinz* early in July, 1903, with Captain Richter. Two incidents, though insignificant, cling to my memory. When the big vessel slid slowly down the Hudson River, a little tug-boat, under full steam, scuttled in the wake of the liner, with its shrilling whistle wide open. It had a passenger on board who had missed the liner at the pier, and was trying to reach it while it was slowly steaming down the harbor. The liner slowed down to let the little dwarf come alongside, and dropped a tow-line and a rope-ladder. The passenger, a stout woman, climbed vigorously. When she was near the top, a gust of wind blew her broad-brimmed straw hat to the side of her head. All the passengers, of course, were intently watching the dapper lady, who seemed a little embarrassed by her wobbling headgear. Another gust of wind blew the already dislocated hat over her face and blinded her. She stuck where she was, between gurgling water and heaven, and would have stayed there as long as her arms could hold on had not a sturdy sailor come to her rescue. Climb steadily and strenuously as you may to your goal, a treacherous chance, a wind that "bloweth nobody good" can spoil your life's work.

The steamer was crowded, and the stewards were kept busy accommodating the many passengers at the tables in the dining-hall. At that time the *table d'hôte* was still in vogue. One of the passengers refused to be seated between a doctor and an engineer!

"Give me that seat," I put in.

"But here is a letter for you, Doctor Lorenz, in which Captain Richter says he wants you as his neighbor at the table."

"Why not give the pretentious gentleman that seat?" said I.

"Because the captain would refuse to sit at the side of this conceited fellow," rejoined the steward under his breath. A severe but just judgment from a man who is wont to see people of all standards of life.

My fourth voyage across the Atlantic was smooth and

quiet; it was the only time I saw the North Atlantic smiling and basking in warm sunshine—but that lasted only a few days. It would not have been the Atlantic had it not caused the mighty ship to bow devoutly and persistently for two days to the tumbling waves of its majesty. Marconigrams told of the dying Pope, Leo XIII. Captain Richter complained that his ship was a big coal-eater, fifty-six railroad cars per day, which may be the reason why the big ship had to stop her cruises. I stayed one night in Cherbourg. I felt already at home because I was in Europe again.

The clippings from the American papers concerning my voyage filled three mighty volumes, and I could have filled three more with what I discarded. I thought to myself, when I put the volumes into my library, that if I had the money that these clippings would have cost an advertising business man, I would be a millionaire. Though I had paid only for the clippings, these books were by far the most costly in my library.

There was much to do, as many patients were waiting for me. Mrs. L was in such good health that she was able to take part in my work as assistant in spite of her condition.

XVIII

LORENZ HALL OR BUST!

My spare hours were all taken up with planning a new house, that is to say, an addition to my peasant house, which was to be left unchanged and merely adapted to the new building, as an appendix. Plans were drawn, architects consulted. They wanted, of course, to build a house in a more or less modernistic style which would have been an eyesore to its owner. So I changed my advisers until I found a man who understood and appreciated what I wanted. A house in a style which would remind you of a Fischer von Erlach structure, but lacking, of course, monumental dimensions; it should be a bit like the quaint old Viennese houses built in the time of Empress Maria Theresa. The site of the house, with its beautiful view, seemed to demand some architecture striking from outside and not less surprising when you entered it. It must not be a palace, to bring ridicule on an upstart owner, but it might well be like a little castle on the slopes of the Wienerwald, overlooking the broad valley of the Danube, the Tullnerfeld, and rising out of a nice garden with beautiful old trees. As the old and the new building were to form an entity, it might well give the impression of a small castle, the real size of it being veiled by linden trees. To tell the truth, I preferred, in my imagination, a small castle to a big villa. Of course, I could have bought one of the many aristocratic castles in Austria not far from Vienna, but the nearest place would have been too far away for one who had to commute every day of the year, summer and winter. The new house was to be no bungalow, but a solid, year-round abode.

In spite of my descent from peasants, or perhaps because of it, I had always held aristocratic families in high respect. Weren't they peasants themselves, peasants of a higher order, living upon their own fields for centuries —just like my grandfather's great-great-grandfather? But the latter had no family tradition, no family history. And that is why I envied the aristocrats. To have a family history, to have ancestors, as idols to be followed as a type—what spur that would be! And therefore I was a very harsh judge of any aristocrat, young or old, who went wrong in any way, forgetting the traditions of his family.

The vaulted cowstable and annex on the ground floor of the old peasant house were to be a part of the foundation of the new house. Of course, this must have a hall, if not finer, at least better provided with daylight and sunshine than the hall in the Gould house. Lorenz Hall would not be a bad name for the new house, I thought—not unaware, however, of my ridiculous fancy. Yet I turned a deaf ear to Mrs. L who had good judgment on the new house before it was built; her judgment on the old house had been no less accurate. "Your new castle will be nothing but a big hall, just as your old peasant house is nothing but a big dining-room, and the family will have to be content with tiny little bedrooms!" But her hall-crazy husband saw nothing but the hall on the Danube. It must be beautiful beyond description, was my resolve. "But you will spend all the money you have on your crazy idea!" protested Mrs. L.

"The money changed into the hall of my fantasy will be much nicer to look at than the state securities which I have never yet laid eyes on," answered her obstinate and spendthrift mate.

"Can't you appreciate the necessity of having some money for your old age, old man that you are? Don't you give a thought to the fact that you are going to be the father of—most probably—a daughter in your old days? A daughter for whom you must put aside some dowry?"

"I am sure your prospective daughter will be a son; have I not baptized him 'Der Amerikaner' beforehand? That surely means a boy! And to prove that I am not the old man you like to call me, nor you the old girl you pretend to be, you will be a young mother and I a young father, and we shall have time enough to procure for our old age. Am I not earning every day by my work? Why should I deny myself the realization of the dream I have cherished ever since I built our 'dining house'? And this dream is going to become a reality on the banks of the Danube, forty minutes from Stefan's Platz by car. The money won't be blown up, it won't vanish, but will take another, probably more durable shape."

That was the final word of the determined hall-dweller. It was Lorenz Hall or bust! But it is to be noted that, at the close of the World War, the state securities were entirely lost and only Lorenz Hall remained.

There was nothing more to be said. The hall was built on that side of the old house where the large verandah had been situated. It is true that the bedchambers had to sacrifice some of their roominess to the big hall; they became tiny, but cozy, very American bedrooms, with a wonderful view. By means of this sacrifice, we avoided impairing the roominess of the hall by an inside gallery to give admittance to the bedrooms. The hall was, of course, to be the center of the house. The big dining-room and a small music-room belonging to the old house opened into it, as did a big library—my study and real dwelling-place. A nice roomy breakfast-room, two sides of which were windows reaching from the floor to the ceiling, was a good substitute for the verandah, and could just as well have been called a sun-parlor. So it was rather an exaggeration—something much indulged in by Mrs. L—for the lady of the house to call the new addition a mere hall. A large anteroom gave admittance to the hall from the garden. Above the entrance door there glistened in golden letters the sentence from Horace: "*Lucro appone quem fors dierum cumque dabit*" (Consider as gain whatever chance may bring). When you are past fifty years, you have to make the most of the time left you.

To come back to the incriminating hall: It was, of course, two stories high, and from the outside was as much the center of the house as it was from within. Its smaller side commanded the view of the Danube, and was practically one big window, consisting of an upper and a lower part divided by a broad cross-bar of artificial stone. This cross-bar was the subject of a furious battle between the architect and myself. The former had arranged the cross-bar just at the height of my eyes, so that the view was lost to me when I passed the landing-place of the broad staircase which led around two sides of the hall up to the bed-chambers.

"This cross-bar is too low; it must be placed higher up, so as not to shut out the view when I pass the landing place," I said.

"The cross-bar must stay where it is, or the proportion of the upper to the lower part of the window will be spoiled. Every professional would say I am a bungler," said the architect.

And when I insisted upon my right to have a window I could look out of, the architect threatened to drop his work and let me do it at my own risk—which really would have been the better solution of that wrangle. If the owner was hall-crazy, however, the architect was crazy all round, as was proven by the next few months; his irritability was one of the first symptoms of a progressive brain paralysis. But the broad cross-bar mars the view from the hall to this day!

The walls of the lower part of the hall were panelled in light-brown oak. One big panel was measured to hold the most precious picture in the little gallery I had collected; a few words will have to be said about this picture a little later on. One long side of the hall was occupied by a broad staircase made of oak, with nicely carved railings of the same material. The other long side held a rather monumental fireplace, topped by a copper hood reaching up to the second story. On both sides of the fireplace, high-backed chairs were integral parts of the woodwork which enclosed the hearth. A carved oak chest of drawers, a big carved clock-case in a corner enclosing a clock with a melodious chime, some big easy-chairs, and two little tables were the only furniture, so that the furnishings consisted practically of staircase and fireplace. The floor was made of squares of inlaid wood, the polishing of which is a science in itself.

The panels of the hall had to be filled with tea-green cloth. The largest panel was to frame a picture which had been the cause of a severe quarrel with Mrs. L when one day I had brought home a wooden column about two and a half meters high and a half meter thick. The column was hollow; it was nothing in itself, but was the skeleton, as it were, of a colossal canvas which was wound around the wooden drum. When you tried to unroll the canvas, a rain of little particles of oil-paint dripped from its surface on to the rug of the drawing-room. Mrs. L had nearly fainted when she saw the business—and her husband radiant over what he called a find and what was, in her eyes, nothing but heaps of dust and untidiness. I had found the half-forgotten canvas in the garret of a house in the city which belonged to a dealer in works of art and which was to be wrecked. I bought it for a song, because of course nobody could make use of it except a future hall-owner. So this old picture had become one of my clandestine reasons for building a hall, since it required a hall for its resurrection.

"Wait until the picture is restored and you will see a wonder of art," I had said consolingly to my wife.

"And where will you put it? There is no wall big enough in our flat."

"You wait and see," had been my enigmatical answer.

Now the time had come for the resurrection of a fine old picture, the painter of which was entirely unknown. By mere chance, I found out who had painted it on one of my frequent trips to Italy, long after the picture had become "*le clou*" of the hall. In a large room of the Palazzo Bianco in Genoa, I found a collection of pictures which evidently had been done by the same artist because they had in common the same yellowish coloration. I was very much surprised when I discovered several pictures among

the collection which had the same figures as mine, and told
the same story, though they were in somewhat different
positions from my own picture. Pictures as well as books
have their strange fates. How had the *clou* of my hall
come to Vienna—after what wanderings? And how long
had it slept rolled up in a garret? The painter of these
pictures and of the picture in my hall was Lucas Cambiaso
of Genoa, who had lived in the sixteenth century. The
painting told a heart-rending story; it was a document of
the typical malicious spite of women for a sister who has
succumbed to forbidden love. Its title is "The Judgment
of Diana." The goddess Diana, with a golden half-moon
on her head, stands at the left corner of the picture, lazily
leaning toward the center and looking rather indifferently
at the scene which is taking place between three of her fellow huntresses. You know that the playmates of Diana
were pledged to chastity. It seems that they must have
watched each other very closely in this regard, or they
would not have detected so early that one of the girls, who
is crouching on the ground in the center of the scene, her
beautiful, yet anxious and reproachful face upturned to
her remorseless and menacing comrades, has sinned against
her vow, perhaps six months before. The two indignant
maids seem to know the truth, and are trying to pull a
blue cloth off the abdomen of the crouching sinner to make
her shame patent. These three central figures of the picture are of an exquisite beauty. It is to be hoped that
Diana will have mercy upon the fallen maid, since she
knows for certain that so much beauty is doomed to bloom
and bear fruit before it fades away. Three other very
young girls in the background of the picture are indifferent
lookers-on. They don't understand yet—but they will

learn from their comrades! In the left corner of the canvas, a nice little boy with a broken bow on his lap, the god *Amor*, cries bitterly, for he is the only one who sympathizes with the fair sinner.

To have saved this picture from ruin was worth the scolding I got. Other panels on the ground floor of the hall were adorned with many other pictures—too many, as Mrs. L thought. But if you have pictures, where can you put them but on the walls?

The second story of the hall was lighted by the monumental window consisting of one single pane of plate-glass. "If some accident should smash this pane, the new one will wreck your finances," remarked Mrs. L. "And you will have to engage acrobats to clean it," she added, always eager to dampen her hall-crazy husband's ardor. But I turned a deaf ear to the mockings of my hall-opposed wife. While, on the ground floor of the hall, oak pillars with carved heads supported the mighty staircase, the second story boasted of marble columns, which supported the ceiling. On one long side, these columns supported the arched openings of a corridor which ran around two sides of the hall and gave access to the bedrooms. Opposite the mammoth window, this corridor had a little balcony overlooking the length of the hall. This balcony was the place where the owner of Lorenz Hall took his guests to show them the most beautiful picture in the house, one which changed at every hour of the day and every day in the year—the view over the Danube and the woods on its banks. "So you see, Mrs. L, the mammoth window is of some use!" It had to be of plate-glass, like all the other windows in the house, because the windows are the eyes of a house and should be clear.

On the other long side of the hall, flat columns in relief-work supported by the arched niches. Mrs. L scoffed at the marble-pillared hall, because the pillars were not real but imitation marble, though made with such wonderful technique that they excelled the real material in beauty. I admitted that any material you use should be genuine—but this principle cannot possibly be pushed to the extreme, or you would have to renounce all silvered and gilded things. You cannot make a wooden building look like a stone house, because it is silly to try to make two absolutely different materials look alike—but why should one care if the artist successfully substitutes for one material another which is very similar, or rather identical? Why not substitute a composition stone for natural stone? Artificial marble is even more beautiful than the natural marble block.

The ceiling of the hall was the subject of intense deliberation. It was to be made of oak, but solidly vaulted between iron bars and then covered with elaborate stucco-work. The trochilus was to be made of square plates to connect the walls with the ceiling; from these plates broad bands of stucco ran up to join the solid frame of an oblong medallion corresponding with the size of the hall. This medallion was to prove very expensive, because it fairly cried for a picture some two meters long and six meters wide—a picture to be painted on canvas and then made fast to the ceiling by a special method. As the painter whom I had chosen lacked an *atelier* of sufficient size, the picture had to be painted from the top downwards—as it were, by installments. But the subject of the picture was worth painting. I conceived the idea of realizing the sweetest dream humanity ever dreamt—at least on the

canvas: "The Victory of Peace over War." The Angel
of Peace, soaring in the air on spread wings, is surrounded
by the Three Graces and by personifications of music,
painting, sculpture, histrionic art, architecture, science,
and commerce, all of them beautiful, more or less naked
women with their respective properties in hand. The
Angel of Peace hurls, with a sweeping gesture of his right
arm, palm branch in hand, and kicks, with his right foot
an iron-clad man in red mantle, War, into a dark abyss
below. In company with War are dashed into the depths
all the bad sequels of War, first of all Viciousness, represented by a woman clad in green drapery up to the waist,
plunging headfirst down to where Hell may be supposed
to be; she has a flowing abundance of reddish golden hair,
and a complexion like the surface of ripe peaches. Though
the personified Viciousness shows only her voluptuous
posterior, she must be a beautiful woman. A darkish man,
tumbling down with contracted limbs, bears her company
and so do other less clear-cut figures. Terrified little angels are fleeing from the scene of destruction.

Though critics said that the Angel of Peace ought to
be a fair, light, celestial creature, instead of the dark-
winged youth upon the picture, who might be taken for
a bat with spread arms, the composer of the painting defended his angel and said: "Let us suppose it is the Archangel Michael who is killing War with his flaming sword."
The picture was painted in 1907, when unsuspecting people could still believe that the Archangel Michael would
never be called upon to achieve the business painted on the
ceiling of the hall. Can humanity hope that the League
of Nations will efficiently play the part of the Archangel
Michael?

LORENZ HALL AND THE LION STAIRCASE IN THE GARDEN OF THE
LORENZ HOME AT ALTENBERG

ONE OF THE TERRACES AT LORENZ HALL SHOWING PART OF THE
ELISABETH BRIDGE RAILINGS

The fastening of the large picture to the ceiling was quite a problem. Scaffolds had to be built to reach the ceiling; when the canvas adhered to its bed, it was covered with tissue paper and thoroughly ironed to obviate any bubbles. When the scaffolds were removed and the picture looked down upon the hearth of the hall like a bright assurance of an everlasting peace, Mrs. Lorenz could not forbear saying: "Herr Professor, the Easter cleaning of this picture is up to you. My maids cannot fly, nor can I."

"But that is my least concern," answered her husband. "There are other parts of the walls which seem too bare, for instance, the four arched niches along the ascent of the staircase. Don't you think it would be nice to cover them with pictures representing the four ages of human life?"

"I should prefer to leave those niches as they are," opined the unsophisticated housewife. "You will overdo the hall as you like to overdo anything you lay your hands on."

But the four paintings were ordered none the less. It took the painter a long time to finish them, as he could not come to an agreement with his patron as to their composition.

Meanwhile the "hall-decorator" had acquired another rather large picture representing the Goddess of Fortune, who from the blue sky drops roses on to the earth; humanity in all stages of life tries to gather the flowers, each interpreting the gifts in his own way. A pair of lovers crouch in happy forgetfulness at one corner of the canvas; at the other squats a drunkard with a bottle of wine in his raised hand. Other figures are singing, playing instruments, enjoying life, while old couples with white hair are lifting their arms in prayer to the wilful goddess, who lets them have not one petal of her flower-gifts. This picture found its place above the cupola of the fireplace.

Rugs, some marble busts, and smaller pictures for the lesser panels completed the decoration of the hall. If you entered it from the garden, passing through the glass-panelled folding-doors of the large anteroom, you got the impression of a lofty, light-flooded, colorful room, into which nature, always beautiful, peered through the large plate-glass window. "This is really a beautiful room!" exclaimed many an American guest when he had looked it over. The picture on the ceiling was, of course, lost to the guest, but the owner of the hall would not spare him the trouble of leaning far back in an easy-chair and looking at the "Victorious Peace" without twisting his neck. On the whole every one had to admit that the hall was a sight to be seen—though the most superfluous and pretentious room in the house. True as that was, I nevertheless felt delight whenever I ascended the carved stair-case. Beauty within and beauty without, what more could you ask of a realized dream?

While Mrs. L fought for her four bathrooms in the house, since the guests and the servants must not be forgotten in a country-house, her husband was intent on decorating the dining-room, which, because of its dimensions, demanded some embellishment. First of all, the ceiling had to be raised to correspond in height with the rooms in the new house. In this rather complicated pro-cedure, the first story of the old house was involved. The ceiling of the dining-room had to be covered with stucco work, framing four medallions. For each of them a big picture was ordered, representing the four seasons of the year: Spring, a beautiful young girl strewing flowers common to our meadows; Summer, a ripe beauty leaning on a sheaf of wheat, scythe in hand, while swallows dart about in fear of the coming thunder-storm; Fall, a middle-aged man, whose features showed a resemblance to the householder's, bearing a plate with fruits as gifts of the season; Winter, a winged, darkish angel—an exceptional angel with a white beard because he represented the father of Mrs. L—strewing snow upon the house, in the hall of which shines the lighted Christmas-tree.

"Stop decorating," admonished Mrs. L, "or you will have to mortgage the house before it is finished."

"Right-ho," answered her husband. "I leave all the other rooms to you except my study, which in time will get finished."

The house had five attic rooms. One of them was called "The Poet's Den" because there the famous Austrian playwright, my old friend Doctor Karl Schoenherr, wrote and finished his gripping play, *"Die Erde."*

But there were things to be done outside the house. The marble railings had to celebrate their resurrection upon the edges of the upper and lower terrace, and the two caryatides and eight sandstone pillars had to be disposed. Four of them, the smaller ones, were destined to be a pergola on the flat roof, from which the view over the Tullnerfeld, with the Danube and its surrounding hills, was most beautiful. The caryatides and the other big columns were arranged along the wall of the upper terrace, as parts of a vaulted corridor to be used as a walking-passage in rainy weather.

When all was completed—as far as a new house can be completed—the first guest arrived. He did not come too soon, as unbidden guests sometimes do, but instead had tarried a little and had postponed his expected arrival.

XIX

AN ARABIAN NIGHTS FANTASY

IT was, of course, the "American" who entered the house as the first permanent guest. His mother had had a very hard time. Women should have their children before rather than after their thirtieth year, let alone the fortieth. You are never quite sure either of the mother or of the child. Mrs. L came within a hair's breadth of dying of an embolism in the lungs, but her sound constitution was victorious at last. As his father had expected, the "American" was a boy, who received the name Konrad. He was just as frail and thin, with arms and legs like a spider's, as had been his brother Albert, nearly twenty years before. When his brother was born, Albert was just about to begin his military service as a dragoon in the Austrian army. At the end of the year, the young soldiers had to pass an examination to get the degree of an officer of the reserve. As their service lasted a year, these soldier-boys were called the "yearlings," or "voluntary yearlings." When the young dragoon Albert, some months later, was photographed with his baby brother in his arms, the picture was known as that of "the two yearlings."

As a reward, Mrs. L was given a furlough of five years to attend her little son in the green paradise, as the house in Altenberg was called. During this time she made only occasional appearances in town, to look after the accounts. I missed her very much in my practice, because

231

nobody understood so well how to soothe frightened little children when they were taken out of their bandages and were crying like fury. In three days, under her care, the worst of them used to be tame and laughing. Hirelings usually failed in this difficult task; men were absolutely unfit to handle these children. Not until then did I realize how much I owed to my wife as assistant in the after-treatment of children with congenital luxation of the hip-joints. Very often the mothers as well had to be educated, taught how to attend, feed, and wash their ailing little ones. This task was often the hardest.

In her retirement from business, as it were, Mrs. L became a very critical Minister of Finance of the Household. She found the finances rotten from top to bottom.

"You have saved nothing so far but your park, your marble railings, and pillared hall. If anything should happen——"

"Then," interrupted her husband, "the park and the hall so near to Vienna should be worth something. The money is not squandered; it has only changed its outer appearance, not to its detriment, I should say."

But I had to admit that the first visitor to my house—second house, second child—commanded his father to build up bank-accounts instead of pillared halls.

According to a former agreement, the Chicago princess was to spend part of the summer in Vienna under my care. She arrived with her parents, her governess, and a maid. The lovely little girl was not haughty at all, but mingled gladly with her fellow-sufferers and was just as friendly to them as they were to her. During the hot months she and her staff stayed at Lorenz Hall, which was to have a guest worthy of the frame it offered her. When the whole family had paid a visit to Altenberg, all were satisfied with what they had seen. The householder led his distinguished guests through the big garden which extended along the sloping hillside. The foot of it is transformed into two terraces, the upper of which, as you know, bears the hall; so the guests had to ascend and descend. The father of the princess was a young man in the vigor of life; yet I, who walked at his side, observed compassionately how out of breath he was while slowly ascending a gentle incline. "The young man's heart is not of the strongest," I thought, and slowed down, saying, "You should be careful about getting a cold; an inflammation of the lungs would be a bad thing if your heart cannot stand such a slight effort."

The little princess, then about eight years of age, was the liveliest creature you can imagine. Now and again, her laughter would ring through the big house. She was always in a hurry, and never got through with her business. When I went to the Danube bathing, I took her with me, carried her into the rushing waters, and let her float, holding her fast. The princess screamed with pleasure. Her bulldog Bluff, though he had come across the big pond, seemed to know nothing at all of the water and simply walked in, though he could not swim a stroke. But for me, Bluff would have been drowned then and there. Later on the little dog learned to swim, for the summer being rather hot, the water of the Danube was warmer than usual.

The princess had some little particularities about her food; she liked sweet, fat, floury dishes, which were by no means the right thing for her, as she had a tendency to get fat. On an excursion into the Wienerwald, the party of the princess stopped at a place which was famous for a *Wienermehlspeise* called "*Kaiserschmarrn*," a poem of flour, eggs, milk, butter, almonds, raisins and what-not. This time I, who liked the dish very much myself, had not the heart to stop the princess from indulging in the *Kaiserschmarrn*, though she managed to get a glossy, shining face with some raisins stuck upon her cheeks. Later I was sorry for my negligence, as the poor child had to go through the same sequel that I knew of from my own experience.

To honor the queen during her short stay in Vienna, I invited the American physicians in Vienna and many of their friends to attend a garden party in Altenberg. There were more than a hundred guests. Part of them, especially the ladies, were driven in carriages from the railway station to the hall, although it took only fifteen minutes to walk there, while the majority of the guests, the queen included, followed me on a detour over a hill, the top of which commands one of the most splendid views in the country. You follow the band of the Danube up to the little city of Tulln; you see Zeiselmauer, the Zeiselmure of the *Nibelungenlied*, where Brunhilde spent a night; you see where the Romans had their fortifications against the Alemanni; where Emperor Karl der Grosse fought the Tartars, and where Saint Severin came to the country to preach Christ. Quite a historical landscape, with the hills and the last outpost of the Alps, Mount Oetscher, in the background.

But my guests would not listen to my explanations because at the moment when the party arrived at the top of the hill a Viennese waltz broke loose in the nearby bushes, where the musicians had been hidden to greet the guests with Viennese music. Coffee, tea, sweets, fruits and "*Kugelhupf*" were served under the beech-trees of the adjoining forest. On the way down to the hall, I had to assist the queen, who was not prepared for climbing a mountain and was tottering on high heels. Arrived at the house, the guests assembled in the hall, taking seats where they could find them. The queen refused the throne offered to her because she had taken a fancy to sit on the lowest step of the staircase. Perhaps it was the best place for her, because the railings of the staircase at her side and a large picture at her back made a rather conspicuous setting for the elegant and beautiful lady. After a few remarks of greeting from me and some words of thanks from the guests, the party dispersed to stroll through the grounds, play tennis, or exercise in the bowling alley to prepare themselves for the dinner, which was served in the open air on the tennis court. Japanese lanterns hung across the large place made a colorful picture of the scene. Excellent original Pilsner beer was drawn from ice-cooled barrels, wine which had grown on the neighboring hills of Klosterneuburg sparkled in the glasses, the musicians played and sang Viennese tunes, and the young people scarcely waited to satisfy their appetites before they began dancing on the smooth floor of the tennis court. It was a beautiful feast, the first and the last glory of the hall! If it had been held one day later, all the beauty of it would have been dashed to pieces by a thunderstorm and a diluvian rain. The glory of the place withstood the rain and the storm of that day only to be shattered later on by an earthquake which nobody at that time could dream of.

The princess was really charming in her attitude toward the baby boy. She would stand beside his bed for a quarter of an hour at a stretch, watching his sleep, playing with him when he was awake, frowning when he was naughty, as was often the case. To commemorate this fact by a picture, I decided that one of the paintings which were to fill the four arched niches in the hall should be "Childhood"—little children playing in a blooming grove upon flower-sprinkled meadows. Among them is a beautiful little girl with the face of the princess, sitting in a two-wheeled golden cart drawn by little winged angels, while little Konrad is left behind, sitting on the grass, his face distorted by crying—document of a naughty boy! The other three pictures represented Youth, Manhood, and Old Age, the latter signifying my approaching future. An old man with a white beard sits on the shore of an endless ocean while a big somber angel, descending from the heights, shows him the run-out hour glass, and a small angel crowns his head with a laurel leaf.

On an excursion to the monastery of Klosterneuburg, the princess happened to be walking with a sister of Mrs. L's through the streets of the little town, curiously observing the shops at the side of the street. Suddenly she stopped and pointed with her forefinger at a little silver cross on a thin silver chain. "Oh, how charming, how beautiful this little cross is! How I should like to have it!" Aunt Hedwig entered the shop and bought the cross for a song. The little girl could not have been more delighted with a diadem of diamonds than she was with this poor little silver cross.

On her eighth birthday, a masquerade was a feature of the program of festivities. The princess was to be a peasant-girl of Lower Austria. She looked charming in her colorful frock, with silk apron and variegated silken neck-cloth. Round her neck she wore the little silver cross; there was no other peasant girl in the country who could compete with the disguised princess. But the silver cross seemed to put Miss Biller, her governess, in fear of evil spirits. Only a cross of gold could make her safe from them. The princess had to sacrifice her treasure to the superstition of an otherwise very intelligent woman. Opals and silver crosses, it seems, always forebode evil.

It was not difficult to make the little girl do her exercises. Only one thing was taboo. As soon as you tried to explain anything to her, for instance day and night, or the moon, or the seasons, or something regarding geography, she seemed to take offense; she would put her forefingers in her ears and refuse to listen. And yet, she became an accomplished lady. When, in the autumn, I parted with the princess and her staff, I did not know that it was for good. Twenty years later I received a picture from Mrs. M which showed that the little princess had become a beautiful lady.

The next few years were eventful as far as my work was concerned, but brought no further changes in my life. I scarcely ever had a vacation in the summer. About Christmas time I used to go to the Côte d'Azur, or spend a week or two in Egypt, seeking the sun—with the absolute certainty that Ra is not to be found unless you go to Upper Egypt, at least as far as Luxor. One time I tried to find hot sun in mid-winter in Khartoum, but had to turn back at Wadi Halfa because of an offended stomach —always the least dependable of my organs.

One of my visits to Egypt united pleasure with work. The Khedive of Egypt, Abbas Hilmi, invited me to see one of his children who was suffering from a congenital ailment. An operation was suggested and authorized. A room in the Khedival palace at Kubbe had to be converted into an operating-room. Plenty of tepid water was to be available—that had been my order. When, with an assistant, I entered the big hall of the palace, resplendent with oriental pomp and luxury, I thought of my own much smaller, but more tastefully furnished hall at home, and preferred it. I was astonished that there was nobody to welcome me. I had to find my way by the metallic clinking of jars and bowls coming from where I assumed that the operating-room had been installed. Striding through the empty hall, I had the keen sensation of being watched by more than one pair of eyes, lurking behind holes in the curtains. In the operating-room I found all the orders I had given the previous day well carried out. There was nothing in the large, clean room but an improvised operating-table and another small table for instruments and bandages. But when I turned my eyes to the wall which faced the windows I was startled by a sight which seemed like a fantasy out of the Arabian Nights.

Along the wall stood a row of very tall negroes, each with the red tarbrush on his woolly head. In one hand every one of them held a large silver bowl, while the other hand lifted a silver jar, ready to pour out the tepid water upon anything that had to be cleansed! Living wash-stands without soap and brush! But they were more than wash-stands; they were also eunuchs, watchmen of the harem, though the Khedive had only one wife. All of them were very friendly and serviceable, but I let them do nothing but pour water into the basin, and in order not to offend any one of them, I washed in rotation, and oftener than even a conscientious surgeon would have deemed necessary. When all was finished, I left the child to the immediate care of the family doctor; I said I would see the patient again in the evening. When I left the palace, the big house was wrapped in silence. Nobody came to say "Goodbye," or, "How did you succeed?" or "Come again!" But afterwards I was told by the Khedive's surgeon that the mother of the child had been very anxious about the operation and had certainly seen the "giaur" entering and leaving the hall. But the custom of the country did not allow a mother to say "I thank you" to her child's surgeon.

As rumor had it, the Khediva was once a Circassian slave-girl of extraordinary beauty in the harem of the Khedive's father—but who can fathom the truth or untruth of oriental stories? Certain it is that the Khedive had made all efforts to elevate the family of his wife. A brother of hers lived, not at the palace, but in one of the adjacent low buildings, in surroundings which were all but princely. The Khedive did not make much of his brother-in-law, but asked me to see him. The man was later sent to Vienna to get treatment there at the Khedive's expense. All oriental inconsistencies!

On that trip, I also visited a former patient whom I had cured in Vienna, a rich Egyptian princess. Her first name was Tauchida. As their palace was under repair, the family of Tauchida lived very comfortably on a large *Dehabie*, sailing according to where the wind blew from. Tauchida, nearly a grown-up girl, promised to have the beauty of Cleopatra. What may have been her fate?

The Khedive, Abbas Hilmi, a very pleasant and affable man, spoke German with a Viennese accent, as he had been educated in the "Theresianum" in Vienna. He was well aware of his situation, and used to say: "The first man in Egypt is Mr. Cook; the second man is Lord Cromer, and the third man is I!"

Starting for home, I arrived in Alexandria to find a furious sea. A cousin of the Khedive, bound on a political errand, had to sail, whether the sea were smooth or rough. But I turned my back on the raging Mediterranean and returned to Cairo for another week of sunshine. I was glad I was not a cousin of the Khedive of Egypt.

The memory of my operation on the Khedive's child brings back to mind my frustrated hope of being called to the Russian imperial court for consultation. A Russian noblewoman had told me that the Russian Empress wanted to consult me about one of her daughters, and that I should be prepared for the call at any time. The summons never came, doubtless because of the war and the sinister situation of the Russian imperial family. I had nourished the hope that I would be called and thus would be enabled to see the Czarevich, who was suffering from hip-disease. The treatment of the unhappy imperial boy consisted of being dragged around on the back of his servant, an old sailor. What agony that child must have gone through, and how much he could have been benefited by the soothing fixation treatment! The Czarevich, who would allow nobody to come near him, was poorer than the poorest child of the slums, who could get proper hospital treatment. In the end, however, the imperial sufferer could not have been saved from his terrible and untimely death by all the surgeons in the world. And yet, perhaps if he had been in better health, the whole situation might have changed.

One call to treat royalty I kept very quiet about. It reached me by way of a long-distance call from a prominent military surgeon who lived in Trieste.

"The Archduke Joseph has had the misfortune to break his leg while hunting in the Karst Mountains; he has been transported to Trieste, where he impatiently awaits your instant visit. You are not too late for the night train—come at once!

"All right, I'll be off in a minute. Thank you!"

With all my paraphernalia to meet any emergency, I travelled the whole night. I began to feel a strange misgiving, however. I knew personally the doctor who had called me, a prominent man, and it troubled me that I had not recognized his voice over the phone. During a sleepless night, my suspicion grew. At the depot, I inquired whether the Archduke had arrived at Trieste—on a stretcher, of course, as he had broken his leg. The official stared at the foreigner who was so obviously out of his wits. He answered mockingly: "The Archduke has not arrived either on his two legs or on a stretcher," and added that as far as he could tell by the morning papers, the Archduke was in Budapest and had no intention of breaking his leg in his bathroom.

I stood perplexed. I had fallen into a trap, a victim of my faith in some invidious fellow, evidently a friendly colleague. I could imagine the malicious fellow laughing somewhere to his heart's content. I had finally to admit that some one had put "a good one" over on me. But it must be hushed up—nobody must know anything about it except me and the other fellow, who would keep quiet.

It was all between me and one other. When I left the
depot to refresh myself, a tropical rain set in and drenched
me to the skin in a moment, but that helped to quench my
fury rather than to inflame it.

I never learned the name of the practical-joker. If I
had known it, I would have complimented him on his
cleverness—but only some years later.

On my winter trips after a wilfully elusive sun, I often
thought I should have to go back home to the warmer
climate of my roomy house, with its good central heating.
One of these winter trips took me to India. I crossed
and recrossed it from west to east and from north to
south, but cannot record all my impressions. Only once
did I feel overwhelmed—in Dhawalagiri, where I saw the
virginal snows of the Himalaya mountains. I was struck
by the poverty of the people, but also by their corporeal
shapeliness. The naked backs of the Hindu women showed
no lateral deviation of the spine, but a very nice model-
ing of it. Their hips projected widely enough to provide
a seat for a little son or daughter. There were no congenital hip dislocations, so far as I could observe. In contrast to their shapely trunks, the Hindus seemed all to be
more or less bowlegged. As this is not a pathological but
rather an ethnological feature, I came to the conclusion
that an orthopædic surgeon could scarcely make a living
among the Hindus!

It was in India that I was first reminded of my approaching old age. I became aware of being an object of
common curiosity to the indigenous people, not because
of my height, or my white clothes, or my large sun-helmet,
but manifestly because of my long, flowing white beard;

I was a bearer of a white flag, as it were. To make myself less conspicuous, I had my beard trimmed down to an unobtrusive, short full-beard. Former experience had shown that the sensitiveness of my skin did not allow daily shaving. When I came home my short beard aroused the curiosity of my family and my friends just as much as my long, white beard had set the Hindus wondering.

From my trip to India I brought back a stack of photographs of which only one was worth keeping and looking at sometimes. Two young Hindus had carried their dying father on a stretcher to a holy river—not the Ganges—and had set the four posts of the litter into the shallow water. They were watching over the dying man, their lips moving in prayers ending in an outcry to God's mercy. The dying man was unconscious and his agony seemed endless. The setting sun made the world glare with color, with the loving sons still singing their holy tunes at the death-bed of their father. There was something to learn in this for the foreigners who are apt to despise the Hindus. By their appearance, these two loving sons must have been *pariahs*.

Meager and not especially impressive as my remembrances of India may seem, they remain tinged with regret because I was disappointed in my hope of seeing the Lady I had fallen in love with some years earlier when I paid her a visit in Canada.

On a visit to Ottawa, I had received an invitation to the house of His Excellency, Lord Minto, then the Governor-General of Canada. I owed this honor not to his Lordship but to Lady Minto who, with her lovely daughter, wanted to know me.

When I arrived at the Governor's house, which looked

rather simple, I learned from Lady Minto that her husband was out fishing, but would be back very soon. I forgot all about the Governor-General and was rather glad that he did not make his appearance. My attention was entirely concentrated upon Lady Minto, who made me sit beside her in front of the fireplace. She was glad to see me, she said; she had heard so much about me, and so had her daughter, the rosebud at her side. "I have read and heard so much about you" was the standard introduction at that time.

When Lady Minto saw that my English was not faultless, she changed to German which she spoke to perfection, not marred but enhanced by a lovely accent. I never knew that the German language could sound so sweet as it did in the mouth of this beautiful woman. She was tall and slim, as are English sportswomen. Her radiant, rosy face was lighted by large blue eyes, her nose was a bit aquiline, her lips lovely and red.

How did she like the Canadian climate? She was not quite sure whether or not she preferred the damper and warmer climate of England to the cold Canadian sun and the biting frost. But the wife of an English official may not ask about the climate of the country her husband has to go to—even if it be from Canada to India. I was simply enchanted by the noble lady and felt that I had seen a most beautiful flower of English womanhood.

As Lady Minto had guessed, her husband was made Viceroy of India and was reigning there at the time of my visit in India. Of course, I must see Lady Minto once more. In Calcutta, where the Viceroy resided at that time, I went to the royal palace to ask for an audience with her. I was so awed by the many guards and soldiers, by the blast of trumpets and the beating of drums, by the loud commands of officers, and by the turmoil of the place, that I felt almost a sense of relief when I was told that the Viceroy and his wife had left for the mountains. I am not quite sure whether the remembrance of my visit to the quiet house of the Governor-General of Canada would not have been spoiled by an audience with the First Lady of India in the gorgeous, royal palace.

On my way to the south of India, I passed through the domain of the Maharaja Adscha of Hydarabad, at present his Majesty the Nizam of Hydarabad, one of the richest men, if not the richest man, in India. Besides his possessions of land, palaces, securities, and ready cash, he has priceless collections of diamonds and pearls, and with what he receives from his twenty million subjects, he is surely able to make both ends meet.

I had no idea at that time that many years later—to be exact, in the spring of 1935—the Nizam of Hydarabad would "come to my lane," as the Viennese phrase so aptly puts it.

All his riches could not protect the Nabob from acquiring an ailment of which only modern orthopædic surgery could cure him. So he came to Vienna for help. I was absent at the time, but considered it a great honor to my school that the Nizam went to my former first assistant, Professor Julius Hass, who had won his confidence. Hass performed a very difficult and delicate operation on his Majesty the Indian King and got a result which to the Nabob must have been most gratifying.

I am afraid that my excellent pupil knew better how to perform the operation than to ask a fee worthy of the occasion, which would have freed him from care for the rest of his life. Everybody is visited at least once in his life by good luck, but it is of no avail if you don't know how to grasp and hold it.

En route to Ceylon I had some difficulty in getting permission to sail from Tuticorin to Colombo, because I had recently been to places which were infected by cholera and plague. The inspecting physician, who knew me by my name, granted the sailing-permit after a perfunctory examination. The captain of the little steamer plying between Tuticorin and Colombo welcomed me to his boat. When asked whether he knew the name of his passenger, he answered that he read newspapers. It had not escaped his attention that a surgeon had earned a million dollars with one stroke of his hand. It seems that only business men and financial geniuses are allowed to earn money, while a physician is forbidden to get a good fee once in his life. To make a fortunate man more guilty and abominable my one good fee was many times multiplied.

My uneventful stay in Colombo was cut short by symptoms of malaria, cholera, dysentery, Madura foot, and other tropical diseases. If you burn your intestines with curry for three months with nothing but biting whiskey to cool the internal furnace, you come to understand why so many foreign residents in India become hopeless victims of Devil Alcohol. As a Westerner you are forbidden water, milk, salads, fruits, and many other good things you see in the vegetable markets. It is all right if you can travel in India in your private car, with your own cook; for sightseers with moderate means, however, India is the country where the mind may feast while the stomach suffers. The only cure is to get away as soon as possible in a North German Lloyd liner, where oriental splendor is easily forgotten over well-cooked western food—in the long run, the best means of keeping your mind easy-going and impressionable.

All memories of India faded in the course of years, but the colorful, embroidered silk curtains which I brought from the Himalayas and put up in the arches of the hall are just as nice and fresh as they were twenty years ago.

XX

THE CONFLAGRATION

"*Wer lang bittet, dem wird gegeben,*" says the Bible, to the effect that if one entreats for a thing long enough, he will receive it. But this did not apply to my wards. For a long time I had resigned myself to my fate to cure my patients without having wards. And of a sudden wards were given to me. Some large rooms, or rather large halls, hitherto parts of closed wards for internal diseases, had to be adapted for orthopædic purposes. It was a rather difficult task in which my first assistant, Doctor H, took part so fervently that in truth he must be called the builder of the new institution. Operating-room, bandage-room, waiting-room, X-ray department, a room for men and one for women, left nothing to be desired. For children, both boys and girls, a new barracks was to be erected in the ninth court of the general hospital, opposite the wards. The gymnastic room was the only item which fell short.

It was with rather bitter feelings that I took possession of my realm. What a pleasure it would have been twenty years ago! Being not far from sixty, I thought it a little late to begin studying orthopædic surgery on a larger scale. Who could foresee that even this late beginning of work on a wider field was to be denied the old man to whom former pupils in Germany, working themselves in big specialized hospitals, had given the title "The Father of German Orthopædic Surgery."

This honor, great as it may have been, did not make an

old man conceited. He very well knew that unploughed acres yield rich crops to easy labor and deny it later on to hard efforts.

Albert, my first son, whom we still thought of as one of the two yearlings upon the picture described, one day introduced a young lady to his parents and said: "I want to marry this girl." Albert was a nice healthy boy, as tall as I am. To me he seemed a reincarnation of my own father. He had become a doctor of medicine and did postgraduate work at a surgical clinic; later on he became an orthopædic surgeon, and my assistant and follower. There were no financial hindrances to the boy's wish, the less so because the young lady belonged to a well-to-do-family. Of a peculiar, one might say ethereal beauty, though she had rather a dark complexion and dark hair, she was what the French call a *"beauté journalière."* One day she looked like a blooming rose, with flushed cheeks and sparkling eyes; next day, she herself did not know why she looked so pale, faded, and sickly. The girl being of amiable character, I did not know exactly what objection I could make to the marriage; so I said "Yes." But I could not get rid of the uneasy feeling that something must be wrong with the girl, or rather with her constitution. The following year seemed to belie my apprehensions. Elizabeth grew stronger and was the picture of health, as if love had cured her of some unknown disease. The young couple loved each other dearly, but there were no children. The old doctor thought that Elizabeth was too active a woman, crazy for automobile driving, an art quite unknown among women at that time. She became the most reliable chauffeur of the house, spent much of her time in the open air, always had a good appetite, and never complained of anything. I regretted having said to Albert, when he declared that his fiancée would be she or nobody: "Are you not physician enough to see that the young lady enjoys poor health?"—the only reproach I had to offer to the future daughter-in-law. Of course, I was glad to have been wrong. The near future was to show that the silent Elizabeth was by no means the weakling the family thought her to be, and that there was more will-power in her than in many a man who boasted of it.

The years of the beginning of the second decade of the twentieth century seemed to place me at the very summit of my life. At least, I said so to myself and to my wife, after reading two letters. One had come from Bangalore, in southern India. A committee of English ladies in Bangalore were caring for the five-year-old daughter of a Christian Hindu, a teacher, and wanted to send the girl with her father to Vienna in the hope that I would not miss the opportunity of building for myself a step toward heaven! The other letter came from Perth, West Australia, from a committee of English ladies who were caring for a paralyzed child, the daughter of poor English parents, and wanted to send the child with a nurse to Vienna, if only I would make it possible by not increasing the expenses of the committee. A doctor with nothing but these two letters in hand could claim to be at the height of his professional life, even if the patients from South Africa, South America, and Japan whom he had treated should fail to convince him of his excess of modesty. By return post, I answered that I fully appreciated the honor conferred upon me by the ladies and that I would do my best to justify their confidence, which to me was worth more than any big fee that an Indian nabob or an Australian wool-king could pay me. They were to sail as soon as possible for Genoa.

Phœbe Krishna Rau Jumna Bey, with her father, arrived in Genoa before the door to the East was closed. But the ship' which was to carry the Australian patient to Europe had to stop on its way and turn its bowsprit homeward again because the earthquake which had its center in the Balkans was being felt at the Antipodes, and was teaching them that if there was still any safe place in the world, it was home. The whole world had to stay at home, except those who had to take up arms.

The murder at Sarajevo of the Archduke Francis Ferdinand and of his wife fell like a spark into the powder-magazine of European political tension, which had been accumulating during the last forty years. Just as the occupation of Bosnia had been the pivot on whose turning old Austria was eventually driven to destruction, so the murder of the Archduke drew the monarchy into the vortex of the World War which led to Austria's almost complete annihilation. Declaration of war followed declaration of war until the whole world seemed to be flaming. Though it was the fate of Austria to prelude the coming "Gehenna," Austria was much less guilty of the World War than was the Kaiser, through the alarming bombast of his speeches and his crazy rivalry with his nephew Edward. Nevertheless, it would be unjust to accuse the man of being the only and unique cause of the World War. The political tension between all European nations was at the root of it. France and England were afraid of Germany; Germany was afraid of France and Russia. All were afraid of each other. This fear could not continue indefinitely, but must needs find vent in a general explosion. Without the intervention of America, the belligerents would have bled themselves to death. America had to be the quick decider—and the victor!

In the early days of the war, there came back to my mind a half-forgotten incident in my theatre-going experiences of many years before.

I had always liked the theatre, and as a patron of the Hofburg Theatre, I could boast of friendship with most of the prominent members of the staff, such as Baumeister, Devrient, and others. But I did not neglect the private theatres. I wanted to hear a famous and lovely operetta singer who, in the rôle of *"Die Schöne Helene"* (Helen of Troy), had dared to split her gown on the left side from her waist to her ankle, so that the audience could see her beautiful, well-stockinged legs when she walked across the stage! The whole theatre-going world was in a state of mild excitement. What Fräulein G had dared was unheard of—so exacting were men in those times so far as nudity of operetta stars was concerned. For my part I did not go to the theatre to see the legs of the fair singer. Legs of all forms and sizes are the daily fare of orthopædic surgeons. I went to hear the singer.

But my attention was held by the occupants of the imperial loge—a picture which I can never forget. I sat in the parterre quite near the loge, and could watch the occupants very closely. I forgot all about the stage, and stared at the unique sight with the respectfulness of an American newspaper reporter.

In the middle of the loge sat a man who looked young when he laughed—which he frequently did—and old when the vanishing smile revealed a deeply lined, careworn face, pale and sad. He had a thin, fluffy beard; his head showed signs of beginning baldness. In spite of his brilliant uniform, he gave one the impression of a tired-out and *blasé* young man. He was Rudolf, Crown Prince of Austria.

To his left was another young man of very different appearance. He sat erect in his tight-fitting uniform, smiled complacently at the efforts of Rudolf to amuse him with the newest Viennese anecdotes, and then immediately reverted to his stern and unamiable attitude. He was young, healthy, and rather good-looking, with his curled hair and small moustache with its upward trained points. He was Crown Prince Wilhelm of Prussia, later Wilhelm II.

To Rudolf's right sat a blond, rather fat young man, somewhat bald, with a short, well-trimmed, thin beard. His full lips were more or less continuously smiling, and he looked as if he were about to kiss the whole world—a picture of self-content and good humor. He was not in uniform—he seemed not to be made for one—but wore elegant clothes, a little too large. He was Albert, Prince of Wales, later Edward VII.

As I studied the trio, my thought was: If these three young men will clasp hands and stick together, the peace of Europe will be secured for a long time to come.

When Rudolf preferred death to the throne, my hopes were still unshattered, but they fell to bits when the Kaiser chose to adopt a policy of rivalry with his uncle, who alone of the three reached the goal of his life.

Austria's declaration of war was felt by all sensible men to be a catastrophe. Nobody had the faintest idea of what a modern war would be. Most people thought that two or three frightful clashes of armies would clear the air and determine the victor. A winter campaign was considered practically out of the question. "In the late autumn we shall know how the hare runs," I used to say. But the war continued, in trenches below instead of on the surface of the earth. It was something new to the laymen and made them drop their hopes of a quick knockout, this way or the other. The first enthusiasm of the people in the streets soon died away, for the sequels of the war were felt at once. Certain commodities of life had to be renounced once and for all. There were no more private automobiles; the distance between Altenberg and Vienna was tremendously increased, and became impossible when the railroad was used exclusively for the transportation of the soldiers going to the various fronts. Mrs. L would send down coffee, cakes, cigars and cigarettes, salami sausages, etc., to every train that stopped at the station. A general request to take in convalescent wounded soldiers was answered by Mrs. L with an offer to accommodate six officers in her house. Great provisions of foodstuffs, such as coffee, tea, cakes, beans, sugar, flour, tins of every kind, tobacco, etc., had to be provided. As these officers never came, Mrs. L had a good stock with which to meet the pinch of the later war-times—the work of the ominous man Tirpitz, who because of his decision, which reeked of insanity, deserved to be the captain of the first vessel sent to the bottom of the sea. Doctor Albert Lorenz received orders to march as an officer of dragoons, although since doing his military service he had become a doctor of medicine. I assured him that his life from now on was worth just as much as a hare's in a drive-hunt. He must manage to be transferred to the corps of military surgeons. He did succeed in being sent as such to the northern front, and Elisabeth, his wife, went with him as a nurse. They were allowed to keep their automobile, and had the good fortune to be assigned to headquarters.

It was no longer possible for me to stay at my country-place. There was no light, because there was no carbide to make acetylene gas; there was no water, because there was no gasoline to drive the motor. There was no coal, no carriage, no car, and nothing to buy at the market. The family left Altenberg for the city. There, without Nature to console one, it was worse. One morning I read of a very peculiar incident. A peasant in high, dirty boots had entered the shop of the finest jeweller of the city and had bought the biggest diamond to be had in the shop.

"What incredible profligacy! The peasants are getting rich and no longer know what to do with their money," I remarked.

My wife disagreed. "The jeweller was a fool to give the peasant a good diamond for his bad money." The woman's judgment had been clearer than the man's: Mrs. L was right, for the peasant was the wise man and the jeweller was the fool. "Our money gets more and more worthless," continued Mrs. L. "You ought to sell all your state securities and purchase Swiss money!"

"If the Swiss banker were as much of a fool as the Viennese jeweller was, ready to give me his good money for my worthless money, I should feel like a crook," I retorted. Nothing was left but to stick by—and be stuck by—the Austrian money.

I had got my wards at last, but they were of no use to me. Instead of my orthopædic patients, they were filled with wounded soldiers. Wounds did not interest me very much, especially if they had been made not by a deliberate knife but by a raging bullet. I always tried to be very kind to captive wounded soldiers, because they had lost not only their health but also their home as well. On the wound of one such poor "floored enemy," I learned a very important thing. The man had got a bullet through the hip-joint. The head and neck of the thighbone were smashed to pieces; the femur had no support in the socket, but slid up and down along the surface of the iliac bone, resulting in the complete uselessness of the peasant's entire leg. From this case, I got the idea of forming an artificial head for the femur by severing this bone opposite the socket and placing the lower end in the socket, while the upper end was so displaced as to unite with the lower end immediately underneath the artificial head. In this way, the pelvis had got a firm bony support and the leg had again become a useful prop to the body. Later on, this method, called bifurcation, was frequently used in cases of irreducible old hip-dislocations, of severe cases of *arthritis deformans*, and in cases of fracture of the neck of the femur. Again it was made possible to substitute for dangerous, so-called "reconstruction" operations on the hip-joint, a harmless and mild procedure which incurred no danger. Old people with a fractured hip are not fit to undergo "reconstructions," and the "bifurcation" is a blessing to them.

The first Christmas during the war was a great feast in the wards. The patients were all stout young fellows, more or less ready to go home as invalids for life. There was music, dancing, and more to eat and drink than was good for the patients. Every one tried to make the soldiers forget their present situation.

Winter was at its worst when one morning a big car, dirty from top to bottom, drew up at my flat in the city. At the steering-wheel sat Elisabeth, clad in a rough fur coat and looking like a dirty Eskimo woman. On the bottom of the car, upon a heap of straw, coats, and furs, lay her husband, Albert, pale, haggard, but smiling. What a surprise!

"What is the matter?" I asked. "Nothing serious, I hope?"

"No longer serious now," replied Elisabeth. It developed that over-exertion in a draughty place had brought Albert down with pneumonia; the Austrian army had been retreating, and both Elisabeth and Albert had been in immediate danger of being taken into Russian captivity as prisoners of war. Elisabeth bedded her husband, who was nearly unconscious with fever, in the automobile and drove him in a non-stop run through the train of the retreating Austrian army, across the Carpathian Mountains, and through Hungary into Vienna. Albert had passed the crisis of his illness while he was being bumped and jolted in the car along war-torn roads. The courageous little woman's feat did not go unrecognized; she received five war decorations, authorized by Franz Joseph, one of them the *Goldenes Verdienst Kreuz mit Schwerten*" (Golden Service Cross with Swords), which is awarded only for bravery at the front—and Elisabeth was the first Austrian woman thus honored by the Emperor.

When Albert recovered he got a furlough of some weeks

and then was sent on to the Serbian front, where he and his wife worked in a hospital until the end of the war.

Little Phœbe of Bangalore had arrived in Vienna in the early autumn, but before undergoing treatment, she had to become acclimated to the temperature of the place. She had come in her Oriental webs of thin, floating veils; her nice brown face was framed by a tinselled net of lace, and was much wondered at by her Viennese fellow-sufferers. One day I had the honor of a visit from the Archduchess Zita, at that time the wife of the heir to the throne, Archduke Karl. When the Archduchess passed through the ante-room, I drew her attention to the little Hindu girl. The Archduchess, who liked children very much, knelt down by the exotic figure and spoke some soothing words to Phœbe. The girl of course could not understand her and seemed to be afraid; yet she uttered not a sound, but with a dignified, slow, oriental gesture of her arm, refused any further tenderness from her Imperial Highness. "Phœbe is only shy," I said, to excuse her. "She does not even know that she is English and my 'prisoner of war' for as long as the war lasts." It did not take long for Phœbe, clothed now in the Viennese fashion, to become a school-girl; she forgot all about Bangalore and her mother-tongue, and spoke the Viennese *patois* fluently. There was time enough for perfect success in her treatment.

In due time, at the end of hostilities, Phœbe and her father returned to their native home. I heard from her occasionally. After a long interval, in October 1935 dear Phœbe sent me a picture of herself, accompanied by a letter telling me that she had become a professor of languages specializing in Hindu dialects, and was teaching in a high-school.

My interesting work often made me forget that darkness reigned everywhere, in the country as well as in the city. The streets were very dimly lit, and you could scarcely find your way about. Vienna, city of light and laughter, had become a city of darkness. On a Saturday some young friends of mine had gone skiing upon the Rax Mountains. When they came back to town on Sunday night, they found Vienna deeply snowed-in and dark, with nobody on the streets. They put on their skis again and went from one end of the city to the other; it was not much different, they said, from skiing between the rocks of the mountains, for on this winter night, Vienna was as lonely as the wintry plateau of the Rax.

It was a dreary pleasure to take a walk in the streets of the city in the evening, paying visits to different churches. There were more people kneeling before the altars and praying than in the forgotten times of care-free peace. One could easily guess what they were praying for—husbands, fathers, sons, bridegrooms, all lying somewhere in the muddy trenches. Why? For what? seemed to be written upon their faces. When I came upon little shops of dealers in antiquities, I often went in and bought old altar furniture, sculptured angels, cups, tabernacles, chasubles, censers and what-not, scarcely knowing why; perhaps in reminiscence of the happy days of youth when I was a choir-singer and a ministrant, perhaps to while away the dreary time and hear the dealers lament about their sluggish trade.

The war dragged on. No one knew for certain how matters stood, for every one knew that he was being fed with lies whenever he looked at a newspaper. One thing was certain; the old Emperor Franz Josef was dying, and by his death the old monarchy was doomed to perdition, no matter how the war might end. The noble old man, who had always worked hard in the hope of keeping the monarchy together, was spared seeing his life-work go to pieces. His firm belief in his "By-the-Grace-of-God" vocation had never been shattered. He was a bit like his famous ancestor, Emperor Maximilian I, called "the last knight." Franz Josef was no less the "last knight" of his epoch, as well as practically the last emperor of the Hapsburg dynasty. But for the Spanish etiquette which was so holy to him, he might have been a lovable Viennese instead of a lonesome half-god, living above the clouds, with but few personal friends. There was only one lovely woman in the world, Katie Schratt, who was able to bring some human warmth and a gleam of happiness into the life of this lonesome recluse. What the Emperor had said of himself was true: "Nothing was spared me." His wife murdered, his son a suicide, his successor murdered, let alone other severe misfortunes in the family—the Emperor seemed sanctified by an undeserved martyrdom. When the Austrians spoke of the "sanctified person of his Majesty, the Emperor" it was no empty phrase; they meant what they said.

The old Emperor was unfortunate even in his death. By dying two years too soon, he missed the unique chance to exchange his emperor's crown for the crown of a martyr. Had he lived a little longer, long enough to see the general break-down, he would, to be sure, have been dethroned. But it seems incredible that any Austrian would have lent a hand in throwing the "sanctified person of his Majesty" out of his country. Even the fiercest social-democrat would have hesitated to inflict upon the helpless old man the necessity of leaving his historic Schloss Schönbrunn, where he had been born almost a century earlier. The old Emperor would probably have been left where he was during the numbered days of his unhappy life. If Franz Josef had not missed the crown of his martyrdom, he would be the most tragic and therefore the most famous figure in the history of mankind.

Could his successor be less unfortunate? Could he help it that his abilities were not equal to the responsibilities he had to meet, since he had not been educated to and thoroughly prepared for his high position?

The war went on and people forgot to ask: "How much longer will it last?" They forgot everything because of the more immediate problem: "What are we to live on?" The supply of foodstuffs was getting shorter and shorter. Men and women would form long queues along the street to be able to buy something at a certain shop, and after hours of waiting on the cold pavement would come home with nothing in their baskets. Woe to the man whose shoes were worn out—he had to stay at home because leather was not to be had. I went out to my country-place one day to get some old clothes and shoes to take to the city; I was going to give them away, but found that burglars had visited my house and had taken away everything not riveted down—not only clothes, but all the linen. I thought: In the end it comes to the same thing. Giving was the only pleasure you had in those dreary times. The fortunate thing was that all those who had were willing to give. Patients from near and far came and brought all kinds of foodstuffs which, of course, were shared with the needy. There was no tobacco. I grew my own in my garden and learned how to cure it. The plants were beautiful to look at, and the cured leaves equally dreadful when lighted. Better renounce it entirely than get poisoned! I was more fortunate in growing my own potatoes—a very much appreciated article in those days. Saving coal and light was an imperative necessity, and so the rooms were just as cold as the baths. Searching for a book in my library one night, I found it necessary to turn on a second electric light. Not five minutes later a spy was in the room to rebuke me as a squanderer. There were times when no street-cars ran, no railway-train started, because there was no coal available. And the war went mercilessly on.

Christmas at the clinic had lost its splendor. There was scarcely anything with which to improve the patients' meager diet. Without the gifts from my private patients, I had not been able even to light a Christmas-tree. Quite in contrast to the general carnage at the four ends of the world, I got a cablegram from Canada inquiring about the life and welfare of a little Hindu girl who presumably had been in Vienna since the beginning of the war. An English subject is not lost sight of in any corner of the world, even during the fiercest war. I replied that my prisoner of war was all right and was developing into a Viennese school-girl, as far as language, habits, and costume were concerned. Phœbe was indeed in danger of forgetting her South Indian home. Her father used to give lessons in English, and it was said of him that his exotic brown color, black hair, and white teeth had not failed to make an impression on some of his pupils. He was really a very nice man and seemed to like Vienna even in war-time not less than did his daughter Phœbe.

During the last two years of the war, Doctor Albert

Lorenz and his wife Elisabeth were, as I have said, at the Serbian front. Albert was the chief surgeon in a *Hinterland* hospital, Elisabeth his permanent assistant. Both of them had led a strenuous life all the time, but were well supplied with all they needed. Albert looked at the war no less pessimistically than did his father, who was wont to say, "Many hounds are the death of the hare," but when America entered the war, he modified his saying to: "The hare is dead already!" Among other things, Albert told me of an experience with an Austrian Archduke whom he had met at his hospital. The news had just been received that the Polish fortress with the unpronounceable name had again been taken by the Austrian army. When Albert, the chief surgeon, alluded to this news, the Archduke deigned to remark: "*Ganz nett!*" (Quite nice). The chief surgeon was furious at that answer, and thought to himself: "This man would thank the Austrian army, if it were to win the war, with a gracious 'Quite nice.' "

Though the Austrian army was defeated, it had achieved one thing worthy of being written on a special page of the history of the World War: it had stopped the sweeping wave of Russian Bolshevism. One might call that a glorious feat—and an Austrian Archduke had acknowledged it with a "*Ganz nett!*" If the ragged and hungry trench-dwellers had cried out sooner, "We won't be abused any longer," the war would soon have come to an end, and the result could not have been worse than it proved to be.

Albert and his wife came home from their hard work tired to death. Elisabeth had become thinner than she ever was. The health of the frail woman seemed to be declining. She did not complain of anything, had no pain whatsoever, but lost color and looked yellowish. Albert seemed oppressed by some clandestine grief. When I asked him what was the matter with Elisabeth, he gave evasive answers. The years of war had told upon her, though she had not spent them on the battlefields where death is meted out, but in operating-rooms where it is fought against. At last Albert told me that Elisabeth was suffering from an incurable malady—at thirty years of age. Death surprised her when she was arranging her toilette to receive some friends at her home.

I took leave of Elisabeth in her coffin, a picture not to be forgotten. Her pale face, dignified by death, was framed by a wreath of lilies-of-the-valley, her favorite flower. Her head was slightly tilted to the left side, and on her lips was the faintest smile, as if she would say: "Was I not right? Didn't I say to Albert before he married me that I knew for certain I would not live long? And yet he married me! Thanks for my short happiness at his side, though it was marred by the war!" I had never seen death look so beautiful.

XXI

LIFE IN THE ASHES

THE armistice was a relief to the defeated, regardless of what was to come. President Wilson's fourteen points read marvellously. Who did not appreciate every word of them? Even the defeated could breathe again. What was left of these noble declarations after their interpretation in Paris was not a modification but an inversion. Four million Germans, the most cultivated and richest part of the population of Bohemia, ruled by the Czechs! I had become a Czecho-Slovakian because I had been born at Weidenau in Silesia, where at that time the children of the place hadn't even known that there were Czechs living anywhere in the world. The fate of some 250,000 Germans in Southern Tyrol did not touch me personally, but aroused my deepest compassion as a German. And today—the flower of Tyrolean manhood must fight in Ethiopia, side by side with the native African troops!

Every sensible man had hoped that the new states, former parts of the great monarchy, would continue to be an economic entity to insure general welfare, because general welfare is supposed not to restrict but to enhance national independence. Instead of this, customs barriers were erected to separate neighbors, and Austria, with six million people, of whom one-third were living in Vienna, the Hydrocephalus, was left a helpless little relic of the great monarchy. The customs barriers applied not only to commercial goods but also to patients in the respective

states. People who wanted to consult a Viennese specialist were not given visas or could get them only with
great difficulty, let alone expense. Stay in the country,
our physicians are good enough for you!—was the general regulation, which obviously is wrong, because only
the best physician a patient can find is good enough
for him. Not only the specialists and leading physicians,
but also the general practitioners grew needier from day
to day. If the people grow impoverished, the physician
is the first to feel it. Things got ten times worse when the
number of the physicians in a rather diminished population was more than doubled after the breakdown. All
German physicians who had been living for decades in
the new national states were expelled from their homes
and sought shelter and bread in Vienna. There were
cases too terrible to be described.

I had never in my life touched the interest on the capital I had saved. And now, when I was in dire need, there
was no more interest to claim. My whole fortune, invested entirely in state securities, had melted into the air,
or to be exact, had been reduced to less than one four-
teen-thousandth part of its former value. Not enough to
buy a family breakfast with. The rents from Albert's
house were nothing because the social-democrats had declared the houses to be, so to speak, the property of the
tenants. It became impossible to earn the fundamental
necessities of life.

Looking back on those years, it seems that the remembrance of them is more terrible than they were in reality,
because the whole middle-class was in the same plight. I
had things which could be sold, as was the custom among
all needy people.

"We have too many pictures," I used to say to my wife.

"Try to sell them," was her reply. "Your big canvases may be very decorative, but who can accommodate them? They are without intrinsic artistic value!"

"Then I'd better keep them and sell the silver plate," I put in. "It represents quite a treasure, heaped up through nearly forty years; some gifts from thankful patients are really valuable and will fetch a good price!" At this suggestion Mrs. L would remonstrate with wet eyes. One day the question whether to keep or to sell the plate was completely solved. Burglars had once more visited the house in Altenberg and in the dead of night had carried off the whole "*Nibelungen Schatz*" without the watchdog's taking any notice. Curious to say, the sleepiness of the watchdog was more than made good by the alertness of a police-dog, who was put on the track of the burglars and found the whole treasure deposited in a secluded nook in the woods on the bank of the Danube.

So the silver-plate was retrieved, and Mrs. L no longer ventured to take more than a certain part of it from the city to the country-place. But the thieves seemed to be well informed as to these household dispositions; they called a third time for that certain part of the treasure, and this time got it for good. You cannot eat from silver plate without being molested if other people have nothing at all to eat. One of the burglars, poor devil, was caught later on. He was a one-armed war invalid. When the judge asked him why he didn't try to get some honest work instead of burglary, the boy answered: "Try to get work with both arms if you can!" And when the judge ventured: "If you had lost both your arms, you would be taken care of and would not need to steal."

"Oh, then," the boy answered, "I should steal with my teeth!"

I understood the unfortunate young man and was glad that the silver-plate had done him some good. Desperate people need not necessarily be bad people and you never know how you yourself would behave in a desperate situation.

By good luck, Mrs. L did not have to part with the rest of her silver-plate. The medical profession cannot help one man's nightingale being another man's owl, for if it were not so, physicians could not exist at all. Before the silver-plate could be put up for sale (the house in Altenberg had to be considered unsalable, unless you wanted to throw it away), it happened that a noble Italian family paid a considerable fee due me for services in pre-war time. With no offence to my debtors, I had thought this money lost, but now it meant rescue from the worst.

As if they had known of my plight, two exceptionally good cases, one in Switzerland, the other in Italy, applied for help. Regardless of cost, I was to come and treat the patients at their homes. At that time travelling through Austria meant hell! Crouched upon my suitcase, I had to spend sleepless nights in the side corridors of a third-class car. The toilets were inhabited by as many persons as could be pressed into the small closet; human necessities had to be satisfied on the steps of the platform. At the frontier the passengers were driven like cattle into a wooden shed and there examined, body, soul, and visa.

In Switzerland you felt as if you were in heaven. Although you could get a slice of real bread at the Austrian frontier-station, a delicious and opulent Swiss breakfast, with plenty of coffee and milk, fruit-jam, butter, and eggs, was awaiting the hungry passengers at the Swiss frontier-station. This breakfast alone brought to your mind the realization of what drab misery you had lived through during the last few years.

I used to combine my visits to Italy and Switzerland. In Rome, I paid a visit to one of my patients, upon whom I had operated more than ten years before. I found the lovely little girl grown up into a perfect Italian beauty, famous in Roman society as a most graceful dancer! An aunt of the young lady lived at the Italian court and told her Majesty, Queen Helena, that the doctor who had performed that miracle on her niece was staying in Rome at the moment. I was asked to pay Queen Helena a visit. This time there was no Austrian ambassador to interfere with the visit of an Austrian subject to the Queen of Italy. Eternal Rome was then the city of the Pope and of the King of Italy, and not yet the city of Duce Mussolini.

I was curious to see the splendor of the Quirinal and of the rooms in which the Popes had once lived, and I was disappointed when a lackey took me by a lift directly to the Queen's apartments. When a tall and noble lady in black, with a sparkling diamond star upon her breast, entered the vast and dimly lit room, I went forward to meet Queen Helena with an appropriate compliment and addressed her as "your Majesty." Whereupon "her Majesty" began to laugh heartily, took my hand, and patted it caressingly. When the lady turned her face to her visitor, I saw features which any queen need not be ashamed of.

"*Ma, dottore,*" the lady said laughingly, "*io non sono
la Regina, sono la zia di Miranda*" (I am not the Queen,
but Miranda's aunt).

"I hope you will not take offense because I took you for
the Queen," I laughed. Then the aunt introduced her
new friend to the Queen, whom I found sitting on a splendidly decorated estrade in the next room. The Queen allowed the visitor to kiss her hand. As far as size was concerned, this queenly hand seemed rather majestic and
reminded me of the hands of Nikita, the King of the Black
Mountains, and of one of his sons whom I had known.
Aside from her liberally proportioned family hands,
Queen Helena, even in middle age, did not belie her reputation of being one of the most characteristically beautiful Jugo-Slavian women. The conversation was somewhat
handicapped by my inability to speak fluent Italian,
French, or Serbian. Yes, the Queen had been in Vienna,
and loved Vienna; she hoped that the city would rise
from its ashes again, and so on—until the visitor was
graciously dismissed.

Though part of my money was stolen at a crowded
office in the Questura, there was still quite an amount of
good Italian banknotes for me to take home. By mistake
I missed the direct train to Montreux and got into a local
train which definitely stopped at the frontier station,
Domodossola. Just a week earlier, Senatore de Regno
had been examined as to the amount of Italian money he
had in his purse—about 2000 *lire.* Nearly the whole
amount had been confiscated, in spite of the protests of
the Senator, who was on his way to the French Riviera
and could not possibly live there on an empty purse. The
great question was, how to get the considerable amount

of money which I had on my person across the frontier.
It was practically all the money I possessed in the world;
to smuggle it over was a question of life and death. The
danger was more acute as I was nearly the only passenger
who got out of the train at Domodossola. My little trunk
was thoroughly examined. Would there also be an examination of my purse, or of my person, as was the custom
in those times?

"How much money have you?" asked the customs officer. "Count it yourself, please," was my answer. Nothing
to be confiscated! But would I be ordered to strip off my
clothes? I had taken measures of precaution to meet this
danger: I was holding the banknotes crumpled into a
ball, hidden in my right armpit. Nobody could, or would
lift my arm on account of a very painful, though pre-
tended, rheumatism in the right shoulder.

But nobody asked me to strip off my clothes. By a
slow train I proceeded the same evening to Brieg in
Switzerland, where heaven was again open to me. The
Lorenz family now had enough to live on for at least a
year. I had to rely on random earnings, since there was
no regular paid work to do.

All of life had become a haphazard game. I did not
mind, but tried to make the best of it. The adventurous
side of the new life even appealed to me to a certain degree. Nor did I wail about my lost fortune. This loss is
reparable, I said to myself, even if you are very nearly
seventy—always provided you can go on working and
continue healthy. *Are* you healthy? I asked myself. Once
in a while a flicker of lightning on the dark horizon would
make me thoughtful.

In Vienna the condition of the impoverished people improved after the American world relief activity set in, in the grand style worthy of the American people. The little barracks containing the gymnastic room of the Orthopædic Institute was transformed into a magazine for food. Sides of bacon, beans, flour, condensed milk, etc., and even clothes were sent for the poor. I stopped my orthopædic work on the children and became a dispenser instead of a surgeon. One day a picture was made of me standing in a crowd of my youthful patients, all with upturned faces, while I was busy cutting thick slices of American sides of bacon for the children, who held cans of American condensed milk in their hands. This picture will be historic later on, and will remind a happier future generation of the hard post-war times which an older, less fortunate generation had to go through. I captioned this picture as follows: "Professor Adolf Lorenz performing bloodless operations on American sides of bacon."

In Vienna, distribution committees were organized, the members of which met regularly to dispense the foodstuffs equably. Many an old professional colleague came with his bag. They had no need to feel ashamed, for we were all equally poor and the dispensers were not the givers but only the transmitters; so the receivers felt encouraged. Among them were more than a few priests. One of the members of the distribution committee was the venerable Mrs. Hainisch, who did not know that her son, Doctor Michael Hainisch, was destined to be the first President of the Austrian Republic for eight years. Another member of the committee was Herr Arthur von Rosthorn, my former pupil, then his Excellency the ex-Austrian Ambassador to China, who because of the war had fallen from his high position as a representative of his Sovereign to the position of a scantily paid pensionist. Though in need himself, his Excellency was unselfishness personified. After a meeting of the committee during which many hundreds of dollars' worth of foodstuffs had been distributed, his Excellency said to his former teacher: "Isn't it curious that we have distributed so many sacks of flour today and her Excellency Frau Rosthorn has not an ounce of it in her larder!"

"You are a fool, my dear Arthur," I said, "to renounce what you are entitled to. I myself was a fool to renounce my salary as the chief of a university institute. If you refuse to partake of the goods distributed by the committee, I condemn you to accept some stuff which I can dispose of at my own pleasure."

Another member of the committee was my honored friend Hofrath Professor Anton von Eiselsberg.

One shudders at the memories of that dreadful time. The Americans sent not only foodstuffs (the name Hoover was pronounced by all the Viennese in a different way) but helped also to restore libraries and laboratories. The Orthopædic Institute has the Rockefeller Foundation to thank for a modern set of X-ray apparatus.

Slowly the darkest times began to clear up. On my own horizon, however, the black corner got blacker still, and was more frequently shot with ominous lightning flashes. But my attention was diverted from these symptoms into a more agreeable line of thought when I found my son Konrad, who had grown up into a tall boy, studying a tiny little pamphlet.

"What is the matter? What are you studying, Konrad?"

"I want to be a ministrant at Mass!" said the boy.

"Let me have a look at the prayers," I said. There it was: *Introibo ad altare Dei, ad Deum qui laetificat juventutem meam.* "Do you know the meaning of it, Konrad? I did not, though I said a thousand times: 'To God who gladdens my youth.' . . . If I were a ministrant today, I should have to change that text and say: '*Ad Deum qui laetificet senectutem meam:* To God who may gladden my old age!'" Not a bad prayer, I thought. It would look nice printed in gold letters on green brocade and put in those beautiful baroque metal frames which I had bought a long time before.

This little incident was the genesis of something new: a little vaulted room on the ground floor of the house was converted into a chapel. All ecclesiastic furnishings and paraphernalia—tabernacles, crosses, angels, saints, candlesticks, laces, chasubles, brocades, etc.—were artistically arranged to build up three altars one of which was really a nice baroque picture worthy of being painted. The chapel that the house acquired in this way was not meant especially as a place for religious services (I preferred to pray in God's open nature), but as a little ecclesiastical museum. A prayer-mill, some pictures of Indian gods, and Mohammedan veils with the halfmoon were given a modest place in a dark corner, for I remembered having seen oriental people pray to God more fervently than Christians ever do.

But there was now no longer any doubt that for me the time had come to pray to God not only in the great open temple of nature, but also in the houses especially devoted to Him.

The lightning flashes on the black horizon increased

in force and frequency. My first theory that a temporary muscular cramp was the underlying cause of my symptoms had long since been dismissed. There was no doubt that I had become the fellow-bearer of a cross which weighs upon many men on the wrong side of fifty and beyond, no matter whether they have been good boys or bad. My age of nearly seventy corroborated the diagnosis. No constitutional disease, no cancer, God be thanked! Only, as it were, a mechanical defect in the machinery of the body. Yet it meant a rather serious operation, to which, of course, I at once consented.

I had just had a letter from New York: The Committee for the Relief of German and Austrian Children asked me to come there, the idea being that by the free treatment of poor American children I was to try to express the thanks of the Viennese children for all the benefits they had from America. I knew perfectly well that such a project could mean only a *beau geste,* but one which might appeal to the American benefactors. Furthermore, I had already entertained the idea of going to America in the hope that some of my former colleagues would, for "auld lang syne," be helpful to me and thereby help stave off my impending state of penury, which at the age of seventy seemed to me the almost unavoidable termination of my story. In fact, I had gone so far as to write to my dear friend Doctor Virgil Gibney and to several others. Unfortunate and uncontrollable circumstances surrounded my correspondence with Doctor Gibney, and further on you will see that it all turned into another unwelcome piece of publicity. At the same time, I had applied for reinstatement in the American Orthopædic Association, who had stricken my name from their list as a "war

measure." Too bad, my request was refused—perhaps the
Association did not realize that the World War had come
to an end!

I accepted the invitation on two conditions: First, money
must be sent to me, because with my own I could scarcely
reach Hamburg; nobody must ever ask me to pay it back,
but in the unlikely event that I should be able to refund
it, I would consider it my duty to do so. Second, I must
not only be alive, but also fit to work the next autumn;
they must allow me five months to recover from the operation which I had to undergo as soon as possible.

In spite of their strangeness, these conditions were accepted with best wishes for my recovery. But everything
came within a hair's breadth of going wrong. I thought
that Easter week would just be the suitable time to suffer
with Christ; I asked my friend, Professor Victor Blum,
of Vienna, to perform the operation on Maundy Thurs-
day. The surgeon excused himself; he couldn't do it on
that day, feeling not quite well himself; he asked his patient to wait until after Easter. But on Good Friday, I
suddenly fell very ill. My ailment proved to be a bilateral
flu-pneumonia. In my feverish dreams, I congratulated
Professor Blum on his foresight and prudence in not having operated upon a man who would have been doomed to
get bilateral pneumonia the day after the operation, because his patient would then most probably have died. I
did not congratulate myself upon my good luck at having
escaped a great danger, but rather upon the fact that I
would escape the operation because I was going to die of
pneumonia. We never know where death is waiting for
us—*nescimus ubi mors nos exspectat*. Sometimes death
seems to trap you, to snatch at you, and you escape with-

out any merit on your part, and often without your knowing of it. Never forget a line from Horace: "*Omnia sunt
hominum tenui pendentia filo*" (All human affairs are
hanging by a thin thread).

But this time the old man pulled through bravely. The
curious thing was that during the week of high fever the
dark corner of my horizon had become clearer; there were
no threatening lightnings at all. Had the fever perhaps
cured me entirely? Every sick physician is liable to think
as any layman would, without being ashamed of his futile
hopes. After this recovery, however, the old symptoms set
in with renewed force. The operation could not be delayed
any longer, and the day was set. Physicians are often
afraid of their colleagues as patients, because they are
obstinate and think they know better. I did not belong to
this class of patients, but acquiesced unconditionally in all
of Professor Blum's arrangements, even to his suggestion
that he perform the operation under a local anæsthetic.
On the whole, local anæsthesia is a bad business, at least in
severe operations—certain cases, of course, excepted. The
worst thing is that the patient has to live through his
operation instead of sleeping it off. I knew and felt every
act of the operation. When it came to the worst item of
it, I begged for ether, for I could stand the pain no longer.
After a few deep breaths, the drugged old man felt as if
he were painlessly melting away into nothingness. My last
thought was: If death is like this, nothing could be more
agreeable! . . . But it was not death yet. I awoke before
the dressings were finished, to accept the congratulations
of the surgeon and of my son, Doctor Albert Lorenz, who
was a great solace to me in the bleak hour.

The first three days after the operation, the slightest

movement caused me pain. I had known happier days than these. Although my convalescence was uneventful, I had to put in some restless nights in a condition of half-consciousness. My mind seemed to be set free from my ailing body, and seemed to rove over space and time, hovering over eternal questions and solving them on the spur of the moment.

Soliloquy: You will die and your family will be left in misery! Most probably, but can I help it? I did my best. . . . Don't you fear punishment? What for? As far as I know, I never did anything to deserve punishment. . . . Don't you hope for some reward? Oh, no, I am sure I don't deserve it. . . . What about your life after death? I am not so sure about that. . . . Don't you believe in immortality? Oh, yes, my body is certainly immortal, as far as the material it is made of is concerned. . . . And what about the immortality of your soul? Oh, there is no doubt of it, my soul is immortal because it is God-like. The faint God-like spark which animated my body until it was worn out can't die because it is a part of God. . . . Is it not a blessing to know that one is immortal? *Taisez vous!* I can't conceive a thought more ghastly, more terrible and desperate, than that of living through all eternity. In the end, all human beings condemned to eternal life would be driven to try suicide. Nobody but God can conceive eternity. Human beings are crushed by the mere thought of it. . . . And yet, you believe in immortality? Yes, I believe in it because its terror dissolves in the thought that we shall not be conscious of our eternal life! . . . What is the use of being immortal if you know nothing of it? Please stop torturing me, my head aches and I am not quite sure where I am, who I am, what I am here for or what is the matter with me.

I felt a tug at my arm and heard Mrs. L say: "I thought it better to wake you, to put an end to a torturing dream." I tried to sit up, but the pain caused by the brisk movement told me at once where I was and what was the matter with me.

Under the solicitous care of Professor Blum, I made a quick recovery and six weeks later was fit for work again. I had been in the deepest hole a man can be in—that of being old, sick, and poor. "*Alt, krank und arm, dass Gott erbarm!*" (Old, sick and poor, God have mercy)—this German saying clung persistently to my mind. Both gloves were gone. To be old, sick, and poor is the most terrible trial that can befall a man—and yet I was not hopeless. Get well again, get fit to work again, and old age and poverty lose their terror. Old age cannot be remedied, but it can be made happy, provided it be filled with work. The working man will never be a poor man. Work breaks poverty. To be able to work means to be healthy. "Time is money" is a false saying. It should be: "Good health is wealth!" By the blessed aid of surgery, I had regained my good health; I did not mind my old age nor my poverty any longer; was there not the prospect of overcoming the latter obstacle through my trip to America?

XXII

RECONQUERING AMERICA

I T was agreed that I should travel in the company of Mr. Anton Wedl, a Viennese who lived in New York as an importer of Austrian goods, and of his charming wife, Mrs. Magda Wedl, who has to play an important part in this story later on. Wear and tear, thefts, and the impossibility of obtaining new clothes had made the wardrobe of the old doctor more than scanty. Surveying my suits, I found only one worth being turned about. It looked very poor, nevertheless. As you have to be doubly careful of borrowed money, I accepted Mr. Wedl's invitation to be his guest as far as Cherbourg. Paris with its lights and luxury impressed upon me that I had been living in a dim, poor nook for the past six years. The splendor of the new SS. *Paris* taught me that refinement had not come to a standstill in this part of the world. *La cuisine était merveilleuse!* There were revelations without end for a man accustomed to the Viennese war diet. The most inviting feature upon each table in the dining hall were two open bottles of wine, one red, the other white. Just common ordinary *"vin de France,"* not good enough to be educated and sent to foreign countries, destined to be consumed on French soil. But how delicious, how helpful in digesting French delicacies!

On the last day of the passage the tables assumed, as it were, a stern countenance. The picture had lost its color; all was white, even the two bottles with their contents— tepid water. It was the first welcome of a dry country to a newcomer who had as yet no conception of what prohibition meant. A rather agreeable side of it would be no longer to hear: "Have a drink, Doctor!" After a few days on shore, I had to learn one of its many drawbacks: A rather rich and not over-carefully cooked diet, sprinkled with ice-water, is apt to make even a good stomach rebel after a while, let alone the sensitive stomach of an old man who is still a bit shaky from a severe illness. After a few days, I got sick. For me, prohibition and not alcohol (one small glass of a light wine) was the poison. But everything comes to an end, and so did prohibition.

I put up at the old Murray Hill Hotel, where the management still remembered me. Mr. S was glad to offer me a nice sitting-room and bedroom, with bath. "Thank you very much, Mr. S, a small back room will do for me," I said. "This time I am a doctor of the poor." But Mr. S insisted upon giving his old customer of twenty years ago a nice front room and on charging him no more than for the back room. I had to thank the management of the hotel not only for this but for many other kindnesses.

My arrival in New York was accorded unexpectedly eager attention by the papers, and the comments were rather friendly. The newspapers, which always had been kind to me, gave me a surprisingly warm welcome. I was even given a title that was far beyond my ambition: "Lorenz comes to America as an 'Ambassador of Peace and Mercy'"! What higher achievement could a man strive for? However, one of the greatest calamities that can befall a physician is to be termed a "miracle man," and have the ever-zealous American reporters take notice of him. At that time there were no gang wars, no Lindbergh kidnappings, no Hauptmann trials, and the four-thousand-mile journey of an old man seeking to mend the broken links of two nations and to assure for himself a livable old age seemed to appeal most dramatically to the American press. I could not leave my hotel without being thoroughly photographed, and curious crowds followed me wherever I ventured. Usually I had to enter my hotel by a side door. I was photographed examining patients, and to my utter surprise and astonishment newspaper reporters and photographers were even permitted to enter the portals of the operating-room in reputable hospitals in order to photograph and interview me while I worked. When occasionally I refused an interview, I was given the choice of granting it or having the reporter write his own statement—it was much the lesser of the two evils to grant the sought-for interview! In no country in the world do newspaper reporters and photographers enjoy such freedom as in America.

But there were also opinions less pleasant to read. A very conspicuous physician of Philadelphia, once a staunch friend of mine, wrote a furious article. He denied ever having been a friend of mine and wanted to have nothing to do with the Hun! Some utterances were even more straightforward: "Go home, Teuton, we don't want you." Others said that the "Ambassador" so far had done nothing for his science; at the best, he could only be called a routinist. I was prepared for even worse reproaches, but was spared them. I did not take such welcomes much to heart, because they came from the rank and file of my dear colleagues, who could not resist venting their war psychosis. To some old men who seemed to be over-excited, I would say: "Spare your breath vociferating; better use it to thank God for the blessing that you still see His sun." It was not to be hoped that physicians would be entirely immune from war psychosis, but a humanitarian vocation should at least have made them less likely to be infected with the war mentality. If the links between fighting nations be broken, the physicians should hold on, because they, in spite of their patriotism, should be able to feel themselves cosmopolites, their noble vocation being just as international as are human ailments. It cannot be denied that the physicians in the whole world, with due exceptions, have failed to acknowledge this point of view.

I did not worry on account of the contradictory newspaper articles, and waited quietly for the excitement to abate. I knew that my mission would meet with difficulties, and I felt reassured when, time and again, I was recognized in the streets by the people, to be surrounded by young boys and girls who shouted: "Don't worry, Doctor Lorenz, let them cry, the people are with you." The great question was: Which hospital would grant me its facilities for seeing patients? In the meanwhile I was besieged by them in the lobby of the hotel, and the management justly protested: "We are not a hospital, but a hotel!"

One morning a pleasant young man who called himself Doctor X forced his way through the crowd to introduce himself to me as a messenger from the Commissioner of Health, Doctor Royal S. Copeland, who sent his compliments to me. The message of Doctor X was, of course, highly appreciated by me, the more so as Doctor X was to put himself at my disposal. He at once became my secretary and proved to be very useful. After protracted negotiations, at last I got permission to see patients at a certain hospital. With my new secretary, I drove there every morning, to see, in crowded wards, at least a hundred patients who wanted to be examined and advised.

The work was exhausting, the overheated air in the wards unbreathable and nauseating. For many days I had been living on tea and biscuits because my stomach was not only out of order, but refused to work entirely. Several times I had to interrupt my work and lie down or I should have fainted. I felt sure I would die, then and there. The curious thing was that it did not matter to me: it would be, in a sense, dying in the battle against human disabilities. At my age of seventy, it would not have been too early, either.

Lying exhausted on a couch behind a curtain, I overheard a discussion between two of the leading physicians of the hospital. One of them spoke in my interest. "It is a shame," he said, "to let the old man ruin himself. No man can stand this kind of work for any length of time. He must have a day of rest once in a while." The other man showed less concern about my shattered health when he replied: "Let the old fellow work; he won't live much longer anyhow!" (And that was over fifteen years ago!) No wonder this aroused my anger, and I tried to conceal the condition of my health as much as I could. The number of patients increased from day to day. They stormed the hospital so that policemen had to intervene to maintain order. They waited patiently for many hours, had to spend the night somewhere if they had come from out-of-town, were accommodated in the hospital and were charged for it. At the same time the management demanded of the patients I saw a donation for Viennese children, from ten cents up, according to their means. Many refused to pay for a free consultation. It got into the papers and the consultations had to be stopped. As it was impossible to give the donations back, the amount was delivered to Mr. Wedl, who was cashier of the Lorenz Fund for the Relief of Poor Viennese Children. So it came about that the free patients seen in the hospital contributed to poor Viennese children.

As no other hospital would open its wards to my patients, I had to consider my mission a failure. I wanted to go home—I was so sick and felt so miserable that I was more or less indifferent to everything. In this stage of affairs, my friends Mr. and Mrs. Wedl intervened. "We brought you here," they said, "and we must take you back home safe and sound." And it was Mrs. Wedl who, by her art of cooking nice dishes with sweet butter, disavowed medical science and its phenic acid and pills and restored her thankful friend to full health. Since God has mercy on confessing sinners, Saint Volstead cannot possibly be less gracious if it be confessed in due contrition that the ice-water on the table was four-quarters light wine, proving the truth of what Saint Paul said: "Use a little wine for thy stomach's sake"!

By and by the broken spirit of enterprise became alive again in the old man. I laughed heartily when I was told that my secretary, Doctor X, was not a doctor, but a well-known swindler who had duped, among others, an Afghanistan Princess, introducing her to the President of the United States in the disguise of an officer in the navy. This was, of course, considered his chief crime. I had rather liked my secretary on account of his willingness and pleasant behavior, and the boy had not even asked a fee for his services. "Why should he have asked one," said Mr. Wedl, "if he could take it? Was not the secretary also your cashier?"

More serious was the blow dealt me by the Board of

Medical Examiners at Albany, who said, "Your practice in New York is illegal, you have no license!" This time I was not to be arrested, and was told that I could go on with my charity work, but that I must not see any private patients. As I could not live on the crisp air of New York, I immediately applied to be admitted to the examination. A bit late at seventy, I thought, but hoped that the examiners in Albany would be no less human than their colleagues in Chicago had been twenty years before. I thought of suggesting to them the expedient of an examination for Docentship as it is used in Vienna, and as the examiners in Chicago had done without their knowing.

In the meanwhile, I was co-operating in Newark with one of my friends, Doctor Keppler. In Kings County Hospital, in Brooklyn, I had to work under the blinding glare of electric lights while the movie operators worked on me. These moving-pictures were much applauded in all American theatres as proof that my mission appealed to the American people. A year later I operated in Vienna on a patient who came from southern Chile. "How did you get my name?" I asked. "I saw you operate in the movies at Valparaiso," was the answer. And so successful was that operation recorded by films, that the young man who had suffered with congenital club-feet came to me in 1935 and said that he was joining the United States Navy. Not a vestige of his handicap remained.

Having some leisure now, I granted myself an audience with President Theodore Roosevelt at his small iron-grated residence in the cemetery at Oyster Bay, Long Island. American graveyards are an eye-sore to Europeans, for they lack entirely the poesy pervading well-cared-for European cemeteries, as the secluded, impressive, dignified resting-places of one's ancestors. Roosevelt's grave made me very sad: in spite of the heavy iron bars which surround it, the grave looked neglected. Two small discolored American flags on tiny little staffs flanked one side of the place where the grave was supposed to be, while the corresponding two flags at the other side had been swept to the ground by the wind. No withered flowers, as a sign of loving care. I thought of my father's grave in a beautiful old churchyard in Styria. All year round, flowers are blooming upon the tomb, and at this time of the year the last chrysanthemums would be fighting against the winter's frost. I soliloquized: Well, Teddy, here I am again, whom you once greeted as the famous doctor. When I saw you at that time, I didn't think I should outlive you. But were you really as strong and healthy as you looked? Your force of will did a great deal to strengthen an originally not over-exuberant health. Did I not remark some scars behind your strong jaw? How could you succumb to the first blow dealt to your constitution which you had mastered successfully for so long a time! Well, *omnes eodem cogimur*—we all are driven to the same place, whether we be emperors or presidents or just human beings!

At Sagamore Hill, Mrs. Theodore Roosevelt said she was glad to see me and gave me as a souvenir the family photo entitled: "Three Generations: Three Theodores"— the senior, the junior, and the third. Mrs. Roosevelt showed me over the house. President Roosevelt's study, a big room richly adorned with African hunting trophies, was not heated.

"Coal is too precious nowadays," remarked Mrs. Roosevelt.

"I feel very much consoled" I put in, "for the fact that the big hall in my house has been below zero in every winter, since the war." I told Mrs. Roosevelt that I saw her husband the last time in Vienna at a reception at the American embassy, and that Mr. Roosevelt had recognized me at once.

The Board of Examiners in Albany graciously and unanimously granted me a New York license by making my Illinois license valid for New York State, a courtesy which I felt very thankful for. I now had the license, but as yet no working-place in New York. But for the protection of Doctor Royal S. Copeland, I would have had to go home. Commissioner Copeland opened the palace of the Board of Health to my patients. One story of the huge house was converted into the largest office I ever had. To save time, it was arranged that the patients were to be put on many linen-covered couches ready for examination. Stenographers followed me as I went from one patient to the other and noted my diagnosis and advice. On some cases I operated myself. The great bulk of the patients were advised to apply to excellent local specialists who, of course, were to be free to accept or reject my advice. That is the way in which I injured the practice of the local physicians!

I could not undertake to operate on the hundreds and hundreds of patients who wanted to be advised, but I was really surprised to observe that the great majority of the patients considered themselves hopeless cripples, whereas their condition could at least be greatly improved by harmless operations. I considered it my chief duty to encourage these patients and to advise them to get the proper treatment. I even wrote letters to professional friends of

AN EXAMINATION IN THE CONSULTATION ROOM AT THE BOARD OF HEALTH,
NEW YORK, 1921

PROFESSOR ADOLF LORENZ DISTRIBUTING AMERICAN BACON BY A BLOODLESS
OPERATION TO STARVING CHILDREN AT HIS VIENNA CLINIC IN 1922

twenty years before, recommending patients who could profit greatly by a simple treatment. One answer to a letter to a former friend whom I thought to oblige, I have kept as evidence of the narrow-mindedness of educated people when they misconceive patriotism. The man refused to see a patient sent by me because he deemed it beneath his dignity. Can foolishness be pushed to a greater degree?

When I thanked Doctor Copeland most heartily for his protection, the Commissioner said that he got hundreds of editorials from newspapers throughout the country praising his attitude toward me. In truth, there were some other friends who had remained courteous to me. And one fine morning I received some letters which had been forwarded to me from Vienna. Among them was a most friendly note from Doctor Virgil Gibney, a reply to my aforementioned letter which had been written to Doctor Gibney some time before my departure from Vienna. I unjustly had misinterpreted Doctor Gibney's silence; his reply and I had passed each other on the broad Atlantic. Immediately I got in touch with him by telephone and after due explanations was soon on my way to his office, where we had a long and friendly talk during which he pointed to my picture and told me that all during the war he had not turned my face to the wall. Then he told me, pointing to his examination-table, how well he remembered the day when the Chicago princess had sat on that table and he had told her father that there was but one man in the world who could cure the little girl—and that was Professor Adolf Lorenz. The king wanted to know whether it were possible to bring that doctor to America, and Doctor Gibney told him that he would try.

Doctor Gibney asked me whether I would like to inspect his new hospital—new since my last visit—the New York Hospital for the Ruptured and Crippled. I told him that I would be very glad to do so, and an appointment was made for the following week to inspect that institution with Doctor Gibney. Several days later, I was surprised to receive a note from Doctor Gibney reluctantly telling me that he must rescind the invitation, as the hospital's staff objected to having me even enter the building. Even my presence was anathema. Although this was to be kept quiet, again an enterprising, wideawake newspaper reporter found out, perhaps with the help of a talkative member of the staff, and soon the whole press blurted out the story that the staff had threatened to resign and walk out if I came to the hospital. Just another instance of how publicity was thrust upon me, publicity which the millions of a Rockefeller or a Mellon could not have gained for commercial enterprises. Yet I paid, yes, paid dearly for it all. Something I did not want was eventually paid for in the antagonism of my colleagues, who were all so ready to believe the worst.

Doctor Fred Albee, the leading bone surgeon of New York, did not deem it beneath his dignity to help a colleague in his troubles. My friend and pupil of post-war days, Doctor Walter Galland, also stood staunchly by me and smoothed the way in a manner never to be forgotten. To him I owe much thanks. The Muschenheim family, of Hotel Astor fame, opened their home to me, as formerly.

One morning my work at the Board of Health was interrupted by the ceremony of the presentation of the New York license. To spare me the trouble of visiting different offices in order to put my signature in thick folio volumes, the officials had the courtesy to bring the load of books with them. Each act of the ceremony and the final congratulations were duly photographed, and all were very happy. I had to see approximately a hundred patients in the forenoon and be very careful about my diagnosis and advice, as any mistake might turn out to be a snare.

Before I left Vienna on my mission, the Mayor of my city had provided me with a letter of introduction to the Mayor of New York. To deliver this letter, I had applied for an audience with Mayor Hylan. After this was granted, and when I, in the company of the editor of the New York *Staats-Zeitung*, Mr. Victor Ridder, was driving downtown, I was informed that this audience would not be what I had hoped for—a private affair in the Mayor's office—but a great manifestation in the big hall with many Germans present as guests. And again I found myself unprepared to answer an unexpected speech. It was the only time I was glad of the New York traffic, which grew heavier the nearer I came to the City Hall. The many long stops left me time to pencil some notes and catch-words upon my cuff. The shorter, the better, I thought.

The big hall was crowded with people, mostly Germans, who greeted their fellow countryman frantically. I was told that this was the first mass meeting of the Germans in New York since the war. Mayor Hylan, who looked very democratic, availed himself of the occasion to express his high appreciation of the work of the distinguished guest, which appealed to the American people throughout the country. And then, with harsh words, he chastised those who had had the impudence to call the "Ambassador of Peace" a Hun or Teuton, and wanted to drive him away. Teutons and Huns, he said, were very brave people in their time, but today were beyond good and evil and no longer appropriate for insinuating an insult. No guest of the City of New York should be insulted; they wanted New York to be a hospitable city. "Don't worry"—this to me as the bearer of the letter—"about those damned fools, let them rave! Rest assured that among the one-hundred-and-ten millions of American people, one-hundred-and-nine million and ninety-and-nine-hundred-thousand are of the same opinion as the Mayor of the City of New York in this respect."

In my reply, I thanked the Mayor very heartily for the honor bestowed upon me on this occasion. "I know very well," I said, "that my work can be estimated only as a symbol of good will. If this good will should be appreciated by the American people as a proof that the Austrians in their hearts could not possibly ever have been real foes, then my mission as 'ambassador of peace and mercy' can be considered a success. And in expressing the good will in the only way left to me, that is to say, by my efforts as a physician, I have followed that principle which should be inborn in all physicians—to act as a link between nations, as fighters against the international ailments of humanity. As far as worrying is concerned, my American patients don't leave me time to worry." And when I shook hands with the Mayor, I felt as if the Viennese were shaking hands with the New Yorkers. The ceremony was quite a success, and the culminating phase of handshakes with the Mayor and with each member of the gathering of course was duly photographed.

One day of the week was given to patients in Newark, in the city dispensary. This little service was rewarded in a really royal way by the Mayor of Newark, Mr. A. Archibald, who with Mr. Myron W. Morse, Flag Custodian, arranged a splendid reception in the magnificent city hall of Newark. The climax of the festivity was the presentation to me of a costly silken embroidered American flag, while hundreds of school-children, lovely girls and boys, waving tiny American flags, sang the national anthem in clear young voices. I thanked the children not so much by words as by emotional palpitations of my old heart, which on this occasion proved to be young enough to withstand so great an excitement. Dear Mr. Archibald could not be present on account of a headache, which unfortunately was most ominous, the first symptom of a fatal disease. With the flag I received the key of the City of Newark. The honor of the presentation of the American flag was rivalled by some precious letters which were read to me as part of the ceremony.

Ex-President Woodrow Wilson wrote: "I hope that when the flag is presented to Doctor Lorenz, you will give him my most cordial greetings and tell him how much I share with my fellow countrymen the great admiration they all feel for his genius and for his warm and generous service to suffering mankind. I wish I might share with you and the other citizens of Newark the pleasure of welcoming him in person. He may rest assured that America entertains for him an affectionate admiration, and appreciates to the fullest the great and unselfish service he has rendered."

If the recipient of such a letter does not feel proud, he belongs among the hopelessly modest.

I liked best of all the letter from President Warren G. Harding, because it laid stress upon a merit which I claim without running the danger of being called presumptuous. In his letter, the President expressed his thanks to the committee for calling his attention to the presentation to Doctor Adolf Lorenz of a specially made American flag and asked that they signify to Doctor Lorenz, on the occasion of the ceremony, that he had desired to associate himself with the sentiments which this presentation so effectively suggested. The President continued: "I cannot but feel that in coming to our country and doing this fine work of humanity and charity, he has been contributing much to the re-establishment of those friendly and sympathetic relations which so long subsisted between his own country and ours, and whose full restoration in the new era of peace, we all most sincerely desire."

In reality the aim of my mission was to help, in the only way possible to me, to mend links which had been broken much against the will of every sensible Austrian. That my mission had succeeded was thus testified to by the highest authority, the President of the United States. This is a feat of which an old physician rightly may be proud.

After the presentation of the flag, wrapped in its glistening folds I hurried down the stairs to embrace as many of the children as possible, only to find them gone back to school—a drop of bitterness in the cup of joy, due to the many handshakes I had to endure on my way down to the floor of the hall. But the picture of the children with their fluttering flags will forever cling to my memory.

With the flag I received a calligraphed address which read in part:

"Citizens of the City of Newark, State of New Jersey, through the school children here assembled present to you our National Emblem, the AMERICAN FLAG. The beautiful silk in this flag and the assembling of its various colors were all arranged within the boundary lines of our beloved State of New Jersey. This emblem which represents Sacrifice, Honor, Purity, Courage, Love, and Unity and to which you have expressed such beautiful sentiment, may, we trust, inspire yourself, if possible, to more wonderful deeds of helpfulness in alleviating suffering and distress.

"Seldom do we find men whose God-given talents are so freely given to relieving the afflicted, which deed symbolizes the best instinct in man. May God continue your strength that your noble work may go on for many years. This is a slight tribute to you for your loving sacrifice in the interest of humankind and particularly the children."

The key of the City of Newark, adorned with silken ribbons, is a souvenir no less precious to me than the specially made embroidered silken flag, which beautifies the balcony at the small side of the hall in my house, the same balcony which commands the glorious view of the valley of the Danube—a unique place of honor. Many an American has paid his respects to this flag, whose beauty can rival that of any other flag hoisted in the United States.

Though with the help of my friend, Mr. Wedl, I was very busy augmenting my own fund for the Relief of Viennese Children, I had to accept invitations from other committees whose aim was the relief of German and Austrian children. I had to give some popular lectures concerning my medical work, which were made more interesting by moving-pictures. On other occasions, such as one in a Methodist Episcopal church, to make my speech more attractive I took with me two pictures which had been made in Vienna by Mrs. Strauss, the wife of my assistant, Doctor Strauss. My sermon, or rather lecture, in the church, which was crowded with people, was apparently to be the last item in a concert composed of songs, the melodies of which were first sung and then whistled. After the musical performance, the speaker of the evening was introduced to the congregation by the clergyman, the Reverend Mr. Reisner, and heartily welcomed by them. I felt that I had to win the favor of the many ladies present in order to induce them to loosen their purse-strings at the end of the performance. I told them something of the history of my youth. I hoped it would not matter to them that I was a Roman Catholic, and as such had wanted to become a Catholic priest. As a boy I had ministered to the priest at Holy Mass and later on I wanted to be a Benedictine monk. I told them I had been within a hair's breadth of becoming a monk, and that today I might have been an abbot instead of a children's surgeon. But it is given to only a few to direct fate; most of us are driven by it. And yet, it seemed that fate had not denied me all my juvenile hopes after all, because, now past seventy, I found myself standing in the pulpit of a church!

I had to excuse myself for giving a lesson in geography to my audience before proceeding to the chief subject of my lecture—the dire need of the middle-class people of Vienna and their children. I produced my two pictures— old Austria before the war, and new Austria after the war. The artist had outlined the boundaries of the old monarchy. In one picture the whole space within the old frontiers was occupied by a richly clad lady who was meant to be Empress Maria Theresa in her imperial robes. Her

head, situated in the center of what was formerly the
province of Bohemia, bore the imperial crown. Her left
arm, lengthened by a sceptre, was extended through what
was once the province of Galicia, as if encircling the arch
of the Carpathian Mountains. Her right hand pointed
westward toward beautiful Salzburg and the Tyrol. And
Vienna, with some anatomical latitude, could represent
the heart of the imperial lady Austria, while her costly
gown and scarf covered the rest of the space, reaching
down to the Adriatic Sea as far as the Bocche di Cattaro.

"That was the old monarchy," said I. "Now look at the
new Austria, a poor fragment of the old glory. The proud
empress has become a shrivelled old woman clad in rags,
who, with bowed head, curved back, fettered hands, and
extended legs, sits within a narrow cage. Her head is
very large, like a hydrocephalus, with another geographical allowance representing Vienna; the fettered hands of
the woman seem to protect the western provinces, while
her outstretched legs, shackled by the valley of the river
Inn—practically all that is left of the Tyrol—reach to
the Lake of Constance. The little cage within the huge
expanse of white space resembles a narrow automobile
body containing a fettered passenger, an automobile without wheels and without engine."

After this demonstration of the status of the new Austria, I gave a picture of the misery prevailing there at
that time. At the close of the lecture, the audience contributed toward the alleviation of Austrian suffering,
every one according to his means. There were no millionaires among them, and yet the collection was worth while.

I accepted the invitation of the Mayor of Detroit, Mr.

Couzens, a close friend to Commissioner Copeland, and now, like him, a United States Senator, to see patients in a hospital in Detroit. I was conducted there by a representative of the Mayor, who welcomed me at the depot. The exercise began with a breakfast for which there had to be prepared not only dishes by the cook, but also speeches by the host and the guests. I was aided in my rather hard work by my temporary assistant, Doctor Van Ward. I had to see not only patients but also college boys and girls in their schoolrooms, and address them there. Those were very poor, extemporized speeches, but they met with frantic applause from the youngsters. Here, as in New York, I was impressed by the fact that so many fair and lovely children had received no treatment because their parents thought that there was no helping them. By advising treatment, I had occasion once more to injure the interests of local practitioners.

Of course, I had to pay a visit to the Ford Hospital as well as to the Ford automobile factory. I thought the hospital one of the finest and best equipped I had ever seen. As Ford-Father had just left for Washington, Ford-Son Edsel was the host at a lunch in the hospital, which, to tell the truth, did not measure up to the marvellous equipment of the kitchen. When I saw Edsel and the other guests enjoying it, I cursed Viennese gastronomy, but could not help it. Welcomed to the hospital by Edsel, I replied somewhat in this strain:

"I am not sure whether I heard the name of Henry Ford twenty years ago on the occasion of my first visit to America; but today there is no schoolboy in this great country who does not know the name of Henry Ford, and who has not some knowledge of the machinery of the Ford car.

But America is not wide enough for his name, which has become a household word throughout the whole world. And this is due not so much to the unsurpassed qualities of the Ford car—not even Ford himself would be positive on that score—but to a new branch of science inaugurated by the creative genius of Henry Ford, who has built up his work on purely scientific principles and in so doing has become a teacher to the whole industrial world, a world prophet, not only through his industrial achievements, but also through the high ethics of his principle, 'Live and let live.' He has shown the way to reconcile employee and employer, whose interests are inseparably linked together. In one word, Henry Ford is the father of 'practical' science, which means more to humanity than many a branch of theoretical knowledge."

Edsel thanked me in the name of his father, to whom he said he would relate the happenings of the day.

Visiting the Ford factory, I saw what I had read about many times, and yet I could only marvel at the watch-like precision. The idle visitors walking along beside the moving belt took some casual cuffs in their ribs when they got in the way of the workers, who made no distinction between Ford-Son and one of his guests. The bright, comfortably, but very simply furnished study of Ford-Father seemed even more interesting than the gigantic workshop. In this quiet place the new science was hatched; in the noisy workshop it lived its useful life.

I received a welcome letter from Henry Ford which I consider a very precious document. It reads:

My dear Doctor Lorenz:

It was with very great regret that I found myself absent from Detroit at the time of your visit to our hospital.

Through your courtesy, however, I have been furnished with a copy of your remarks on that occasion and I desire to say, in return, that for your personality and work I have a very high admiration. It is my opinion that your visit to our country has been a strong influence toward more human understanding between the nations. Our people have felt something of your spirit and your strong desire for peace, and I am sure that you had many evidences that your desires were reciprocated. I hope yet to be able to meet you and talk with you face to face.

Sincerely yours,

HENRY FORD.

Whenever I look at the sympathetic face of Henry Ford in his photograph, I wish that Ford-Father may realize his hope of accomplishing as much and even more after his sixtieth year of life than he did before. His letter was a great satisfaction to me because, like President Harding, he had testified to the fact that my visit to America had had a conciliatory effect upon the relations between the United States and my own country.

I paid medical visits to Buffalo and Trenton with the same good intention and with the same good result, irrespective of the fact that—as I had to learn—the local medical profession is not necessarily in the same boat with a well-meaning mayor.

I cannot forbear mentioning a very insignificant theatre experience. Al Jolson, the would-be negro (whom I from the first moment admired as an actor and singer as well as a *conferencier*), took notice of me in an audience and improvised the following acknowledgment:

"Who is the best crap-shooter?"

"Doctor Lorenz, because he knows best how to handle the bones!"

In Vienna this kind of wit is called "*Kalauer*" and whoever undertakes to tell it first asks his audience to lay hold of some substantial object so as not to be floored by it. An American audience is not so exacting, but appreciates every kind of wit. And so did the man at whom it was aimed, and I liked Jolson the better for it.

XXIII

DIMPLES AND INDEMNITY SUITS

In America I was consulted not only as a "bonehandler" but also as a beautifier of the softer parts of the human body, especially the face. Among my many letters was one from a young lady who had only one dimple in her cheek, while her twin sister had two of them. She would so love to be completely like her sister, even as far as the dimples were concerned. "Mother dear is willing to spend some hundreds on the missing dimple. She is sure that Doctor Lorenz can comply with her wishes." It is curious, but true, that beauty and stupidity sometimes go together. In this case "Mother dear," as well as her twins, must have been of extreme beauty! I wrote, through my secretary, that surgery causes scars which are but poor dimples, and therefore I couldn't make dimples which would satisfy the young lady. But "Mother dear" could make lots of vanished dimples reappear in the faces of underfed Viennese children by a contribution to the Lorenz Fund—an invitation which disappointed "Mother dear" did not accept. I wonder if the twin found a surgeon to risk the experiment. Both parties would then merit punishment. Surgery is disgraced in the service of mere— often misconceived—beauty. To lift an old face and give it an unnatural grin ridicules old age and mars its beauty, for old age, in good health, has a beauty of its own. Dignified old faces, though furrowed by lines dug in by the years, are often more beautiful in old age than they were in youth.

Even the legitimate practice of his profession is full of pitfalls for the orthopædic surgeon. Over the head of every surgeon dangles the sword of the indemnity suit. Over the head of an orthopædic surgeon hangs a sharper sword, on a thinner thread, than that which threatens the general surgeon. The patient feels that he should experience not even the slightest disappointment under the care of the orthopædic surgeon. If he thinks that he has been damaged by an orthopædic operation (it need not be true), he shoots a summons to his unsuspecting doctor.

Just as the most skillful egg-dancer must crush an egg once in a while, so the most experienced surgeon must sometimes make an unlucky stroke, overlook something which scarcely could be foreseen, or work on a patient who should have been left alone on account of a delicate constitution. The surgeon must be heavily insured to feel easy at heart when he offers his neck to a snare which can ruin him financially.

It would be a good thing for the medical profession, and for surgeons especially, if their work could be done without regard to money, be it fee or indemnity. The physician should be paid out of public funds so that he has no other care than the welfare of the patient. This communistic idea looks very fine, but has its drawbacks, as communism has in general.

In spite of my utmost precautions, I had to face indemnity suits which, summed up, would have totalled more than half a million dollars.

The most flagrant case happened in New Jersey some

four or five years ago. One day in a hospital in Newark a man slipped a paper into my hands.

It was a summons. The case called for payment of $450,000 for damages by an operation. A like paper was handed to my collaborator, Doctor X, with the same demand.

"But I do not know the patient or the man," I said, nonplussed.

"He claims that you not only know him, but that you advised and performed his operation," retorted the deliverer of the message. I repeated that I knew nothing of the man or of his ailment. On the day of his operation I had not even been in America, but in Italy.

The truth was that I had really seen the man without examining him; I had simply discussed his case with his physician, whom I assured that I did not envy him his task. That seemed enough to drag me into the affair.

The patient complained that he could sit better before the operation than after it. As he loved to drive his own car, he felt very much embarrassed by his straight, stiff hip, which formerly had been flexed, though also stiff. Had the physician asked the patient before the operation whether he preferred comfortable sitting to straight standing, he would probably have left the man alone.

To get out of it, I had to prove, with the assistance of the steamship company, that I had arrived in Naples on the *Duilio* on the very day of the operation. When I was out of the picture, the patient was persuaded that no real harm was done to him and that he had better drop the whole affair.

Another of my indemnity cases was far more expensive for me.

A Hungarian lawyer of middle age wanted me to correct his spinal column, which offered a total kyphosis, the neck included. The patient stood and walked bent forward, with his face turned to the ground; he could not look any one in the face, and he could no longer plead in court. The man was suffering from progressive ankylosis of the spine, a disease which at that time was scarcely known; at least it had not yet been thoroughly studied. The dorsal and cervical vertebræ were absolutely fused in a long curve, convex backward. In the lumbar spine there was some mobility left, though it showed the same kyphotic attitude.

I resolved to redress the mobile lumbar spine to a lordotic position, which would counterbalance the upper kyphotic part of the spine, allowing the patient a more erect posture. The redressment was performed, and in the lordotic position of the lumbar spine, the patient was fixed in a plaster-bed.

The result of the operation was disastrous: Paralysis of both legs as well as of bladder and bowels. My endeavors to help the patient had resulted in putting him in the most terrible condition that could be imagined. I felt like a criminal.

X-ray pictures showed not the slightest lesion of the spine. It is impossible for even a strong man to break the lumbar spine in an adult. My diagnosis was that the redressing of the spine had caused a hemorrhage in the spinal canal and compression of the spinal cord. As the hemorrhage did not show up in the X-ray, my diagnosis was regarded as an optimistic explanation of the symptoms.

It was to be expected that the absorption of the hemor-

rhage would take a long time, while the compressed cord
would need a much longer time to be restored to normal
shape and function.

The lawyer began to become impatient. I had silently
to accept bitter reproaches, for, though feeling innocent,
I was and felt responsible.

Upon demand for indemnity, I offered a considerable
sum, of which half was to be paid immediately; the other
half one year after the operation if he were then not yet
cured. The expenses for the sanitarium, travelling costs,
etc., had naturally to be paid extra.

Shortly after the lawyer's departure, a young actor
came to me for help. He showed the same symptoms, but
in a lesser degree. Should I dismiss him because I had
failed in my first therapeutic experiment?

I decided to accept the case because otherwise the young
man would lose his job on the stage. Had I not learned
something by my first experience? And I am happy to
say that finally this patient was dismissed considerably
improved; he could remain on the stage and was excellent in the part of a stooping elderly gentleman.

In the meanwhile I got occasional reports on the poor
lawyer. His condition seemed to have become chronic.
When the year was up, he was not much better than directly after the operation. In accordance with my promise, the second half of the indemnity sum was paid, and
I tried to get the memory of this dreadful experience out
of my mind. But I could not forget the paralyzed man
—until one day, shortly after the last report, my son,
Doctor Albert Lorenz, met a friend who lived in the
same place as my lawyer-patient, and that man congratu-

lated him on the good result I had attained in the case of ——, who now walked in a fairly erect attitude.

The marvellous improvement had been brought about by the payment of the second half of the indemnity.

I cannot forbear to mention a third case. One day in the gay nineties, I was greatly surprised by the visit of a tall and slender lady. Biologically she belonged to that type of female which grows extremely fast in becoming mature, and accordingly suffers from a certain softness of bone and is liable to get deformities of the knees or the hip-joints.

"What does the visit of a beautiful lady to an orthopædic surgeon mean?" I asked the fair visitor.

"The exterior appearance is deceptive," answered the lady. "Nobody knows that your fair lady has knock-knees well hidden under the long gowns of the present fashion."

"So much the better."

"Not if you have to expose your knock-knees to a critical audience. I must sing the Fidelio in Beethoven's opera —in trousers—as you see! A '*Hosenrolle*' would disclose my deformity. I should rather die than hear people scoff at my knees—even if I should sing like a lark."

My visitor was a famous Wagnerian singer whom I had often admired as Ortrud, Kundry, and in many other rôles. She was the pride of the Vienna Opera, and rightly so. I held the lady in the highest regard, and felt eager to help her.

I advised a sort of apron by which her knees would be covered; I suggested she should always try to turn her profile to the audience, so that the knock-knees would not show.

With a sad smile the lady explained that it was not only the deformity itself which was wrecking her life and threatening to halt her career as an artist, but that she often suffered agonies when forced to stand on the stage for a long time.

I pitied her, but did not refrain from telling her that the correction of knock-knees would be possible only by severing both thighbones above the knee-joints.

"Cut my head off, but relieve me of my knock-knees," said the courageous Madame Octave.

I felt somewhat afraid to attempt it, knowing that nobody could absolutely guarantee a perfect result after this rather severe operation. The slightest restriction of mobility in the knee-joint, as sometimes happens after the supracondylar osteotomy of the femur, would spoil the outcome and would not satisfy her in the part of Ortrud, who must throw herself to the ground in one moment, to raise herself like a flash in the next. I said that I would consider it an honor to operate upon her, without asking any fee, just in deference to her art, but did not say that the slightest accident could bring great disappointment, and that she would have to sue me for damages. I could not afford to pay her high wages from the opera-house out of my own pocket, and so the instinct of self-protection told me to leave her alone.

Still, I hesitated to dismiss her case entirely. I advised Madame Octave to get in touch with a teacher upon whom I had performed the same operation some six months before, and gave her the address in Hungary; I told her to ask about everything regarding the operation—pains, after-treatment and final result, secretly hoping that she would be discouraged by the discomforts of the treatment entailed, and spare me the necessity of refusing her.

But no! The teacher was delighted with the result, and encouraged the singer to carry out her plan. When the would-be patient came back to fix the day for the operation, I finally said, "No!" Then Madame Octave carried out a manœuvre worthy of a cunning woman.

"All right," she said. "If you refuse to operate on me, I will go to Berlin, where Professor Hoffa will be glad to have me as his patient."

She had touched me in my professional jealousy.

"No, that must not be," I replied. "It would be a shame for us in Vienna if our great artist had to go to Berlin to get rid of her knock-knees. I shall operate upon you to-morrow morning!"

When I came into the sanitarium the next day, I found Madame Octave already on the operating table; the anæsthetist was waiting for the signal to begin with the narcosis. While I scrubbed my hands in the anteroom, I was interrupted in my earnest thoughts by my old friend Doctor Z, the director of the sanitarium. He seemed furious with me.

"How can you dare to take upon your shoulders such a heavy responsibility? The lady has a contract to sing *Fidelio* on a definite date, and you know what an unforeseen complication would mean. And besides, opera-singers are naturally difficult to please. I beseech you, get out of this business before it is too late!"

Then and there I forgot her threat to go to Berlin, threw my brush into the wash-trough, and ordered a rich breakfast for Madame Octave instead of ether. She was in her full right when she got furious with me.

Whether I was right to follow the instinct for self-protection may be seen by what came to light the next day. Madame Octave had hired a private nurse, and had engaged the Hungarian teacher as a companion and reader, both of them for three months; she had further rented a nice villa at a distance of about four kilometers from my country-place, so that I could see her every day during the summer. All summed up, it made quite a tidy amount, which must be paid immediately. But I did it gladly. A poor family with many children enjoyed a pleasant summer in the villa, and the Hungarian teacher and the nurse were paid for having a holiday.

The knock-knees did not impair Madame Octave's success in *Fidelio,* and I hope she has forgiven me.

It would require more space than is at my disposal to exhaust all my experiences in indemnity cases. Suffice it to say that I have kept a clear conscience. The physician is so often lauded without having deserved it, that he must make up for it with the injustices which he may have to endure.

XXIV

ABDICATION

BEFORE leaving New York in the spring of 1922, I accepted an invitation to pay a visit to the man-o'-war *Colorado* in the navy yard at Brooklyn. Having never been upon a battleship, I wanted to see all that can be shown to a casual visitor. I could not tell the names of all the compartments I was dragged through—chambers with compressed air, bewildering switch-boards far down below in oppressingly narrow cages, blindly attended to by a young man in response to commands received from another "seeing" man in an iron-clad cage far above. Machinery —confusing machinery—everywhere! And guns, guns to throw mountains of steel perhaps against stronger guns! Ridiculously small guns, their sharp noses upturned toward the sky as the only weapon against the most formidable of all foes to a battleship, the bombing-plane, which by one single hit can send the helpless giant to the bottom of the sea, while the deadly fly, eased of its burden, soars to the sky on widespread yet invulnerable wings!

After this fatiguing visit I felt an overpowering sadness in my soul. All that human science and human ingenuity has to be proud of, condensed, as it were, in a single giant machine, whose only aim, though one seldom achieved, is destruction, and whose sure fate is to be destroyed by buzzing drones! Is there still sense in warships? Is there any sense at all in war upon water or earth, when the airplane can hurl exploding bombs filled with deadly gases down upon innocent Mother

Earth, tormented by a mankind worthy of being extinguished? The globe would become peaceful under the rule of beasts, the cruellest of which are lambs compared with man!

Though mine was a mission of thanks rather than of asking, in that time of eager willingness of the American people to give it was really scarcely necessary to ask. To the donations of my patients to Viennese children (the project which had so nearly wrecked my mission at the beginning) I was able to add many voluntary contributions. The management of the fund was put in the hands of Mr. Anton Wedl, as cashier of the collection committee. I was able to contribute by some lectures, but my chief contribution was possible through the generosity of my honored friend, Mr. George Semler, the very man who had lent me (without my knowing him) the money to come to America. When I tried to pay my debt to him, my creditor said that he had already forgotten what in all probability, or so both he and I thought, would never happen. I then asked to be allowed to pay my debt to him by the letters of thanks from those to whom I intended to distribute the amount, at my own pleasure, while the bulk of the fund was being disposed of by a distributing committee in Vienna. When Mr. Semler later on got stacks of letters, he said he had not known that so much good could be done by such a trifle of money. As generous contributors, though not directly to the fund, must be mentioned Mr. R. J. Kuddihy, the well-known editor, who sent $2000 by my son to Cardinal Piffl in Vienna for the relief of the needy, and Mr. Morgenthau, Mr. Heide, Monsignor Father Schumack, and others. The total of about $25,000 was due to small contributions from everywhere, as a proof that my mission was not unpopular in this country. The greatest credit belongs to Mr. Wedl, to whom the recipients of the benefits are more indebted than to anybody else.

With a happier heart than when I had arrived in the autumn, I left New York in the spring, again on a French boat, in the company of my friends, Mr. and Mrs. Wedl, who considered it their duty to install the somewhat tired doctor in the home from which they had taken him six months before.

Not quite my first but an important concern, which by a sort of superstition I had delayed until homecoming, was to put my turned-about suit in the reliquary of the house and to order my first new skin of clothes in ten years from the best tailor in Vienna—which, by the way, I am still wearing! My part of a shabbily clad old man had come to an end. A very agreeable task was that of being an influential member of the distribution committee which, besides needy children—the Mayor of Vienna had immediately got part of the Semler money for poor children—concerned itself with poor students at the three universities of Austria. The rest of the money was given to starving artists, though they were not on the program. Mr. Wedl and I felt, however, that we could answer to our consciences for this gratification.

The distribution committee had assigned a fairly considerable sum to the Dean of the Medical Faculty for aid to needy students. When I went to the Dean's office to give him notice of the gift, I remembered the day when a ruthless former dean had thrown me out of his room instead of granting my just request as a poor and intimidated boy. When the Dean had welcomed me, this time very cordially, I said rather sternly that I had come to take revenge. "On me? For what?" asked the astonished Dean. "On you, in so far as you are the successor to the dean of fifty years ago," I answered, and told the Dean the story of how nicely a poor, timid boy had been treated by that man whom the world had forgotten, but not I. The Dean of course condemned the behavior of his predecessor, but could only be sorry for it. "No," said I, "you have to atone for it by deigning to accept from that very same boy of fifty years ago a considerable amount of money under the obligation of distributing it 'justly' among the poor students." The Dean told the avenger that he would be only too glad if he could also atone in the same pleasant way for his own sins.

As fate would have it, I was unexpectedly given another opportunity to take a late revenge upon the malevolent dean of fifty years ago. But if the thirst for revenge has once been quenched, nourishing the hatred gives no more pleasure. A prematurely old man, who had been a general in the Austrian army, much feared by his soldiers, came one day to my office, walking on two crutches. His ailment, by the way, had nothing to do with the war. When I looked at the patient's face, I was struck by a memory which had clung indelibly to my mind for fifty years. It was not the malign dean, but his younger brother—just the same croaking, lamenting, never-to-be-satisfied, presumptuous fellow that I thought his older brother must have been, aside from his harshness to poor students. I did my best, treated the brother of my foe with the utmost care, and asked nothing for my exertions, but would have been glad to hear my patient say a word of acknowl-

edgment. But no! I had to force him to admit that the
treatment had some effect when he was able to discard
his crutches. Sometimes it is hard to take revenge in one's
own way. I was often on the point of losing my patience,
but I kept the patient.

In Austria you have to abdicate your position at seventy regardless of your bodily and mental condition. I
had always agreed with this law because it opens the way
to the younger generation and admonishes the older ones
henceforward to spend their time not exclusively in working but also in thinking of the many questions which old
age brings with it, and in thanking God for still being
alive. I refused the invitation of the Dean to take a last
—the so-called "honorary"—year in my position as Chief
of the Orthopædic Department of the hospital. If I were
not good enough at seventy, I would not grow better at
seventy-one!

I would have preferred a quiet and, as it were, clandestine abdication. But no! My pupils, colleagues from Germany and Sweden, urged a solemn ceremony which could
only convey the impression of a funeral in which the man
to be buried vainly cries out: "I am still alive!" The
authorities honoring the ceremony with their precious
presence felt cool at heart because the man to be retired
had been so stupid as never to ask a salary for his forty
years of service. Therefore I had forfeited my pension.
They were the more at ease because they knew that I was
too proud to request a pension of grace.

An old man without even a pension of grace would
surely not have minded being the recipient of the Nobel
Prize for Medicine. God knows I had never had the faint-

est thought of it until one day I was nominated as a candidate. I greeted the information with an incredulous laugh. What should I get the Nobel Prize for? "For your bloodless treatment of the congenital luxation of the hip-joint; send all your writings about the subject to the committee immediately," was the command. I did so, and from that moment on I nourished the hope of getting what I had never before thought of or striven for. I felt nearly certain of it when I was informed that my candidacy was in the inner election. Weeks of elated expectation came to a sudden end when I had word that I would have got the Nobel Prize—but for one vote! What an old fool I was to have allowed hope artificially kindled to grow to a conquering flame!

The missing vote had evidently been given by a man who had not the slightest idea of orthopædics, least of all of congenital hip-luxation. The evil thought shot through my mind that to make that man understand the importance of its cure, all his children, or rather, since he must be an old man with sclerotic brain-vessels, all his grandchildren should— No, you criminal, they should not, must not, atone for their grandfather! Can the prospect of some money convert an honest man so easily into a criminal? No sir, I need no "given" money. I am strong and healthy enough to earn what I need.

Such thoughts as these liberated me from the qualms of disappointment and I dismissed the whole affair from my mind. "As far as the honor is concerned," I said to my friends, "I don't feel disappointed at all. I was a candidate for the Nobel Prize, or rather the recipient of it, but for one vote. Let the real recipient have the money in the bargain."

Vague hopes of your own should never be indulged in, but much less should high expectations ever be kindled in another man who never cherished them. You should not promise a man heaven, nor threaten him with hell, if you are not quite certain about these places.

Throughout my good times, I never forgot a debt which was no less a debt because I could not be sued as the debtor. As a choir-singer, I had had a free place in the St. Paul monastery for four years. I had sung in the choir, but on second thought I realized that my efforts could not have compensated for the food, the housing, and the teaching. I had never forgotten the humiliations a rude monk had thought fit to mortify me with, and the vivid memory induced me at last to make a reckoning of what I should have paid, and the interest. That amount I sent to the monastery as a gift for poor students, with the assurance that it could never equal my indebtedness. When I paid a visit to the monastery, the successor to Abbot Gregor was highly delighted and much impressed by the lasting thankfulness of a former pupil. "Let me have a long and undisturbed look at the green stone in your ring," I said, and kissed once more the emerald which had made such an indelible impression upon the young choir-singer. It seemed to me that the stone sparkled less than it had sixty years before. But that was due to the fact that the eyes of the old man were less sensitive to its splendor than the boy's had been. Dead things are eternal.

Whoever has once been in New York returns to it again. So it came to pass that the next winter found me again in New York. Many of the patients whom I had seen the previous year wanted to be treated. The charity work shrunk by itself to a certain extent, and my work became less exhausting. Nevertheless, I had to return to Vienna for another winter to attend to my practice there. Having retired from my clinic, I found interest in writing on orthopædics. And so, becoming accustomed to writing, I tried myself out in belles-lettres, and finally as clandestine playwright. An old man must have his hobby—why not playwriting? Had I not always nourished a love for the theatre? Afraid of being laughed at, I concealed my writings and, overwhelmed by a new flood of medical work, forgot all about them. After a while, the well-hidden scripts by chance came to light again. Perusing them quite impartially, I felt curious as to the solution of the conflict which I had created and had forgotten—and thus I found out at last that my play was certainly no worse than many I had seen on the stage, and resolved to work on it not as a hobby but as an earnest task.

Spring and summer finds the whole family assembled in their green paradise in Altenberg. Albert's second marriage has borne fruit in the form of a lovely boy, Georg, who is already very much like his father. Konrad, my second son, nicknamed the "American," became a doctor of medicine too, and married his playmate of childhood days, Margaret, who is also a physician, and they have two children, Thomas and Agnes. My wife, because of a medical practice of forty-five years as assistant to her husband, has been designated an honorary doctor through the fulness of the sovereignty of her husband. The five doctors constitute quite a learned family!

The splendor of Lorenz Hall, somewhat faded in the course of thirty years, was temporarily and partially revived by a visit from royalty. When the annual meeting of the German Ornithological Society was held in Vienna, all the members wanted to see the workshop in which Doctor Konrad Lorenz had made his study of the habits and psychology of the heron, which were kept in the garden, free to go or to come. Konrad, though a doctor of medicine, had preferred ornithology to medical practice. I was not over-enthusiastic about his choice and had deeply aroused my boy's anger when I said that it was of no great importance to know whether herons were more or less stupid than they were thought to be. Konrad contends that human psychology has much to learn from animal psychology and that there is no essential difference between these two branches of the science. Through his observations, Doctor Konrad had won the acclaim of the assembled birdmen, and they wanted to pay him and his birds a visit, in Altenberg.

His Majesty, Ferdinand, ex-King of Bulgaria, himself a learned birdman and patron of the German Society of Ornithology, was a member of the party. About a hundred of the guests arrived in buses; his Majesty came soon afterward in a splendid Mercedes automobile. He was very elegantly and correctly attired in a light gray suit, his quite imposing but utterly bald head covered with a wide-brimmed, coquettishly cocked hat. There was a carnation in his buttonhole. His expressive face, of healthy color, seemed to serve the sole purpose of providing a frame for his projecting, aquiline Coburg nose. Of nearly super-human tallness, this lively-stepping old man of over seventy in his brilliant attire gave one more the impression of a well-to-do, self-satisfied nobleman who delighted in his scientific hobby without forgetting many of the other joys of life still left to him, than of a care-worn modern king. It remains an open question whether the ex-King envies his son, the real King, or whether the reverse is true!

After the garden and its feathered inhabitants had been duly visited, the guests entered the house, which had been turned into a restaurant. Chairs, tables, and tableware had been borrowed from kindly neighbors. While the hall was left to the common people, the King and the officials of the congress were seated in the dining-room, which was richly decorated with early autumn flowers.

The King assured Mrs. Lorenz that he felt delighted to breathe a true Viennese atmosphere, for he always felt as if he belonged in Vienna. Mrs. Lorenz begged his Majesty to excuse the frugal refreshments, which the King seemed nevertheless to enjoy.

As the host and master of the house, I felt it my duty to say a few words of welcome to his Majesty the King and to the other guests on this remarkable occasion. I was stung with the temptation to commit an unpunishable *Majestaets-Beleidigung* (*lèse majesté*) against the sovereign. So I said:

"Your Majesty, ladies and gentlemen! Allow me to assure you that I feel quite honored by your presence under my humble roof. The more so, as I cannot boast of any connection whatsoever with ornithology, except the interest which I always have taken in that branch of ornithology whose noble aim is to fill the roasting-pan. If times were not so hard at present, I assure you, Your Majesty and honored guests, that at least fifty-five Styrian capons would have come to believe that they had not been 'caponized' in vain. The times being meager, the refreshments are not less meager, but Viennese ham between buttered slices of good Viennese bread and a glass of Voslan wine are not to be despised anyhow. To any birdman, whoever he may be"—and here I looked at the King— "who is not satisfied with what we have to give, I must answer with the German quotation, *'Vogel, friss oder stirb.'* " (Eat, bird, or die.)

The assembled guests roared with laughter, and the King said affably, "My dear host, all your guests prefer eating!" Doctor Konrad received a nice framed and autographed picture of the King.

Since that time the much discussed hall has been left to its dreams of a glorious past.

XXV

WHAT HOPE FOR THE CRIPPLED?

As far as the question of health goes, cripples are rather a happy family. With the exception of the sufferers from tuberculosis of the spine, hips, or knee-joints, who are subject to sudden but usually harmless pains, cripples as a rule enjoy good health, since the disease which caused their corporeal deformity has long since passed. This is especially true of those crippled by infantile paralysis. Being free from pain, they are usually cheerful and good-tempered and do not greatly mind their disabilities. Their mental development is often far advanced on account of the fact that they find more time to read and study than their more athletic classmates. Lack of physical activity and too rich food often makes them fat and less able to use the muscular force that may be left to them.

The general health of patients with softening of the bones—rickets—is, of course, not so good. They do not suffer, but they are usually under-nourished. A perfectly healthy child has hard bones and will never get scoliosis (lateral deviation of the spine) no matter how uncomfortable the school-bench he may be sitting on.

Children with congenital deformities are usually of splendid health.

The same is often true of the spastic cripples, who are, in fact, brain cripples, as contrasted with patients with infantile paralysis who suffer from a pathological condition of the spinal cord, while the brain is not involved at all.

These spastic cripples have a bad reputation for being difficult to educate; they are often of defective intelligence, in spite of occasional special gifts and talents. In later years some of them show criminal tendencies. In general, they are the cause of all the blame so liberally and indiscriminately heaped upon cripples. A master of character portrayal like Shakespeare has not overlooked the spastic. In Richard III he says:

> Deform'd, unfinish'd, sent before my time
> Into this breathing world, scarce half made up,

meaning a premature child.

Cripples—the spastics excepted—are liable to suffer from an inferiority complex. It is a fable that they are insidious, revengeful and not to be trusted. They are grateful for every word of solace spoken to them and for kind treatment, which they get from all except their schoolmates, because children are cruel. Each feels ashamed of his deformity, whatever it may be. Knowing that the public allows every one to limp as much as he wants, but gets the creeps at the sight of a deformed hand or foot, arm or leg, he tries to conceal his deformity in whatever way he can.

The world-famous cripple Cardinal Richelieu found it easy to hide his crippled foot as well as his political schemes in the rich folds of his priestly robes. Lord Byron found it less easy to hide the club-foot. He even commented on it, and declared that in his whole life he could not put up with two things: first, with his club-foot, second, with the hypocrisy of his own people. Perhaps he would have been an unknown poet had physicians of his time been able to cure him of his club-foot. It seems that poets must have something unattainable to strain and grieve for constantly, to keep their brains fertile.

A German emperor tried very hard to hide the insufficiency of his arm, the result of a birth palsy. However hard he might have tried to hide it, history would have found him out and called him "Imperator Rex Unfortunatus," or perhaps "One-Arm, the Second." But fate decided that history will have no need to give him the name "One-Arm" because the change of his number "Second" to "Last" will be enough to make his name remembered.

If, from the medical point of view, any human being with any deficiency in the "osseous frame in motion" is called a cripple, then the President of the United States at the present time has the privilege of this title. Whenever I see an American mother despondent over her boy's more or less damaged legs, I say: "Don't worry, Mother! Your boy may be President of the United States some day if his brain makes up for his legs!"

Infantile paralysis cannot be cured. However, the normal shape of a contorted, paralyzed limb can usually be restored by a bloodless procedure, but the lost muscular power cannot be restored. One can only improve the mechanical conditions of the function by balancing the equilibrium of the disturbed muscle-power. If all the muscles of a limb are paralyzed, there are usually no contortions, no joint distortions, because there is no disturbance of the equilibrium of the muscle-power. Exceptional contractures in such cases are due to the weight of the body. Totally paralyzed limbs, therefore, need not undergo operations, but must be supported by braces.

Though infantile paralysis will never be cured, some

day it may be prevented by the vaccination of children, just as small-pox can now be prevented despite the fact that no human eye has ever seen the microbe-pest which causes it. That is true also of the microbe of infantile paralysis. It is to be hoped that an electric eye such as that constructed by Vladimir K. Zworykin, the newest ultra-microscope, will leap the barriers of vision, and that the hitherto invisible evil-doers may at last be seen by the human eye. That would be a long step toward their destruction.

It is remarkable and almost incredible that this microbe-pest shows a preference for settling down in the spinal cord. The microbes of infantile paralysis—what gourmets!—prefer the anterior column of the spinal cord, where the motor centers are located. By feeding on them, the microbes cause their destruction, putting out of commission the motor nerves and, consequently, the muscles. Except in fatal cases, they avoid the brain as not suitable to their taste. This is indeed a very fortunate fact, because even if the ravages of the disease leave patients more or less crippled, they are left mentally intact and really bright-minded. It has to be stressed that the patient be kept in good humor, even if condemned to a wheel-chair for lifetime.

Why for so long could nobody see the spirochæta, the dread scourge of humanity, the cause of syphilis? The story I am going to tell here is set down merely to inspire the hope that the microbes of infantile paralysis may be brought to the light of day accidentally and unexpectedly, just as the cause of syphilis was detected one day by a man who was not a physician but a zoölogist. This man was short-lived. I met him on board the *Oceania* on a cruise in the South Atlantic. When I sat down at a table in the dining-room, I saw on the plate next to me a card bearing the name of Doctor Schaudin. When the young, tall, and blond Esthonian giant entered the room, I asked him: "Are you just an ordinary Schaudin or are you *the* Schaudin?" He acknowledged himself to be *the* Schaudin. When his neighbor asked him how in the world it came about that he had found that little microbe which thousands of keen eyes, reinforced by the best and most powerful microscopes, had looked for eagerly for many decades and in vain—although they had mistaken many casual findings for it—Schaudin answered: "Oh, it is not so tiny as my rivals thought. As you now know, it is a brilliant and lively creature about one one-hundred-and-fiftieth of an inch long, resembling a corkscrew. It could not escape anybody's eyes. I found it when, for the first time in my life, I looked through the microscope upon a specimen taken from a luetic ulcer."

"But why," asked his inquisitor, "for God's sake couldn't all the others find it in spite of all their efforts?"

"That" he replied, "was because they were all physicians, while I am a zoölogist who has some acquaintance with the great family of spirochætæ. Physicians are in the habit of dyeing specimens they want to study under the microscope, and the dye-stuffs destroy these transparent little spirals. Now, of course, anybody can see them if he follows my instructions."

Perhaps a zoölogist will also find the microbes of infantile paralysis.

When the steamer was lying off Madeira, Schaudin invited me to go ashore with him to hunt spirochætæ in order to see whether these glittering corkscrews were carrying on better on the sunny island than on the frosty continent. So we "went places," where young and old sailor-boys of the world were trying to forget the hardships of the high seas, and were serving in the exchange not only of commercial goods but also of insular spirochætæ. It would not help much to blow up such dangerous places, for they would only revive somewhere else, like padlocked speak-easies during prohibition times.

But to have found out the fiend does not mean to have destroyed him. We discussed the question whether medical science or law would be most effective in doing away with the fiend. The surgeon held the opinion that the spirochæta must be killed by the natural death of its host—or hostess—, and that such persons should be required by law to stay by themselves, within their own community, and to do no outside business.

In Lisbon, I lost sight of my notable friend. Six months later, in the prime of his life, Schaudin died, not as a host to the restlessly revolving spirochæta, but to the mute and quiet but no less insidious tuberculosis bacillus.

And now, what can orthopædy undertake to do for the crippled?

Since the name and what it implies is not generally understood by laymen—I told you that the Emperor Franz Josef knew nothing about it and had never heard the word—, a general definition would not be amiss. I prefer to derive the name orthopædia from ὀρδός—straight, and παιδεύω—I educate, I train. Orthopædia means, therefore, straight-making or straightening; the orthopædist is a straightener. His realm comprises the human skeleton in motion, that is to say, the bones and their connections, the

joints, and the muscular motor of the same. The orthopædist takes care of the osseous frame of the body and is, so
to say, responsible for its beauty, for the foundation of its
beauty is the skeleton. He studies the attitude or the posture of the body, its normal balance, which still presents
some difficulties for man even though he has spent many
hundreds of thousands of years in lifting himself definitely
on his hind legs to an erect position. The orthopædist is,
in other words, the carpenter of the frame, a bone-carpen-
ter who should elect Saint Joseph as his patron saint.

The head itself he leaves alone, though the skulls of
young children should be a good subject for modelling,
as is proved by the work of priests of savage tribes who
give the skull its definite shape according to the fashion
of the particular tribe. Though the septum in the nose is
very often out of its normal position, the orthopædist does
not dare to touch it lest the rhinologists get provoked with
him. But if the jaw is out of place or locked, he claims
the right to set or mobilize it. If the whole head is out of
place, drawn to one side, turned to the other, and out of
the middle line (as in congenital wry-neck) the orthopædist is the man who can help.

Lateral curvatures of the spine have always been a
subject of profound study and sorrow for him. Rickets
and other forms of bone softness and subsequent deformities find him ready for action. Fresh bone fractures or old
ones badly healed are the orthopædist's delight. All joint
diseases, be they of tuberculous or any other character
(such as arthritis of any origin, etc.) demand his special
care. All contractures of joints (the sequelæ of tuberculosis, infantile paralysis, or the spasticity of muscles), all
congenital foot deformities, and the most frequent con-

genital dislocations of the hip-joint, offer the orthopædist most interesting problems.

Bone diseases of malign character are gladly left to the general surgeon.

We must not forget the fallen arches, the static knock-knees in young laborers, due to the overloading of the feet and knees in weight-bearing. Fallen arches are *"eine Volkskrankheit"* (common disease) of economic and military importance—though in a future war not the soldier but the airplane will have the last word to say. All kinds of contractures of the hands, the elbows, the shoulders, are of even greater importance and certainly more difficult to treat than the deformities of the lower limbs. Add to all of this the successful endeavors to mobilize ankylosed (absolutely stiffened) joints, especially elbow, knee, and jaw joints, and it would seem to be established that orthopædy is, though certainly not the most important, anatomically speaking the most extended medical specialty of the whole body, excluding its viscera.

The straightening of limbs or joints by lengthening the shrunken soft parts is done either by manipulation, of the sort I described earlier, or by machinery which exerts a steady and strong but always controllable force. You need not be an athlete to do that, but you must be thoroughly trained for the bloodless work, the dangers of which must be known if one is to avoid them.

Bones cannot be stretched; they must be cut. Therefore only a relatively small part of orthopædy can be done by the bloodless method. Knife and chisel are indispensable implements. Consequently, I do not deserve the title "bloodless surgeon" which has been given to me in America. I can claim it only in so far as the open operation is not my first resource but my last, and because in the most difficult tasks of orthopædy, such as the treatment of congenital hip-dislocation, congenital club-feet, etc., I rely exclusively on my bloodless methods. Also it is my pride to have substituted for rather grave and dangerous operations, harmless methods which yield results no less satisfactory. I should prefer to be called "highly conservative" (and who is not conservative after eighty years!) rather than a "bloodless surgeon."

Before we try to visualize the future of orthopædy, let us take a look at its past. Orthopædy is probably nearly as old as mankind. The first man who set a broken leg or fixed it to its mate as a brace, was the first orthopædist.

Over three hundred years before Christ was born, Hippocrates, one of the greatest physicians who ever lived and who still lives in the daily routine work of medicine, described the symptoms of congenital dislocation of the hip-joint clearly and impressively, though with some exaggeration, when he said: "They walk stooping, in the manner of animals."

I assume it was Herodotus who told the story that the old Persians cut the heel-cords of their captives lest they run away, unknowingly performing a very important orthopædic operation, though with a purpose just the reverse of that of the present achillotenotomy! The world had to wait until the nineteenth century before Dieffenbach found out how the operation has to be done to assist humans to walk.

In the dark ages nobody cared for any science. As for orthopædics in the dark ages, a picture is carefully preserved which shows some sturdy men forcibly straightening the hunchback of what was probably a tuberculous patient with the aid of a long lever. Nothing to shudder about! It was only at the beginning of the last century that a famous French surgeon repeated the procedure with milder means but with the same disastrous results. Nature does not allow any surgeon to cross her own way of healing—that was learned at least once more.

Not much can be said about orthopædic achievements up to the nineteenth century. Andry, one of the first writers on orthopædics, described his method of curing congenital wry-neck: He advised the mothers of such children to take them to a fire—incendiaries must have been common in Paris at the end of the eighteenth century—and hold them so they could not see the conflagration unless they turned their heads to the other side. In this way the contracted soft parts in the concavity of the distorted neck would be stretched by the children's own efforts. One can imagine what the result of such and other similar treatments may have been.

There was no orthopædy to speak of, though there were cripples everywhere. The great Spanish painter, Murillo, could nicely depict but could not cure a beautiful case of congenital club-foot. Apparently he wanted to recommend the poor boy for public charity, for the picture, now in the Louvre, bears the inscription: *"Da mihi elimosina!"* (Give me alms). The kings also deigned to notice the cripples, not in order to cure them, but to use them as decorations at their courts. The more severely deformed and the more "witty" the *"Hofnarr"* was, the more his services were appreciated, even if they sometimes consisted in telling the bitter truth to the high employer!

Surgery could offer no help to crippled patients. Noth-

ing was left to them but to go to the holy shrines, such
as those at Mariazell in Styria and Lourdes in France,
where patients dedicated silver images of their deformed
limbs to the shrine as a prayer for help, but scarcely ever
as a thanksgiving for relief. Some diseases may be cured
by faith, but it is certain that a visible deformity has never
been straightened out by prayer alone.

Before the Lister era there was little of general surgery
and nothing at all of orthopædic surgery. The joints
always had the bad reputation of being very susceptible to
infection. Blood poisoning was the dreary background of
surgery. The "*Genius epidemicus,*" as the virulent microbes were understood at that time, loomed everywhere,
and the hospitals were so full of it that Professor Nussbaum, a very famous surgeon at Munich, had to close his
wards because he knew from experience that students who
had suffered only a slight sabre-cut on the head would die
in the hospital from blood-poisoning.

The Lister era freed surgery from its fetters. And yet
Listerism, the soul of which was blind adoration of phenic
acid, had many adversaries who claimed to be able to get
equally good results by means much simpler than the
Lister "ceremonies." A French surgeon whose name has
been forgotten preached heat and hot poultices in the
treatment of wounds. Nobody took much notice of him,
though at the present time heat reigns supreme in surgery.
Nevertheless, the name of Lister will always be celebrated
because he was the first to understand Pasteur and defeat
the fabulous *Genius epidemicus.*

Through the antiseptic method, the realm of surgery
seemed to have become limitless. General surgeons became interested in tubercular joints in children. Liberal

re-section of the tubercular joints, regardless of the zones of growth, became the mode of the day. The final results were awful shortenings of the contracted limbs which deterred surgeons from further operations of this kind. In all honor to Professor Eduard Albert, it must be said that he always protested vehemently against this *"furor operandi,"* but his was "a voice crying in the wilderness."

After this defeat of general surgery in the treatment of tubercular joints, interest in all other types of joint diseases seemed spent.

Orthopædic work was left entirely to brace-makers, who then reaped the harvest of their times. I distinctly remember the joyous Viennese *bon vivant* who made the braces for the general hospital arriving at the clinic in an elegant private equipage with splendid Hungarian horses, while Billroth and Albert walked to their work. The young doctors aimed jokes at this upstart of a fellow: "Not only clothes but also carriages show who is who!" The surgeons thought themselves too noble for humble orthopædic work —as if it were a degradation to massage and teach methodic exercises for orthopædic purposes!

Among the brace-makers of Germany who "owned" orthopædics at that time, however, there was one outstanding man who must not be forgotten, because he was really a genius. He was Friedrich Hessing. From a gardener's apprentice, this self-made man became the greatest and most skillful brace-maker ever known. He constructed orthopædic contrivances by which diseased joints could not only be securely fixed but also redressed. These so-called *"Schienen Huelsen Apparate"* (braces which fit the limbs like husks) were unsurpassed in their purposeful construction and mechanical perfection, but were very complicated, expensive, and of little use for hospital work.

When my friend Hoffa in Berlin and I came forth with our results obtained by manual procedures and plaster-casts, Hessing feared for his dictatorship. He told visitors to his great institute in Göggingen, near Augsburg, in Germany, that he had two nails securely fixed in the wall of his atelier. On the one Hoffa was to hang by the neck until dead, on the other Lorenz, if they should ever come within his reach. Hoffa was saved from this dreadful fate by his own untimely death, and I was saved from being hanged by the death of Hessing! In the obituary which I had to write for my implacable foe I said that I should like to hang a marble tablet on my nail with the inscription: "In honor of the genius Friedrich Hessing, the greatest brace-maker of all times!" For in comparison with the Hessing braces for diseased hip-joints, the traction splints devised by other surgeons were but poor and useless contrivances.

When young and enthusiastic doctors, in the eighties of the last century, took up orthopædics as a specialty, manual procedures or open operations more and more took the place of bracework. In the course of time entirely open operations prevailed with the aggressive orthopædic surgeons, to such an extent that the orthopædic brace went totally into the discard. I never approved of this trend, because a brace is indispensable in the orthopædic work.

Thus the dreary past of orthopædic surgery has yielded to a magnificent state of development at the present time. Now let me try to glimpse its future.

If the progress of humanity be not interrupted by another war or by other catastrophes, it is quite possible that orthopædic surgery may have no future at all! When there will be no cripples, there will be no orthopædic surgery. Humanity without cripples is by no means a fantastic dream. Suppose that only half of the cost of war preparation, not to speak of the cost of a war itself, were to be spent for the welfare of the needy, in providing them with proper food, housing, clothes, and other hygienic precautions, such as plenty of fresh air, sunshine, and water, the number of tubercular cripples would dwindle to an insignificant number. By the same means all those crippled by the yielding of soft bones, bones with not enough lime in them to bear the strain of weight, such as cases of lateral deviations of the spine, bow-legs, knock-knees, and deformities of the hip-joint, could be prevented. If infantile paralysis, that scourge of childhood, could be wiped out, there would be very few, if any, paralytic cripples. It yet remains to be seen, however, whether congenital deformities, especially congenital club-feet, can be prevented by eugenics.

Quite a difficult problem is offered to medical science by the spastic cripples. Their muscles are spastically contracted, and disobey the normal reactions in some way or other. The power of the muscles is not diminished; on the contrary, they are always in a state of over-excitement, and therefore the name "spastic paralysis" is misleading. These unfortunate cripples very often are not even able to stand, much less walk. In this respect much can be done for them, but even the best results are not satisfactory because the condition of the patient is due to a pathological condition of the brain which may spontaneously improve to a certain degree but can scarcely ever be cured. These patients very often become half-wits, a burden to their parents, to themselves, and to the community, especially when they reach maturity. To at least diminish their number, some drastic means, such as sterilization, is strongly indicated. Look at Germany! It is even more important that these children, who are usually prematurely born, should not be pampered with all possible means of preserving their feeble lives. If new-born premature children are too weak to stand the conditions of extra-uterine life in which normal children thrive, they had better die than live a life not worth living at all. This seems cruel, but in the end it is better. Believe this, from a man who is rather too soft-hearted to be a surgeon and who has witnessed untold misery and suffering because of children who are unfit for life.

When the obstetrical art shall have freed human females from the fetters of difficult child-birth, the cases of cripples from the process of birth will also be few.

After these achievements, very little will be left for the orthopædic surgeon. Since people will never stop breaking their limbs, they will be occupied mostly in bone-setting, an art which has been brought to perfection by the efforts of orthopædic surgeons. As a specialty, however, orthopædic surgery will have lost its right to existence. In those blessed future days, human limbs will not only "bloom" on Olympus, as Schiller says, but on this earth as well.

This seems rather a strange horoscope to be cast by the so-called "Father of German Orthopædic Surgery." But I would not be the real father of my child if I did not look forward to its future, and endeavor, even though it be through sacrifice, to assist my child as far as possible in the ways of the world.

XXVI

YOUR OWN MISSING GLOVE

IN the late afternoon we like to gather in Mrs. Lorenz's flower-garden, which occupies the site of the former vegetable garden, in the center of a big lawn in the upper part of the park—the sort of place where nobody but the Munich-Vienna airplane pilot could peep in. It is in the late autumn, when two of the doctors are about to leave again for America—always for the last time!—but no longer in search of the missing glove, for as Doctor Albert Lorenz, who accompanies me to New York, asserts: "Haven't you seen, Father, how unreliable the esteem of your colleagues is? If you're a Teuton, the esteem is lost. Stop searching, Father! Don't you know that you have been in possession of the odd glove since the day your first orthopædic achievement proved to be a lasting asset to the medical art?"

"I have put away ambition," I reply. "Life is quieter without it."

Here in the peace of the garden, my thoughts are busy with this question of the search for the missing glove.

He who thinks himself born with two gloves will never search for the missing one. He will be an idler, a good-for-nothing, a zero in the community of men.

To have to search for the missing glove is the wholesome lash hissing through the air, always ready to slash the sweating back of the searcher. You may wince sometimes under the threat of the falling blow, yet in the end you will find it has done you some good. Don't say that only the lazy are in need of the lash. The industrious need it just as much, if their endeavors to find the missing glove are vain and they succumb to despondency.

The lash is necessary not only for people with slow brains, but also for the highly intelligent, because very often it is among them that the laziest ones are to be found. The lash makes their brains fertile. Searching for the missing glove gives your life some purpose, but finding it sooner or later does not necessarily mean that your success will make you happy. The tragedy of your wish may be its fulfillment. All depends on what the missing glove means to you.

Does it mean riches? But, you cannot take them with you at the exit from the stage of life, and money alone does not make you happy. It remains to be seen whether your heritage of poverty and good health and vitality from your own father may not be worth far more than the riches and perhaps poor health which is possibly your own bequest to your children to spare them the trouble to search for the missing glove. I used to say: *"Arm, gesund und jung, giebt dem Leben Schwung!"* To be poor, healthy and young gives life its swing.

Does the missing glove mean power? How long can you wield it? There will always be some one more powerful than you. In the end your power exists only in your own imagination, for you never can be quite sure whether at any given moment your power is still acknowledged.

Does it mean honor? If honor is due to riches and power it is the same soap-bubble that these are. Honor is a very uncertain possession, for it depends upon the good-will of your admirers.

Does it mean fame? A most equivocal aim. The worst specimens of humanity have reached the highest degree of fame, whether as imposters, thieves, or as retail or wholesale murderers, from Tamerlane, Jenghiz Khan, the horse-breaker Alexander the Great, Cæsar, and Napoleon, down to those men who kindled the World War and then concocted a peace every word of which means hatred. They will not outlive their fame. Fame during your lifetime is usually too highly paid for; and as for fame after death, what good can it do you?

Does your search mean the strife to secure the eternal bliss which is promised to you by your religion? A more egotistic aim in life cannot easily be imagined. You work only for yourself, strive and pray for yourself. If you chastise yourself, if you deny yourself the most innocent joys in life, you do it exclusively for yourself. You want to deserve the eternal heavenly bliss for yourself. Such an aim for your life has as its base your selfishness and your Godless, overbearing conceitedness. At the same time, it is, on your part, the most unfair, sacrilegious bargain with things eternal that could be imagined. You short-lived worms which pop up one day, with hardly time to take a glimpse to right or left before you disappear again from the face of the earth, you "magic shadows, shapes that come and go"—*you* feel entitled to heavenly bliss as a reward for your sacrifice of all the joys that your life of scarcely a moment's duration can offer! Don't you realize that if your life were to last uncounted hundreds of millions of years, it would be incommensurably far from being equal to an immeasurably small part of eternity?

How can mortal man even pronounce the word *eternity*

without feeling crushed to atoms? Would eternal bliss to mortal man not seem the same punishment as eternal damnation—just because the one and the other are eternal? Eternity can only be conceived by God, who is Eternity.

So long as man's soul is linked to his body, mortal man should not dare to think of eternity. Only when the soul is freed of its temporary house of clay does eternity without beginning or end unite man's immortal soul with God, to live in Him as ever so small a part of Him. Whether or how the liberated soul will be conscious of its eternity, who can dare to guess? Many a wise man will prefer unconsciousness, that is to say, to be as he was before he came into this world; the best thing would be to know nothing about anything.

It is useless to bother oneself with these questions. Better to rest assured that you will not endanger your soul if you live a righteous, moral life. Whatever religion you embrace, morals go without saying.

Searching for the missing glove is an endeavor to solve the question: What is the sense of life, what is life for in the end?

It is cruel but true that pleasures must be indulged in wisely. It depends on the vitality of the individual how much pleasure he can stand, but not even the weak ones need to be totally excluded.

Everything else in your life depends on your vitality, which you inherited from your ancestors. You are lucky if you come from a hardy race! In one of his best known poems Goethe says:

Was du ererbt von deinen Vätern hast,
Erwirb es um es zu besitzen!

(What you inherited from your fathers,
    Earn it, to possess it.)

That may be all right from one point of view, but from a biological standpoint just the reverse is true. Then it should read:

What you inherited from your fathers,
You need not earn because you possess it already.

Upon your vitality depends also your allotted span of life. Three-score and ten is man's allotted time, but in some of more strength you see four-score. You cannot lengthen the time allotted you individually by ever so careful living. Every living man lives himself to death at last. But you can shorten your allotted time by wasting your vitality. This can be done in many different ways. According to a well-known saying: "The Germans eat and drink themselves to death; the French love themselves to death; the Orientals smoke themselves to death!" I should like to add: The Americans work themselves to death, treating their organism as they treat their steel machinery, for instance, their automobiles. "Step on her" and force her to do her utmost, without rest, without proper care, until the machinery clogs and is beyond repair. The human heart is a wonderful machine, a tireless pump, working day and night without a moment's rest, for rest is death. There is no steel machinery on earth comparable with the human heart as far as steadiness of work and durability of building material are concerned, though it consists only of a convolute of soft fibers, of muscles and tendons. But ruthless treatment brings disorder in its vulnerable working, and nervous breakdown does the rest. Both America's cemeteries and America's automobile graveyards harbor thousands of victims of brutal treatment who could still be alive.

If some people drink, love, smoke, or work themselves to death, most people, regardless of race or religion, eat themselves to death if they can afford it. One can bear with the enthusiastic worshippers of Bacchus or Venus, or even with those who worship both of them, but voracious animals, even if they are human creatures, are repugnant. They are punished by digging their graves with their own teeth. I am convinced that more men have died from over-eating than from starving. To be healthy and remain healthy, you must starve to a certain extent. My happiest moments are passed starving in anticipation of a good meal.

In enjoying your life, you must never forget what Voltaire said: *"Qui n'a pas l'esprit de son age, de son age a tous les malheurs."* He who has not the spirit of his age, has all the maladies of his age. That means that old people must be careful in enjoying their life; they must renounce the spirit of youth as far as enjoying themselves is concerned. Only one harmless pleasure is left to them— that of thinking by which of all possible excesses they would most have enjoyed dying. It would not have been gluttony, it could not have been Bacchantic joys, it could not have been love—though the thought of dying a victim of love has some thrill in it. But it could have been, and in my own case nearly was, the love of that bewitching, brown lady with her sweet, penetrating and empoisoning perfume, which fills your lungs, your brain, and the rest of your system. Like all treacherous lovers, she grips your heart with her thin, snake-like fingers and kills you the more cold-heartedly, the more fanatically you are devoted to her. Beware of Lady Nicotiana. Beware of smoking yourself to death, because this vice overpowers you without your knowing it. And nearly a victim to my own vice, I go on preaching: Don't miss anything, but be moderate in everything!

Another pure joy is left to old people, freed by their age of whatever vices they may have indulged in former years—the love of Nature and its indelible beauties. Old people who are incapable of loving and admiring the beauties of Nature had better die while they are still in harness, because out of harness they would not know what to do with their time, unaware of the fact that the small remainder of their lives should be devoted to thanking God for the blessing of being still alive and of enjoying His sun. If I should ever fail to appreciate the beauty of the setting sun, then I should know my time is up.

But there comes to mind a last question which every human being is very much interested in. Of which malady will you be the victim?

When you come into this world you do not necessarily have good luck. You may be able to turn bad into good luck later on. But at your exit from this world you must unconditionally have good luck, or you will have to lament your sad fate. Instead of being painlessly swept away into eternity, you may be slowly tortured to death by a cruel malady. This fear is shared by everybody.

If I could choose, I should prefer a flash of lightning to any disease. Only a few, beloved of the gods, are awarded such grace by Nature. Those who have bad luck at the exit must hope for and rely on a new medical specialty still in its infancy, namely, "Euthanasia," or the art of making you die in beauty. It is to be feared, however, that this new specialty will not flourish before all physicians have become human angels.

The second part of the question of "What is life for?" is the altruistic part which is even more important than the egotistical part. It reads: Help others to enjoy their lives likewise! In any walk of life you can be helpful to others in some way. The Viennese say: *"Leben und leben lassen."* Live and let live. These few words comprise a sound philosophy.

Most fortunate are those who in any way, as philanthropists, inventors, scientists, artists, teachers, and last, but not least, physicians, can do some good not only for present but also for future generations.

All these may call themselves the truest observers of the law of love which reigns supreme in the Christian religion. Does not Saint Paul say: "If I speak with the tongues of men and of angels, but have not love, I am become sounding brass or a clanging cymbal"?

But we must not think that the law of love is foreign to other monotheistic religions. The Koran tells you that the Lord forgave a woman who was condemned to eternal hell because she had once given water to a thirsty dog.

On the dread last judgment day, humanity will be united in one last prayer: *"Quid sum miser tunc dicturus, quem patronum rogaturus, cum vix justus sit securus?"*

On that crucial day, men to whom the retrieved glove meant not only an egotistical but also, and chiefly, an altruistic achievement, will not only know what to say but what to do. They will not invoke a patron saint to assist them; even though they be sinners—and who is not?— they will feel quite secure, because they need only fling

PROFESSOR ADOLF LORENZ WELCOMED TO AMERICA IN 1934 BY
THE LATE HARRY ACTON, WELL–KNOWN GANGPLANKER

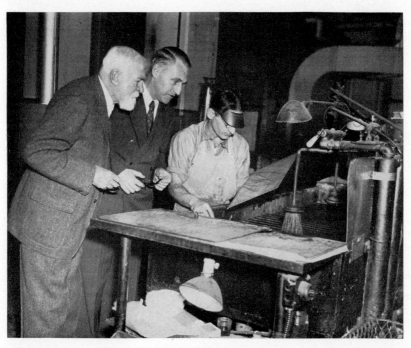

PROFESSOR ADOLF LORENZ WITH HIS SON, DOCTOR ALBERT
LORENZ, INSPECTING A NEWSPAPER PLANT IN THE SPRING
OF 1935

PROFESSOR AND MRS. ADOLF LORENZ, ALTENBERG, AUGUST, 1935

their retrieved glove on the scale rising with their good deeds to make it heavier, and turn the balance.

As God is just, their sins shall be forgiven through all eternity, whether they themselves be denied or granted the privilege of living that long.

The garden, now in the glory of its autumn flowers, looks its best when the sun is setting beyond the vast plain of the Tullnerfeld, as if it were going down in the sea. Of roses, of course, there are none, but there are lilies of all kinds, carnations, gladioli, petunias, begonias, sunflowers, asters in variety, mallows, phloxes, mignonette, and many other commoner flowers, called "peasant" flowers on account of their vivid tints. They all glow in orgies of color in the setting sun. But beautiful beyond all description are the hundreds of dahlias, ranging in all shades from the darkest of the dark to the whitest of whites with just a faint rosy tinge; yellow dahlias with twisted petals, dahlias in all tones of red—a glory to behold.

"Isn't it a pity," muses Mrs. Lorenz, "that the first night frost, to be expected any day from now on, will destroy all this splendor! Must nature die just at the moment when it is in its fullest glory, even though it dies in beauty?"

"Well," answers her husband, "that cannot be helped. Everything that lives is doomed to die, and yet, death is powerless against up-coming new life. Don't I see spring looming in the background only five months from now?"

"And what about us old people?" asks Mrs. Lorenz, pensively. And her husband says: "There is not much to be said in our favor. Our one bit of good luck is that we are not so extremely sensitive to the first frost of the fall as these short-lived dahlias."

Let the coming of our killing frost be veiled by uncertainty—so well expressed by the favorite ending of German tales: *"Und wenn sie nicht gestorben sind, so leben sie noch heute."*—And if they haven't died, they're still alive today.

XXVII

I ATTEND MY FUNERAL

AND now, although I am beyond my eightieth year, I
am not only still alive but am looking forward to
another winter in New York with my student and
former Vienna clinic associate, Doctor Wiesenthal, who
makes me feel quite at home in a typical Viennese manner. I
am not afraid of the treacherous Atlantic, which always is
in the worst of its moods at the time of my crossing. I greet
the awe-inspiring skyline of New York with greater joy
than ever, pleased with the fact that Manhattan, surrounded by water, has ceased to be dry. I flatter myself
that I took a lively part in the fight against the pernicious
drought. I always enjoy the thought that excellent California wine will take the place of the ice-water upon my
table. My only sorrow is, that Americans as a rule do not
fully appreciate this gift from Heaven, but cling to their
abominable whiskey.

Americans have taught us many things, but from us
they have still to learn the art of drinking wisely. They
have to learn not to gulp indiscriminately what they are
drinking, but to caress the wine with their tongues, to
chew it, as it were, and to worship it.

So far as beer is concerned, it will take the Americans
some time to brew beer equal to Pilsener, but the time will
come, and the people will like their good beer and prefer it
to whiskey. Moderate drinking, moderate eating, and moderate smoking will help you all to reach an average age of
eighty.

It is by no means easy to pay yourself the last tribute. Before you can do that, several severe conditions must be fulfilled. You must not only be alive, but enjoying a certain state of good health. You must be able to stand, to walk, to wait, to pray, and even to deliver your own funeral speech. Furthermore, there must be no yawning grave in the depths of which you vanish forever, to rest beneath your grave-stone. The funeral must not make you disappear, but reappear, in a rebirth, as it were—upon a memorial tablet which shows your head and your name, informing passers-by who you were, or are.

On the whole, the procedure, though only a sham-burial, is more painful to the person to be buried than the real funeral, which is painless. But none of us likes to be reminded of it. Yet, the sham-burial is a warning that the real funeral is certainly not far off.

I seemed to have fulfilled all these baffling conditions, and the Board of Aldermen of the little Silesian town of Weidenau, headed by its venerable Burgomeister, Johann Fuehrmann, an old friend of mine, unanimously decided that the front of a certain house on the big market-place was to be adorned with a marble memorial tablet showing the head of Adolf Lorenz, who, as a son of this tiny city, lived in that house up to his eleventh year and from it went forward to face the world, for the most part alone.

I was duly invited to attend the unveiling of the tablet on August 18, 1935, and to deliver a speech on this occasion. Thus it came about that I motored with my son Albert to Weidenau to attend my own funeral.

Memorial tablets and gravestones are condemned to the same fate: that of being forgotten. Yet, there is some difference between a gravestone and a memorial tablet. The gravestone is much sooner forgotten—and removed, if the resting-place is coveted by a successor. The memorial tablet will also be forgotten, but it will take a little longer.

Not only small tablets, but big monuments, dedicated to the memory of great men, kings, and emperors, lose their names and are forgotten by the people. Not two hundred years after its establishment, the beautiful equestrian statue of the Emperor Marcus Aurelius had lost its identity. It was erroneously credited to the Emperor Constantine the Great, and to this mistake the world owes its possession of the finest equestrian statue of antiquity. Had it been known that the statue was dedicated to Marcus Aurelius, it would have been smashed to bits, because a heathen Roman emperor was not acceptable to the people at that time.

Monuments and tablets to the greatest benefactors of humanity have become nameless, and forgotten by the great mass of the people. The people only remember forever the names of the wholesale slaughterers and scourgers of mankind. Napoleon will never be forgotten, memorial or no memorial. Yet great scientists and benefactors are not entirely deprived of immortality, though in a far smaller community: the world of scientists.

For those who are really worthy of honor, tablets and monuments are superfluous. They will never be forgotten, even though the monuments crumble to dust. And though oblivion is the fate of all memorials, there can be no doubt that they are the best means of lengthening the memory of those to whom they are dedicated.

And now let me give you a description of my funeral:

It was a beautiful August morning. The rain had ceased, the air was fresh and balmy, and the sun promised to say "good morning" at any moment. The *Marktplatz* at Weidenau was crowded with people who wanted to hear and see the old Professor and his marble counterfeit.

The front of the old house had been decorated with wreaths, flowers, and flags, and looked quite pretty in its baroque outlines. Behind an artistically folded white curtain the tablet was waiting patiently for its unveiling—and patience was necessary!

First the dear old Burgomeister bellowed his welcome to the many guests. Then followed a Silesian physician, who tried to explain to the people what kind of a man it was they were going to see and to greet. The man he was talking about, an involuntary hearer of the eulogy, would have blushed had not old age deprived him of the ability to do so.

When the eulogist had finished, the Burgomeister commanded:

"Die Hülle falle!"

and amidst the applause of the gathered populace and the playing of the Czechoslovakian national anthem, the veil was slowly withdrawn.

Though the sculptor, Mr. Obeth, had never laid eyes on me and had been obliged to work entirely from a photograph taken in New York, he had succeeded in imparting to the hard marble the characteristic features of his model.

A lovely girl upon whom I had operated many years before recited a pleasing poem and gave me a bunch of roses for which I paid her with a hearty kiss. When the young ladies of the city had sung some sweet Silesian melodies, the Burgomeister asked me to address the audience. I excused myself for not being able to oblige him, explaining that now that the memorial tablet had been unveiled, it had rightfully become the center of the celebration. I added that I wished to disappear and to hide behind it in order to help the "man of stone" deliver the funeral speech. Then I entered my boyhood home, found my way to an open window a little above the tablet, and whispered into the ears of the "man of stone" what he should say to the people.

The loudspeaker droned:

"My dear friends! I thank you very much for the honor conferred upon me by the dedication of the memorial. I am proud, but at the same time I pity myself, just as I pity all men carved in marble or cast in bronze who are doomed to stand, or to sit, sometimes on horseback, in the same unalterable position, with the same gesture of the hand, with eyes fixed on the same point, day and night, rain or shine, winter or summer—for centuries.

" 'Must they not collapse of boredom?' I used to ask myself, without having the faintest idea that I should ever share their fate.

"At any rate, I shall do my best not to collapse of boredom. I shall be busy as the watchman of the market-place. I shall watch the children when they go to school. I shall reprimand the lazy ones and encourage the weaklings. With pleasure I shall see them sliding on the icy pavement in winter. I shall muster them on Corpus Christi Day, and when they sing holy songs, in my heart I shall sing with them. I shall help them work the rattles when, during

Passion Week, the church bells are silent. Though my stony features will seem immobile, I shall frolic in my heart watching the boys playing their games. From my street-corner I shall control the pulse of the commercial life of the city, watching the weekly and annual fairs. I am sure I shall see the lost prosperity of the city return in the near future.

"One sad duty I see heaped upon my shoulders. At this street-corner begins the road which leads to the cemetery. It will be my fate to see generation after generation of the people who lived and died in this city pass this corner on their last journey. I shall have to greet every casket with a word of solace:

" *'Sit terra tibi levis, requiescas in pace!'*

"But my services as a watchman will be rewarded. When one thousand, eight hundred and three years shall have elapsed, I shall quit my job, provided that the hard Silesian granite will have withstood so many severe Silesian winters. After this long time, my reward for the faithful service will be due, and this reward shall be the repetition of the grand spectacle which was the first great event in my life.

"Though I was only four years old at that time, I remember clearly a series of summer evenings which were full of excitement. The whole populace of this city assembled in the market-place, just where you are now. The women and young girls sang holy songs, as at a May prayer. Old men prayed silently over their rosaries; others just stood and gazed at the sky. Little children, amongst whom was myself, partook of the general excitement, flitting hither and thither like summer birds.

"In the heavens hung a mighty transparent disk filled

with a mysterious light and throwing silvery rays over the whole sky. Nobody seemed to know what this celestial spectacle meant—least of all the children. Many years later I learned that this floating star was the big Donati comet of the year 1858. It takes this comet one thousand, eight hundred and eighty years to complete its course, and as seventy-seven years have already elapsed since its last appearance, I shall have to wait one thousand, eight hundred and three years for the next glimpse of the Donati comet.

"This will be a very short time for the man of stone— to whom time means nothing. When the comet appears again, I shall be the only person in the world who saw the Donati comet twice as a reward for services. Then the establishment of this memorial tablet will have been worth while!

"And now, my dear friends, the time has come to condemn my mouth to eternal silence. Before that moment allow me a few more words:

"When the big comet shall have visited our skies another thousand times, not the smallest part of eternity will have passed. Eternity is indivisible! The earth will go on spinning round the sun just as eagerly as ever; time will run as fast as ever; summer evenings will be as lovely as ever, and the Archangels Gabriel, Raphael, and Michael, who speak so impressively in the prologue in Heaven in Goethe's *Faust*, in their united prayer to God, will have to sing once more:

"*Und alle Deine hohen Werke sind herrlich wie am ersten Tag.*"

INDEX

INDEX

Abbas Hilmi, *see* Khedive of Egypt
Achillotenotomy, 330
Advent Bay, 127
Albee, Dr. Fred, 290
Albert, Prince of Wales, 253
Albert, Prof. Eduard, 63–66, 73, 74, 77, 78, 333; his clinic, 81, 92, 95
Alcohol, as an antiseptic, 95
Alexandria, 240
Alfonso XIII, King of Spain, 180, 182–188, 197
Allgemeine Krankenhaus, 92, 93, 130
Altenberg, 80, 86, 140, 233, 254, 255, 268; neighbors in, 134; garden party in, 234, 235; burglars at, 267; family reunion at, 318, 337; royalty entertained at, 319–321; the garden at, 337, 345
Ambassador to Spain, Austrian, 180, 181
America, visits to, 136 ff., 148 ff., 163 ff., 188, 189, 190 ff., 208–214, 280 ff., 311–313; impressions of, 146, 158, 166; desire to see more of, 148; temptation to stay in, 214; medical activities in, 148, 149, 155, 156, 201; and the World War, 252; anti-German attitude in, 282, 290–292
American hospitality, 171
American Medical Association, congress of the, 190–193
American Medical Association of Vienna, 130–133
American Orthopædic Association, 275
American railway travel, impressions of, 140, 190
American relief, in Vienna, 272, 273
"American, the," 205, 219, 231, 318. *See also* Lorenz, Konrad
American traction method, *see* traction
Americans, in Vienna, 130–133; work themselves to death, 341, 342; and drinking, 347
Anatomical Institute of Vienna, 68
Anatomy, 58–60, 62, 70–72
Andry, 331
Ankylosis, 82, 107, 305, 329
Antipodes, the, 178, 251
Antisepsis, 65, 95
Arad, 46
Arches, fallen, 329
Archibald, Mr. A., 293
Aristocrats, 218
Arlington Hotel, Washington, D. C., 157
Arlt, 74
Armistice, the, 265
Art, collection of, 118–120, 222–224, 226–229
Arthur (pupil), *see also* von Rosthorn, 46, 47, 49–53
Ashley, Dr. Dexter, 130
Atlantic City, 169–171
Aunt Karline, 26, 29, 30
Australia, 179; patient from Melbourne, 176, 178; prospective case from West, 250

Austria, 59, 62, 195, 251; declaration of war by, 253; before and after World War, 296, 297; after World War, 265, 268; law requiring retirement at seventy, 315
Austrian Army, 263

Bacon, Mrs. Misa, 142, 143
Bamberger, Prof. Ernst, 73
Bangalore, India, 250
Bank of England, 165–167
Bauch, Herr, 16–19
Belgrade, 37
Bergen, Norway, 128
Berlin, 309; congress of surgeons at, 106
Bey, Phœbe Krishna Rau Jumna, *see* Phœbe
Bifurcation, 256
Biller, Miss, 237
Billings, Dr., 191, 193
Billroth, Theodore, 54, 63, 73, 78, 333
Biskra, 127
Bleeding, 81
Blood poisoning, 332
Bloodless operations, *see* Operations
Blum, Prof. Victor, 276, 277, 279
Board of Medical Examiners, Albany, 286, 288
Bohemia, 265
Bolshevism, Russian, 263
Bone operations, *see* Operations
Bone, diseases of, 329; fractures of, 328; necessary to cut, 329; setting, 336
Bosnia, 62, 251
Boston, 131, 156
Brace-makers, 333, 334
Brahms, 73
Brooklyn, visit to Navy Yard, 311
Bruck-on-the-Mur, 35
Buffalo, 300
Busch, Adolphus, 204, 205
Busch Brewery, the, 204
Busch, Mrs. Adolphus, 204
Byron, Lord, 323

Cairo, 240
California, 148–151; wine, 347
Cambiaso, Lucas, 223
Cancer, 60, 195
Carbolic acid, 76, 77, 95
Carinthia, 2, 35, 36, 112
Carmen Sylva, Queen of Roumania, 186
Carol of Roumania, King, 186, 187
Cases, at the Clinic of Surgery, 65; of wounded soldiers, 256; resulting in indemnity suits, 304–310; selected, 201. *See also* Patients
Cellular-pathology, 75
Cervera, Admiral, 199
Ceylon, 246
Chicago, 143, 188, 190, 205; arrival in, 140; visit to stockyards, 142; resolution of thanks from city of, 156; recalled to, 152
Children, treatment of, 78, 81–85, 141; free treatment of poor American, 275;

soothing frightened, 232; with congenital deformities, 322; at Newark reception for Dr. Lorenz, 293–295; advising treatment of, 288, 298
Chile, 134, 286
Christina, Queen of Spain, 180–186
Church attendance, in Dallas, 202
Churchill, Mr. Winston, 210
Ciudad Porfirio Diaz, 200
Club-foot, 201; correction of, 100–102; congenital, 78, 160, 161, 328, 330, 331
Colombo, 246
Columbia Theatre, Washington, D. C,. 159, 210
Columbia (steamer), 127
Congenital club-foot, see Club-foot
Congenital hip dislocation, see Hip dislocation
Congenital wry-neck, 328; Andry's method of curing, 331
Contractures, of upper part of body, 329
Copeland, Dr. Royal S., 283, 288, 289, 298
Côte d'Azur, 237
Couzens, Mr., 298
Cramp's Shipyards, 167
Cripples, general health of, 322; spastic, 322, 323, 335; world-famous, 323, 324; a result of difficult childbirth, 336; used at royal courts, 331
Crisis, The, 210
Cristóbal Colón, the, 198
Cuernavaca, 195
Custozza, 38
Czarevich, the, 240, 241
Czecho-Slovakia, 59, 265

Dallas, 200–203
Danube River, 37, 80, 122; swimming experience in the, 125
Davis, Mrs. Varina Jefferson, 170
Dean of Medical Faculty in Vienna, 57, 58, 313, 314
Denver, 148
de Regno, Senatore, 270
Dermatology, 70
Detroit, reception at, 298
Diana, 223, 224
Diaz, Porfirio, 195
Die Erde, 229
Dieffenbach, 330
Dillon, Judge, 161, 162
Doctors, American, in Vienna, 130–133, 169; should consider themselves cosmopolites, 283; difficulty with local, 288, 289, 298
Domodossola, 270, 271
Donati, comet of 1858, 352, 353
Dooley, Mister, 212
Drave River, 37
"Dry" surgery, see Orthopædic surgery
Dumreicher, 63
Dupuytren, 66, 68

Eberhardt, Father, 39, 40, 112–114
Edward VII, see Albert, Prince of Wales
Egypt, 99, 237–240
Ehrlich, Dr. Eduard, 2, 32, 34, 35
Ehrlich, Johann, 1, 2 (later Father Gregor)
Ehrlich, Mr., 1

Elisabeth, Archduchess, 115–117
Elisabeth, Empress, 117
Elisabethbrücke (bridge), 119, 208
Esmarch, Prof., 65

Faculty of Internal Medicine, 81
"Father-house," the, see Peasant house
Faust, quotation from, 353
Ferdinand, Archduke Francis, 251
Ferdinand, ex-King of Bulgaria, 319–321
Ford automobile factory, 298, 299
Ford, Edsel, 298, 299
Ford, Henry, tribute to, 298, 299; letter from, 299, 300
Ford Hospital, 298
Francis Ferdinand, Archduke, 120, 121
Frank, Dr., 177
Franz Josef, Emperor, 38, 73, 92, 109–112, 115, 159, 257, 259–261, 327
Fourteen Points, President Wilson's, 265
Fuchs, Prof. Ernst, 74, 130, 131, 151
Fuehrmann, Johann, 348, 350, 351

Galland, Dr. Walter, 290
German and Austrian Children, Committee for Relief of, 275, 295
Germans, in New York, 291
Gibney, Dr. Virgil, 275, 289, 290
Girls, afflicted by dislocation of the hip-joint, 97, 107, 108
Glands, 69; thyroid, 72
Good Samaritan Hospital, 201
Gould, Edith Katherine, 209
Gould, George, 208, 209
Gould Hall, 209
Gould, Helen Vivian, 209
Gould, Mrs. George (Edith), 208–210, 213
Grand Canyon, the, 151–153
Gregor, Father, 2, 32, 37, 39, 41, 112–115. See also Ehrlich, Johann
Graz, 2, 34
Gurahoncz, 49, 143

H., Mrs., 61
Hackett, Mr., 210
Hainisch, Dr. Michael, 272
Hainisch, Mrs., 272
Hans (pupil), 43–45; sister of, 176
Harding, Warren G., 300; letter from, 293, 294
Hass, Prof. Julius, 245, 246
Head, the, parts of, treated by orthopædy, 328
Heart, the human, 341; of the world, 164, 165, 167
Hebra, Prof. Ferdinand, 70
Hedwig, Aunt, 236
Heide, Mr. 312
Heinrich (pupil), 60
Helena, Queen of Italy, 269, 270
Heukoppe, the, 129
Henry, Prince of Prussia, 138, 168
Herodotus, 330
Hessing, Friedrich, 333, 334
Hindus, corporeal shapeliness of, 242
Hip dislocation, congenital, 66, 67, 329, 330; operation for, 96–98, 100, 103–107, 146, 316, 330; lack of, in Hindus, 242
Hip-joint, 98, 322; operations on the, 256

Hip luxation, bilateral, **96, 104, 105, 136**; unilateral, 105
Hippocrates, 66, 97, 330
Hofburg, The, 115
Hofburg Theatre, 252
Hofer, Andreas, 50
Hoffa, Prof., 309, 334
Horace, quotation from, 220
Hohenwart, Count, 195
Hylan, Mayor, 291, 292
Hyrtl, Prof., 54, 70–72
Hyrtl Orphanage, 71

Indemnity suits, 303–310
India, 179, 242, 243, 245; food in, 246, 247; prospective case from, 250
Infantile paralysis, 103, 322, 324, 335; possible prevention of, 325
Italy, 61, 118, 268–271
Ixtaccihuatl, 194

Jaw, the orthopædic treatment of, 328
Jefferson Hospital, 173
Jefferson Medical College, 171, 173
Joints, treatment of diseased, 82; tubercular, 332, 333
Jolson, Al, 300, 301
Joseph, Archduke, 241
Josephine, 43
"Judgment of Diana, The," 223, 224

Kaiser, the, 251
Karl, Archduke, 258
Keppler, Dr., 286
Khartoum, 238
Khediva of Egypt, the, 239
Khedive of Egypt, the, 238–240
"King, the," 140, 142, 233
Klagenfurt, 2, 37, 42, 43–46, 53
Klosterneuburg, 235, 236
Kluss, Mr., 32, 33, 56
Kluss, Sectionsrath, 56, 57
Knee-joint, 98, 307, 308, 322
Knock-knees, 322, 329
Koenig Grätz, 38
Kronprinz, North German Lloyd, 214
Kubbe, Egypt, 238
Kuddihy, R. J., 312

La Cima, Mexico, 194
Lake Pontchartrain, 191, 192
Lakewood, 208
Langer, Prof., 54, 55, 58, 59, 62, 63, 70, 78
Leopold, King of Belgium, 115, 116
Lincoln, Abraham, 37
Lindewiese, 4, 5
Lisbon, 327
Lister, 65
"Lister era," 76, 77, 95, 97, 332
Liverpool, 176
London, 176
Lorenz, Adolf, accidents to, 122, 124, 129; "Ambassador of Peace and Mercy," 281, 292, 294; ambitions, 21, 25, 35, 62, 63, 78; anatomist, 58, 59, 62, 63, 77; appearance, 7–9, 40, 140, 141, 243; appointments: Assistant at Clinic of Surgery, 64; Counsellor to the Government, 109–113, 167; Docent of Surgery, 76; Demonstrator of Anatomy, 59; Professor Extraordinarius, 109; attends Bankers' Dinner, New York, 163–167; birth, 1; "bloodless surgeon," 329, 330; books

and pamphlets, *see* Writings; boyhood, 32 ff., 42 ff.; builds new home, 217 ff.; carbolic acid victim, 76, 77; charity work, 142, 275, 288, 292, 318; childhood, 2 ff., 15 ff.; children of, 88, 231, 249; choice of profession, 54–56; choir-singer, 37–41; clinical work, 60, 63–67, 78, 81, 89; degrees received by, 152, 154; disgust with war and machines of war, 311; education, 13, 14, 37–43, medical, 57–62, social, 60, 61; "Father of German Orthopædic Surgery," 248, 336; favorite study, 58; finances, 10, 34, 35, 39, 40, 42, 45, 52–57, 58, 60, 61, 79, 90, 91, 136, 179, 219, 232, 246; after the war, 266, 268, 270, 271, 276; grandchildren, 318; grandmother, 10, 11, 24, 25, 29; handshaking, 154; health, 10, 11; hobbies, 118 ff.; honors, 109 ff.; illness, 88–90, 98–100, 273, 275–279, 284; illness of father, 21, 22; indemnity suits against, 303–310; invited to treat poor American children, 275; joke played on, 241, 242; journey to St. Paul Benedictine Monastery, 35; leaving home for the first time, 32, 33; lectures, 295, 296; license difficulties in America, 143–147, 286, 288, 290, 291; marriage, 79, 80; medical student, 57–62; memorial tablet to, 348, 350–353; military service, 61, 62; miniature altar made by, 17, 18, 20; missing glove, the, 15, 16, 64, 171–174, 337; mistakes a stork for a ghost, 122, 123; monastery life, 37–41; nominated for Nobel Prize for Medicine, 315, 316; offer from a publisher for book on American experiences, 176; orthopædic surgeon, 78, 80 ff.; paints doors of peasant house, 91; pall-bearer at baby's funeral, 19, 20; parents, 1, 3, 15, 21, 22, 27, 28, 30, 61; pays debt to St. Paul Monastery, 317; philosophy of living, 214, 337 ff.; pranks, 6, 7, 23, 26–31; proposed world tour, 178, 179; publicity of, in America, 148, 149, 151, 153, 155, 161, 174, 204, 210–13, 216, 272, 281, 282; 283, 290; receives tribute for work, 295; remarks on: cripples, 322, drinking, 347; dying, 343, 345, 346; eating, 342; enjoying life, 342; fame, 339; honor, 338; Nature, 343; power, 338; religion, 339, 340; smoking, 342, 343; vitality, 340, 341. Retirement of, 315; royal recognition, 109 ff.; speeches, 166, 167, 171, 172, 292, 298, 299, 320, 321, 351–353; sport ventures, 121–128; students of, 130; summit of career, 250; surgery, 60, 62–64; teachers of, 64–67, 68 ff.; travels: America, 136 ff., 148 ff., 163 ff., 188, 189, 190 ff., 208–214, 280 ff., 311–313, 317; cruise in the South Atlantic, 325–327; Egypt, 99, 237–240; Italy, 269–271; Mexico, 194–197; Spain, 180–184, 188; Spitzbergen, 127, 128; Switzerland, 268, 269; treats brother of old Dean of Medical Faculty, 314, 315; tutoring, 43–53, 58, 60; visits Uncle Eduard, 34, 35; visits American battleship, 311; writings of, 78, 81, 318
Lorenz, Agnes (granddaughter), 318

Lorenz, Albert, 88, 277, 306, 337; on motorcycle trip, 123, 124; in military service, 231; first marriage, 249; in the World War, 254, 255, 257, 258, 262–264; second marriage, 318
Lorenz, Elisabeth (Mrs. Albert Lorenz), 249, 250; service in World War, 255, 258, 263; receives war decorations, 257; illness and death, 263, 264
Lorenz Fund for Relief of Poor Viennese Children, 285, 302; contributors to, 312; distribution of, 313
Lorenz, George (grandson), 318
Lorenz Hall, 218–229, 233, 318, 321; description of paintings in, 222–229, 236. *See also* Peasant house
Lorenz, Konrad, 231, 273, 274, 318, 321; interest in ornithology, 319. *See also* "The American"
Lorenz, Margaret (Mrs. Konrad Lorenz), 318
Lorenz, Mrs. Adolf, 90, 91, 118–120, 126, 135, 170, 220, 222, 254, 268, 345; advice from, 90, 123, 124, 129, 134, 136, 218, 224, 227, 255; as assistant to husband, 78, 79, 136, 216, 232; description of, 78, 79; marriage, 79, 80; second child of, 205, 219, 231; skill in soothing frightened children, 232
Lorenz, Thomas (grandson), 318
Lorz, *see* Adolf Lorenz
Los Angeles, 149, 150
Low, Mayor Seth, 175
Lowe, Mt., 150
Luxor, 238

Madeira, 326
Madrid, 180
Magellan's Strait, Chile, 134
Maharaja Adscha of Hydarabad, 245
Maine, the, 167, 168, 184
Malaria treatment, of the spirochæta, 74
Marburg, 112
Maria Theresa, Empress, 296, 297
Marie, Queen of Roumania, 186–188
Masaryk, Thomas G., 59
Max (cousin), 8
Maximilian, Emperor, 195, 196, 260
Mayo brothers, 191
Medical Association, American, 190; American, of Vienna, 130–133; International, 190
Mexico City, 194
Mexico, diplomatic relations with Austria, 195
Mexico Mining and Exploration Company, private car of, 197, 200
Microbes, 325, 326, 332
Milwaukee, 155, 156
Ministry of Education, Vienna, 56, 57, 109
Ministry of Instruction, Vienna, 93
Minto, Lady, 244, 245
Minto, Lord, 243, 244
Missing glove, the, 15, 16, 64, 171–174, 337
Mississippi River, 80, 191, 192, 203
Monuments, to famous people, 349
Morgenthau, Mr., 312
Morse, Myron W., 293
Mueller, Dr. G., 136
Mur River, 37
Murillo, 331

Murray Hill Hotel, 160, 281
Muschenheim family, 290

N., Sectionschef, 57
Naples, 136, 137, 304
Narcosis, 65
Neusser, Prof., 73
New Orleans, 190–193
New York, 137, 160, 161, 208; impressions of, 138, 139; leaving, 176, 313; resolution of thanks from Board of Aldermen, 175; welcomes Dr. Lorenz, 291, 292; return to, 317, 318, 347
New York Hospital for the Ruptured and Crippled, 290
Newark, 286, 292, 293
Nile River, the, 192
Nizam of Hydarabad, the, 245, 246
Nobel Prize for Medicine, 315, 316
North Cape, 127
Northwestern University, 152, 154
Norway, 127
Nose, septum in the, 328
Nothnagel, 74
Nussbaum, Prof., 332

Odilo, Father, 37
Oetscher, Mt., 86, 234
Operations, 95, 160, 161, 179; bone, 102; "bloodless," 100–102, 107, 141, 142, 146, 329, 330; club-foot, 100–102, 160, 161, 201; congenital hip dislocation, 96–98, 100, 103–107, 141, 142; filmed by movies, 286; on the spine, 305; on wounded soldiers, 256; osteoplastic, 85
Oppolzer, 68
Orizaba, Mount, 196
Ornithological Society, German, 319
Orth, Johann, 135
Orthopædic Institute, 272, 273
Orthopædic surgery, 78, 92, 96 ff., 111; and indemnity suits, 303
Orthopædy, definition, 327; realm of, 327–330; history, 330–334; future, 334–336
Oyster Bay, Sagamore Hill, 286, 287

Pabst Brewery, 155, 156
Pain, alleviation of, 82–84, 102, 104
Paintings, description of, in Lorenz Hall, 222–229, 236
Palazzo Bianco, 222
Paralytic club-foot, *see* club-foot
Paralytic knee-contracture, 103
Paris, 115, 116
Paris, S.S., 280
Pasadena, 150
Pasteur, Louis, 74, 75, 332
Patients, *see also* cases, first, 80, 81; increase in number of, 92, 109, 284; royal, 115–117, 180, 182–188, 238–239; from foreign countries, 135, 179, 238, 250, 268, 269, 286; in America, 136, 140, 201; tubercular bone and joint disease, 81
Peasant house, the, 80, 86–91, 140. *See also* Lorenz Hall
Peasants, 1, 218
Philadelphia, 167, 171; visit to mint in, 168, 169
Phœbe, *see* Bey, Phœbe Krishna Rau Jumna, 251, 258, 262
Piffl, Cardinal, 312

Plaster-bed, 83–85
Plaster-casts, 83, 101, 102, 334
Plaster spica, 84
Plastic Surgery, *see* Surgery
Pollitzer, 74
Pope, Leo XIII, 216
Popocatepetl, 194
Popol, *see* Leopold, King of Belgium
Poppe Inn, 23
Prelate Augustin, 37, 38, 112, 114
Premature children, 206, 207, 336
President of the U. S., 154, 324
Prince Eugenius, 37
"Princess, the," 140, 141, 188, 205; visit to Vienna, 232–237
Prohibition, 280, 281, 347
Pulitzer, Mr., 209
Pulitzer, Mrs., 209

"Queen, the," 140, 234, 235
Queenstown, Ireland, 176

R., Lady, *see* von Rosthorn
Ravold, Dr., 130
Rax Mountains, the, 128, 129, 259
"Redressement forcé," French, 101
Redressment, German modelling, 101–104
Reischel, Herr, 27
Reisner, Rev. Mr., 296
Reporters, news, 153, 155, 156, 204, 281, 282
Richard III, quotation from, 323
Richard, Father, 39
Richelieu, Cardinal, as a cripple, 323
Richter, Captain, 214, 215
Rickets, 322, 328
Ridder, Victor, 291
Rochester, New York, 160, 210
Rockefeller Foundation, 273
Rokitansky, 69
Rome, 269
Roosevelt, Mrs. Theodore, 287, 288
Roosevelt, Theodore, 156, 158, 159, 204; grave of, 286, 287
Rosser, Dr., 201
Rudolf, Crown Prince of Austria, 73, 252, 253
Rudolphinium, 73
Russia, imperial family of, 240
Russo-Japanese War, 179

Sahara Desert, 127
St. Blasien, 38, 112
St. Louis, 203
St. Louis Globe-Democrat, 204
St. Mary's College, Dallas, Texas, 203
St. Paul, quoted, 344
St. Paul, Benedictine Monastery of, 2, 32, 35–37, 42, 56, 112–115, 317; description of, 37
Salt Lake City, 148
San Francisco, 149, 150
San Gennaro, 137, 141
Scabies, 70
Schaudin, Dr., 326, 327
Schley, Rear-Admiral, 198, 199
Schoenherr, Dr. Karl, 229
Schönbrunn, Schloss, 261
Schuh, Prof. J., 54
Schumack, Monsignor Father, 312
Scoliosis, 322
Semler, George, 312
Septic infection, 98

Shakespeare, quoted, 323
Silesia, 158
Silesians, 158
Sims, Marion, 171
Skoda, Professor, 68, 115
Society of Singers of Klagenfurt, 46, 47, 143
Soldiers, wounded, 84
Spinal cord, 325
Spine, the, tuberculosis of, 83, 85, 322; ankylosis of, 305, 306; lateral deviation of, 322, 328
Spirochæta, the, 325–327; malaria treatment of, 74
Spitzbergen, 127, 128
Spofford, Texas, 200
Spondylitis, *see* Spine, tuberculosis of
Sports, automobiling, 124; horseback riding, 121–123; hunting, 126; motor-cycling, 123, 124; skiing, 128
Stefanie, Archduchess, 115, 116
Sterilization, 336
Strauss, Dr., 296
Strauss, Mrs., 296
Stricker, Solomon, 72
Styria, 32
Sudan, 127
Sun-treatment, 83
Surgery, 60, 62, 63, 92, 95, 332; interest of, in tubercular joints, 333; plastic, 302, 303; progress in, 65. *See also* Orthopædic
Syphilis, 325, 326
Sweden, 127
Switzerland, 61, 268–271

Tamalpais, Mt., 149
Target-shooting, 49–51
Tauchida, 239, 240
Tegethoffbrücke (bridge), 119, 208
Tendon transplantation, 103
Texas, 200, 201
Theatre, the, experiences of, 210–213, 252, 300; first impression of, 12, 13; love of, 149, 163; playwriting, 318
Thigh, dislocated, 103–105
Tirpitz, 254
Toluca, Mexico, 194
Traction method, American, 82
Trenton, 300
Trofaiach, Upper Styria, 32, 34, 35
Troppau, Silesia, 1
Tuberculosis, of the spine, 83, 85; of the joints, 81, 82
Tullnerfeld, 80, 121, 126
Tuticorin, 246
Twentieth Century Limited, 140
Tyrol, 49, 50

Union League Club, 167
Unterdrauburg, 35

Vaccinations, 23
Van Ward, Dr., 298
Vera Cruz, 197, 200
"Victory of Peace over War, The," 226
Vienna, 33, 109, 111, 119, 120, 214, 254, 265, 266, 270, 318, 319; as a center of teaching, 74, 131, 133; American medical students in, 130, 169; attractions of life in, 132, 133; impoverished by World War, 259, 272, 273; American relief in, 272, 273; wit in, 301; hospitals in, 177
Vienna Society of Physicians, 64

Viennese children, relief for, 284, 285, 295, 296, 312
Viennese cooking, 150, 157
Viennese Dining Club, 131
Viennese philosophy of living, 214
Virchow, 75
Vogelsang, Captain, 128
von Bergmann, Geheimrath, 106
von Brücke, Ernst, 72
von Eiselsberg, Prof. Anton, 74, 273
von Rosthorn, Arthur, 272, 273
von Rosthorn, Lady, 47, 48, 54
von Wagner-Jauregg, Julius, 74

Wadi Halfa, 192, 238
Waldorf-Astoria Hotel, 138, 160
Wards, orthopædic, 92, 248, 255, 256; lack of, 81, 82, 109
Washington, D. C., 157
Wedl, Anton, 280, 285, 295, 312, 313
Wedl, Mrs. Magda, 280, 285, 313
Weidenau, 1, 4, 37, 56, 200, 348, 350
Western Union Telegraph Co., 161

White House, Washington, D. C., 157, 158
Wienerwald, 132, 194, 234
Wiesenthal, Dr., 347
Wilhelm, Crown Prince of Prussia, 253
Williams, 151
Wilson, Dr., 167, 169
Wilson, Woodrow, letter from, 293
Windhag Stipend, 57, 59, 63
World War, 251, 253, 254, 259, 260, 263; privations in Austria during, 261, 262
World War victims, relieved by plaster-bed, 84
Wright, General Luke E., 204

X, Father, 202
X-ray treatment, 83

Yokohama, potential patient in, 178

Zita, Archduchess, 258
Zworykin, Vladimir K., 325